The Quantum Physicists

THE
QUANTUM PHYSICISTS

And an Introduction to Their Physics

WILLIAM H. CROPPER

Professor of Chemistry
St. Lawrence University

New York
OXFORD UNIVERSITY PRESS
London   Toronto   1970

To My Parents

Preface

Great scientists tend to have a ghostlike presence in modern scientific literature. Though their names appear on thousands of pages in hundreds of books, they are not attached to human portraits, but to equations, constants, effects, and experiments. Erwin Schrödinger, for example, is remembered because the Schrödinger equation is firmly established in the methods of modern physics. His name is before us, correctly associated with his work, but disconnected from the man and his world. This is a practice appropriate for the specialized articles of journals and monographs. Science has a formal structure which can be separated from personalities. To use the theory built around Schrödinger's equation one need not know anything about the complex and eloquent man who invented it.

Is it wise, though, to think that science begins and ends with its formal procedures? Can the story of science be told properly if it is confined to the current theories and their uses? If the methods of science were absolutely permanent and noncontroversial perhaps there would be no practical reason for looking beyond them to the people and their efforts. But the ways of science never have been permanent and probably never will be. If science is studied, then, can the study ignore the creators and the creative efforts responsible for the vital climate of change? I am inclined to think not, and so I offer this brief volume to introduce and bring together the history and formal theory of quantum physics.

The story is told as history in the first four chapters. The initial episode presents two revolutionary geniuses, Max Planck and Albert Einstein, and their two papers that brought forth the quantum concepts. The story then centers on Niels Bohr and his herculean effort to build a quantum theory based on the classical concepts of motion. Bohr was not entirely successful, but his insight and influence contributed in no small way to the next great step in the history, the matrix mechanics of Werner Heisenberg and Max Born. At about the same time, from an entirely different direction, another mechanics enters, the immensely useful wave mechanics of Erwin Schrödinger. The last episode of the story might be fancied as a finale: the principal characters, Einstein, Bohr, Heisenberg, Schrödinger, and Born participate in a lively and sometimes amusing effort to extract a word and conceptual picture from the mathematical equations of quantum physics.

What was achieved in the thirty "heroic" years of this history is not perfect, but it is a working system of quantum physics with vast scope. In the last two chapters of the book the formal basis of the theory, the postulates and the main arguments of the theorems, is displayed. The theory emerges, from all the accidents, mistakes, and controversies which brought it into being, like a great painting materializing from the chaos of the artist's studio, with pure, beautiful lines and magnificent vision.

Some readers will want to look beyond the introductory story told here, especially to the solutions of the equations of quantum physics and their applications to atomic and molecular problems. I can recommend for further reading: *Fundamentals of Modern Physics* by Robert M. Eisberg (Wiley), *Quantum Chemistry* by Henry Eyring, John Walter, and George E. Kimball (Wiley), and *Quantum Mechanics* by L. D. Landau and E. M. Lifshitz (Addison-Wesley). The Landau-Lifshitz book is to me the best available general treatment of nonrelativistic quantum physics.

I also recommend frequent browsing in the "Notes and Comment" section at the end of the book, where many more reading references are cited. And allow me to include an advertisement for the two volumes which are planned as sequels to this one. They will, I hope, more or less complete the story of quantum physics.

It is a pleasure to mention those whose fine help I received in preparing this book: Professor James S. Evans of Lawrence University, who found the time for a perceptive, literate and detailed reading of the manuscript; Michael McKean of the Oxford University

Press, who tolerated several false starts and various strange ideas on how textbooks should be written; Caroline Taylor, whose phenomenal copy editing eliminated some appalling errors; Frank Romano, whose lucid drawings enhance the text; and, most of all, Evelyn, who understood the story and the writing problems so well, and couldn't have cared less about the physics.

Cranberry Lake, New York   W. H. C.
November 1969

Contents

The Quantum Physicists

Foreword

Messages

Suppose the day arrives when radio signals actually originating from intelligent beings are received from outer space. An unusually tangled intellectual problem arises: how are we to form an image of a world that may be totally different from our own and most likely we will never see? The transmitted signals presumably carry a message, but what are the words and what are the meanings? Perhaps we have nothing in common with these other-world beings, not even the same perception of color, sound, and form. Our words cannot ever fit their world exactly, perhaps not even approximately. Yet we have no choice but to extract words from some earthly vocabulary and fit them as well as possible to our limited impressions. To some extent these words and descriptions will be appropriate, but there will always be an element of ambiguity. A world so remote and different can never be understood completely.

The modern physicist faces a problem which is quite similar. He communicates with a remote inner (not outer) molecular world too minute to be observed directly. He has no reason to believe that the physics of this world—what has come to be known as "quantum physics"—resembles the physics of the familiar world more than slightly. In fact, his observations sometimes imply complete inconsistency with the behavior of ordinary things. Erwin Schrödinger, one of the greatest contributors and personalities in modern physics, tells of this: "As our mental eye penetrates into smaller and smaller distances and shorter and shorter times, we find nature behaving so entirely differently from what we observe in visible and palpable bodies of our surroundings that *no* model shaped after our large

3

scale experiences can ever be 'true.' A completely satisfactory model *of this type* is not only practically inaccessible, but not even thinkable. Or, to be more precise, we can, of course, think it, but however we think it, it is wrong; not perhaps quite as meaningless as a 'triangular circle,' but much more so than a 'winged lion.' "

To communicate with the molecular world the physicist goes to the laboratory. The "messages" he receives are experimental results. To help organize the rather long and tortuous story told in the next chapters, three of the clearest and most useful of these laboratory messages will be summarized here. They are phrased in a language which has served physics for hundreds of years, a language that fits laboratory events and speaks of such things as particles and waves, energy and momentum, position and time, continuity and discontinuity. But remember that these are words of an earthly vocabulary with no precise guarantee of validity in the other-world realm of quantum physics.

In the first place there is the quantum concept itself: the entities of matter and radiation usually exist in states which do not range over a continuous spectrum of possibilities. This "quantization" aspect appears in a long and varied list of experiments. Almost every property associated with molecular and atomic motion—particularly energy and angular momentum—is quantized under one set of conditions or another. The molecular world is not to be understood as a continuum; it is a world with a discontinuous, fine-grained quantum structure.

Second, it appears that matter and radiation are subject to a strange kind of wave-particle duality. A beam of electrons, for example, in one experiment resembles nothing more than a chaotic crowd of particles: when it falls on a fluorescent screen it produces a vast number of very tiny, random scintillations. But when this same electron beam is passed through two narrow slits situated close to each other, an ordered pattern of maximum and minimum electron intensity appears which is very difficult, if not impossible, to understand with a particle image. This ordered pattern is exactly like the "interference" pattern produced by a system of waves in the same situation. We are left with the strange conclusion that no single physical image suffices. Depending on the experimental arrangement, electrons (and light as well) may display either a wave or a particle manifestation.

The quantum and the wave-particle concepts force a third fundamental conclusion, the so-called "uncertainty principle." No attempt to make a simultaneous measurement of where a particle is and where it is going can ever be entirely successful. If, for example, a measuring device is invented which succeeds in locating precisely the position of an electron it inevitably causes a drastic change in the electron's velocity. We can no longer imagine an electron or any other small particle following a definite trajectory because no conceivable measurement can supply the simultaneous position and velocity information required to define that trajectory.

These are somewhat staggering concepts. They seem to raise more questions than they can possibly answer. How can anything be a particle and a wave at the same time? If waves are involved what kind of waves are they? Waves of what? How can the idea of a particle's motion make any sense if the particle has no trajectory? Why discard the trajectory concept in the first place just because it cannot be measured?

Physics has faced these problems for many years, some of them since 1900. By and large, especially when there has been no risk of chasing "winged lions," physicists have been astonishingly successful in dealing with the mysteries of the molecular world. These successes have always been most impressive when the language of mathematics could be used. Here, and throughout physics, mathematical equations accomplish calculational miracles without venturing into the realm of conjecture. An equation works (it agrees with experiments) or it doesn't. If a simpler and more efficient equation appears, the obsolete one is, with minimum fuss, discarded. The immense advantages of mathematical statements in quantum physics and elsewhere seem to teach the lesson that if our universe has a comprehensible pattern it must be a set of mathematical equations. Paul Dirac, whose synthesis of the mathematical structure of quantum theory is one of the monuments of modern physics, remarks that "One could perhaps describe the situation by saying that God is a mathematician of very high order and He used very advanced mathematics in constructing the universe."

But the human intellect, unlike Dirac's divine intellect, demands something more than solving equations and fitting experimental data. The organization of equations and data is, in a sense, only the beginning stage. Beyond lies the problem of translating the mathematical language of the equations into a verbal and *conceptual* language. Here we tread on very difficult ground, where the inadequacies of the conventional physical vocabulary become profoundly limiting. Many attempts have been made to construct an "interpretation," a general conceptual basis, for the equations of quantum physics. The efforts of Niels Bohr in this direction are particularly important. His so-called "complementarity principle" is a special logical system which sets out to rationalize the entire body of quantum phenomena. For most physicists Bohr's interpretation is acceptable, but there have always been dissenters, among them an impressive list of Nobel Prize winners whose criticism cannot wisely be ignored.

The modern physicist is forced to admit, with some embarrassment, that although he can formulate a powerful and beautiful mathematical theory of atomic and molecular behavior, he cannot be sure he knows exactly what that theory means. Perhaps it is in the nature of quantum physics that this state of affairs will persist, or perhaps the conceptual meaning of quantum behavior will eventually be defined to everyone's satisfaction. Until that happy day arrives we can certainly admire and use almost endlessly the mathematical theory. And we can listen with appreciation and enjoyment, and sometimes with dismay, to the story of the struggle to understand what it all means.

1

Two Papers

"Today I have made a discovery as important as that of Newton."
This is Max Planck speaking to his son as they walk on the outskirts
of Berlin on a winter day late in 1900. Planck had come to the end
of "a few weeks of the most strenuous work of my life," and had
reached a conclusion which he described, with the more characteristic modesty of his public statements, as having an "unexpected
vista." There have been few, if any, accomplishments in physics
with results more unexpected and implications more far-reaching.
Planck's postulates destroyed some of the most fundamental principles previously thought to be valid for dealing with problems on
the atomic scale. Not the least impressive aspect of his accomplishment is that Planck seems to have recognized from the outset the
immense importance of his work. For five years he was practically
alone in this recognition, except for a junior patent examiner in the
Swiss Patent Office at Berne. To the patent examiner, whose name
was Albert Einstein, Planck's theory was inevitable but appalling;
it was "as if the ground had been pulled from under me, with no
firm foundation seen anywhere upon which one could have built."

It was far from Max Planck's conservative nature to be a revolutionary; it was not his original intention to construct a new general
theory. His concern was with the specific problem of the energy
spectrum of thermal radiation, or, as it is generally known to the
physicist, "black-body" radiation. It was here that Planck was
confronted with the puzzle that inspired his intense efforts in the
winter of 1900. To reconstruct this story a few comments on previous
history are needed.

Thermal Radiation

When an object is heated it emits radiation with a broad spectrum of wavelengths lying mainly in the infrared region. This spectrum becomes independent of the shape and composition of the object, and dependent only on the temperature, when the radiation field is generated with equilibrium conditions inside a heated cavity. This state of affairs is approximately satisfied in a very hot oven. No matter what is in the oven—coal, glass, or metal—a uniform red color is emitted; reflected and transmitted light can no longer be used to recognize materials. The radiation contained in the cavity is in equilibrium with the materials present, including the walls, and, as Gustav Kirchhoff proved in 1859, the energy spectrum is entirely independent of the chemical properties, the shape, and the size of the materials.

Thermal radiation is emitted most intensely by a "black" object, one that absorbs, but does not reflect or transmit, incident radiation. (The blackness is, of course, actually seen only when the object is cool.) The study of thermal radiation has always been done with various "black-body" devices. Familiar black materials, such as carbon and platinum black, cannot be used because they are changed at high temperatures. The blackness is therefore created by closing the heated cavity except for a very small hole. This hole is black at low temperatures, regardless of the contents of the cavity, and shows the characteristic spectrum of thermal radiation at high temperatures.

As the temperature of the cavity is increased, the color of the emitted thermal radiation changes from red to white in a way which is familiar:

550°C.	dark red
750	cherry red
900	orange
1000	yellow
1200	white

To express the changes in the radiation spectrum quantitatively an "energy distribution" function $\rho(\nu,T)$ is defined such that $\rho(\nu,T)d\nu$ is the radiation energy per unit volume (the "energy density") with frequencies in the range between ν and $\nu + d\nu$ found in the cavity when its absolute temperature is T. The total energy density in the cavity, counting all frequencies, is the integral

$$\int_0^\infty \rho(\nu,T)d\nu.$$

An analysis of experimental work reported in 1879 by Josef Stefan, and a theoretical treatment by Ludwig Boltzmann published in 1884, had established that the total energy density increases very sharply with the temperature of the cavity—in fact, as the fourth power of the temperature:

$$\int_0^\infty \rho(\nu,T)d\nu = \sigma T^4, \tag{1}$$

where σ is known as the Stefan-Boltzmann constant.

In 1893 Wilhelm Wien had proved that the distribution function $\rho(\sigma,T)$ must have the general form †

$$\rho(\nu,T) = \nu^3 f(\nu/T), \tag{2}$$

the function $f(\nu/T)$ necessarily depending only on the ratio ν/T (and one or two constants). The far-reaching importance of Wien's derivation was quickly recognized. Its line of reasoning is entirely rigorous, beginning with nothing more than Kirchhoff's theorem and the second law of thermodynamics. It points to a function $f(\nu/T)$, which must, in view of the universal character of the black-body radiation, have fundamental significance. One of the major unsolved problems of nineteenth-century physics was the empirical and theoretical specification of the correct form for Wien's function $f(\nu/T)$.

Using a rather dubious theoretical argument, Wien himself proposed in 1896 that the unknown function should be given a certain exponential form,

$$f(\nu/T) = \alpha e^{-\beta\nu/T},$$

in which α and β are constants. The energy distribution function becomes

$$\rho(\nu,T) = \alpha\nu^3 e^{-\beta\nu/T}. \tag{3}$$

This distribution law was found to give an accurate representation of the black-body spectral data as known until about 1899.

---

† This equation and several others are given without proof because the proofs would lead us too far astray from the main argument. For advice on where to find the omitted proofs consult the Notes and Comment section at the end of the book.

Planck's Radiation Formula

With the Kirchhoff-Wien-Boltzmann-Stefan work as a background, Planck began his attack on the black-body problem in 1897. Taking advantage of the assertion of Kirchhoff's theorem that a black-body emits radiation which is independent of the wall material, Planck represented the molecules of the wall as simple harmonic "resonators" interacting with the radiation field of the cavity. When the wall and the radiation field are in equilibrium this simple model leads to the energy distribution function †

$$\rho(\nu,T) = (8\pi\nu^2/c^3)E(\nu,T), \tag{4}$$

where c is the velocity of light and $E(\nu,T)$ is the *average* energy of those resonators whose vibration frequency is ν. As indicated, this average energy also depends on the cavity temperature T (*not* on the temperature of an individual resonator). With the cavity walls and the radiation field they contain in equilibrium, the frequency takes on a double physical meaning: it not only represents a radiation frequency but also a possible vibration frequency of the wall resonators. (The symbol ν will refer to both meanings in what follows.) Equation (4) applies to a fictitious wall composed of simple harmonic resonators, but once a valid frequency-temperature relation is obtained for the average resonator energy $E(\nu,T)$, it must also, in the light of Kirchhoff's proof, apply to a cavity formed by any real kind of wall.

From here the principal task was to evaluate the average energy $E(\nu,T)$ of the resonators in equilibrium with the black-body radiation field. Planck's inclination was to approach the problem from the viewpoint of thermodynamics, particularly making use of the entropy concept. Much of his earlier career (he was thirty-nine when he started his work on the black-body problem) had been devoted to an attempt to clarify and broaden the significance of the second law of thermodynamics. This work had been frustrating—a major part of it had been anticipated by J. Willard Gibbs—but Planck had acquired an appreciation and a mastery of the thermodynamic method shared by few of his colleagues: "As the significance of the concept of entropy had not yet come to be fully appreciated, nobody paid any attention to the method adopted by me, and I

† Reference to a proof of this equation is given in the Notes and Comment section.

could work out my calculations completely at my leisure with absolute thoroughness without fear of interference or competition."

One of Planck's thermodynamic building blocks was the equation

$$dS/dE = 1/T,$$

which states the fundamental relation between entropy and energy for a system of constant volume. Differentiation of this with respect to temperature leads to another equation of fundamental significance,

$$d^2S/dE^2 = (-1/T^2)(dT/dE)$$

$$= -[T^2(dE/dT)]^{-1}$$

The derivative dE/dT can be evaluated for an harmonic resonator by combining Wien's radiation formula (3) and Planck's equation (4):

$$(8\pi\nu^2/c^3)E = \alpha\nu^3 e^{-\beta\nu/T},$$

so that $$E = (\alpha\nu c^3/8\pi)e^{-\beta\nu/T},$$

and $$dE/dT = (\beta\nu/T^2)E.$$

The entropy-energy derivative is

$$d^2S/dE^2 = -1/\beta\nu E$$

$$= -1/CE,$$

(5a)

where C depends on the resonator frequency but is independent of the temperature.

Planck was impressed by the simplicity of the last equation; however, he also came to recognize that the Wien formula (3) did not have a firm theoretical foundation and that even its empirical validity might be limited. Efforts were first directed toward improving upon the theoretical basis, but spectral measurements at low radiation frequencies by Otto Lummer and Ernst Pringsheim in 1899 made it apparent that the Wien formula had serious experimental limitations. In 1900, Planck's good friend Heinrich Rubens, with Ferdinand Kurlbaum, by extensive and precise work showed that, at high temperatures and low frequencies, the distribution function is clearly not an exponential function of the temperature, as Wien's equation had implied; instead, there is a simple dependence on the first power of the temperature: $\rho(T) \propto T$. This implies, with the assistance of (4), that the resonator energy varies in the same way with the temperature, $E(T) \propto T$, that the derivative dE/dT is constant, and that

$$d^2S/dE^2 = -1/C'E^2, \tag{5b}$$

where C' is another temperature-independent constant.

There are evidently two simple limiting cases: at relatively high frequencies (and high energies),

$$d^2S/dE^2 \propto -1/E, \quad \text{or} \quad (d^2S/dE^2)^{-1} \propto -E,$$

and at low frequencies (and low energies),

$$d^2S/dE^2 \propto -1/E^2, \quad \text{or} \quad (d^2S/dE^2)^{-1} \propto -E^2.$$

Planck noticed that a single equation sufficed to express both cases:

$$(d^2S/dE^2)^{-1} = -E(a + E), \quad \text{or} \quad d^2S/dE^2 = -[E(a + E)]^{-1}, \tag{6}$$

where a is a constant which is independent of temperature, but perhaps dependent on the frequency.

From the thermodynamic equation (6), together with Wien's law (2) and his own equation (4), Planck constructed a major part of the line of reasoning on which his quantum theory was based. The insight Planck displayed in these deceptively simple maneuvers is difficult to appreciate fully. To Max Born, "this adding up [leading to (6)] was one of the most fateful and significant interpolations ever made in the history of physics; it reveals an almost uncanny physical intuition."

Integration of (6) leads to

$$dS/dE = (1/a) \ln [(a + E)/E] + b,$$

in which b serves as a constant of integration. The derivative dS/dE is also equivalent to $1/T$. Therefore,

$$\left(\frac{1}{a}\right) \ln \left(\frac{a + E}{E}\right) + b = \frac{1}{T}.$$

The integration constant b is evaluated by recalling the Rubens and Kurlbaum discovery that at high temperatures the distribution function, and the average resonator energy as well, are proportional to the temperature. As T becomes large and

$$1/T \to 0,$$

E also becomes large and

$$\ln [(a + E)/E] \to 0.$$

Both sides of the integrated equation must approach zero at high temperatures; it follows that the integration constant must vanish: $b = 0$. The appropriate equation for the resonator energy is, finally,

$$E = a/(e^{a/T} - 1)$$

and, with (4), the energy distribution function is

$$\rho(\nu,T) = (8\pi/c^3)[a\nu^2/(e^{a/T} - 1)].$$

Wien's law (2) makes it clear that the "constant" a must depend on ν, $a = B\nu$, with B a true constant, since this supplies the necessary ν^3 in the numerator and the ν/T function is

$$f(\nu/T) = 1/(e^{B\nu/T} - 1).$$

The distribution function assumes the general appearance

$$\rho(\nu,T) = A\nu^3/(e^{B\nu/T} - 1),$$

where A is another frequency- and temperature-independent constant.

Planck found this radiation formula to be in complete agreement with the new spectral data of Rubens and Kurlbaum. Notice particularly that when ν/T becomes small (at low frequencies or high temperatures) there is, as the Rubens-Kurlbaum data require, an approximately linear dependence on the temperature:

$$\rho(\nu,T) = \sim(A/B)\nu^2 T.$$

The Road to the Quantum

Planck had confidence that his radiation formula was absolutely correct. In the first place, it was strikingly effective with the exceptionally precise spectral data obtained by Rubens and Kurlbaum. Planck relates that Rubens "checked my formula against the results of his measurements and found a satisfactory concordance at every point. Later measurements, too, confirmed my radiation formula again and again—the finer the methods of measurements used, the more accurate the formula was found to be."

Thus it was clear that Planck's equation was a fine empirical formula. But did it have a more fundamental significance? Could it be used as a guide for *theoretical* arguments? To Planck, with his incredibly sharp, intuitive understanding, the thermodynamic simplicity of his formula [as displayed in (6)] left no doubt concerning its theoretical credentials. It was *the* radiation law: there was no

other. It could be used as a basis for the development of a theory —
even one with revolutionary implications.

With no hesitation Planck set out in pursuit of a theory: ". . . on
the very day when I formulated [the radiation] law, I began to devote
myself to the task of investing it with true physical meaning."
Planck attempted to develop the physical meaning with an argument
he had long been reluctant to use. He turned to the statistical and
probability interpretation of entropy that had been introduced by
Boltzmann. The concept of entropy from the probability viewpoint
was difficult for Planck to accept: "I had not cared about the connection between entropy and probability. . . . There was nothing
tempting about it for me because every probabilistic law admits
exceptions, and at that time I attributed universal validity to the
second law of thermodynamics." Yet the statistical method suddenly
and dramatically opened the way to a derivation of the radiation
law. Planck's use of the statistical approach was roughly this.

Take it that there are N resonators in the walls of the black-body
cavity. The resonators have an average energy E and an average
entropy S, so that the total energy E_T and the total entropy S_T are
$E_T = NE$ and $S_T = NS$. The total entropy is also, according to Boltzmann's statistical method,

$$S_T = k \ln W.$$

The factor k is a proportionality constant now known as Boltzmann's
constant; it is related to the gas constant R and Avogadro's number
N_0, $k = R/N_0$. W measures the "disorder" by counting the number of
ways the system can be rearranged on the microscopic level without
changing its macroscopic state.

The counting procedure Planck used for obtaining W was similar
to a method devised earlier by Boltzmann. Consider, at least temporarily, that the total energy E_T is made up of n small *indivisible*
units, each one of magnitude ϵ: $E_T = n\epsilon$. If the two expressions for
the total energy,

$$E_T = NE \qquad \text{and} \qquad E_T = n\epsilon,$$

are equated, the numbers n and N are seen to be related by

$$n/N = E/\epsilon.$$

The central problem is to calculate the number of ways n units
of energy can be distributed among N resonators. One possibility
is that a single resonator can have all n energy units and the $N - 1$
remaining resonators have none. This arrangement can be realized
in N different ways by giving the full energy in turn to each of the N

resonators. Another possibility is to give one resonator $n-1$ energy units, another 1 unit and leave the rest with no energy. This distribution of the energy can be achieved in $N(N-1)$ ways. If the counting is continued so as to include all of the possible distributions within the macroscopic requirement that the total energy be exactly n of the ϵ units, the result is †

$$W = (N + n - 1)!/n!(N - 1)!.$$

In Boltzmann's treatment the small indivisible ϵ energy units were invented entirely for computational convenience: "This fiction does not, to be sure, correspond to any realizable mechanical problem, but it is indeed a problem which is much easier to handle mathematically and which goes over directly into the problem to be solved, if one lets the appropriate quantities become infinite." In Planck's problem the "fiction" could be removed by allowing the energy units to become infinite in number $(n \to \infty)$ and infinitesimally small $(\epsilon \to 0)$. This establishes the seemingly reasonable condition that a continuous range of energies is available to the material resonators.

To make this procedure possible, the equation for W must be manipulated to a form containing ϵ. Both of the numbers N and n are very large, so that

$$W = (N + n)!/n!N!$$

is an accurate approximation. Stirling's formula,

$$\ln(x!) = x \ln x - x,$$

can also be used, making it possible to rearrange the $k \ln W$ expression through the following steps:

$$k \ln W = k[(N + n) \ln(N + n) - n \ln(n) - N \ln N]$$

$$= Nk \left\{ \left(1 + \frac{n}{N}\right) \ln \left[N \left(1 + \frac{n}{N}\right)\right] - \left(\frac{n}{N}\right) \ln(n) - \ln N \right\}$$

$$= Nk \left[\left(1 + \frac{n}{N}\right) \ln \left(1 + \frac{n}{N}\right) + \left(\frac{n}{N}\right) \ln N - \left(\frac{n}{N}\right) \ln(n) \right]$$

$$= Nk \left[\left(1 + \frac{n}{N}\right) \ln \left(1 + \frac{n}{N}\right) - \left(\frac{n}{N}\right) \ln \left(\frac{n}{N}\right) \right]$$

$$= Nk \left[\left(1 + \frac{E}{\epsilon}\right) \ln \left(1 + \frac{E}{\epsilon}\right) - \left(\frac{E}{\epsilon}\right) \ln \left(\frac{E}{\epsilon}\right) \right].$$

† For more on this equation and the Boltzmann method, see the Notes and Comment section.

In the last step the ratio E/ϵ has been substituted for n/N throughout. What has been calculated is the total entropy,

$$S_T = k \ln W.$$

The entropy of a single resonator, $S = S_T/N$, is

$$S = k\left[\left(1 + \frac{E}{\epsilon}\right) \ln \left(1 + \frac{E}{\epsilon}\right) - \left(\frac{E}{\epsilon}\right) \ln \left(\frac{E}{\epsilon}\right)\right]. \tag{7}$$

Convert this entropy equation into an energy equation by forming the derivative dS/dE (at a certain resonator frequency ν),

$$\frac{dS}{dE} = k\left[\left(\frac{1}{\epsilon}\right) \ln \left(1 + \frac{E}{\epsilon}\right) + \left(\frac{1}{\epsilon}\right) - \left(\frac{1}{\epsilon}\right) \ln \left(\frac{E}{\epsilon}\right) - \left(\frac{1}{\epsilon}\right)\right]$$

$$= \left(\frac{k}{\epsilon}\right) \ln \left[\left(1 + \frac{E}{\epsilon}\right) \Big/ \left(\frac{E}{\epsilon}\right)\right],$$

and equating the result to $1/T$:

$$\left(\frac{k}{\epsilon}\right) \ln \left[\left(1 + \frac{E}{\epsilon}\right) \Big/ \left(\frac{E}{\epsilon}\right)\right] = \frac{1}{T},$$

or

$$E(\nu,T) = \epsilon/(e^{\epsilon/kT} - 1).$$

Recall Wien's law (2) and Planck's equation (4); combination of these equations leads to

$$E(\nu,T) = (c^3/8\pi)[\nu f(\nu/T)].$$

The last two equations are both written for the average resonator energy, $E(\nu,T)$. They are compatible only if the energy units ϵ are proportional to the resonator frequency ν:

$$\epsilon \propto \nu \qquad \text{or} \qquad \epsilon = h\nu,$$

where h is a proportionality factor. The energy expression is now

$$E(\nu,T) = h\nu/(e^{h\nu/kT} - 1),$$

and, with this substituted in (4),

$$\rho(\nu,T) = (8\pi\nu^2/c^3)[h\nu/(e^{h\nu/kT} - 1)]. \tag{8}$$

This energy distribution function has exactly the form required by Planck's radiation formula. Notice also that it changes into the form of Wien's radiation formula (3) in the low-temperature, high-frequency region (i.e. when ν/T is large):

$$\rho(\nu,T) \rightarrow (8\pi h\nu^3/c^3)e^{-h\nu/kT},$$

implying that the constants α and β of Wien's formula are evaluated

$$\alpha = 8\pi h/c^3 \quad \text{and} \quad \beta = h/k.$$

Boltzmann's counting procedure now dictates that the "fictitious" indivisibility of the energy units be removed by allowing them to become infinite in number and infinitesimally small in magnitude. The condition $\epsilon \rightarrow 0$, or $h\nu \rightarrow 0$, or $h \rightarrow 0$, must be introduced. But this has the astonishing effect of destroying the general validity of the derived equation:

$$\lim_{h\to0} \rho(\nu,T) = 8\pi\nu^2 kT/c^3.$$

What results from this holds true for the behavior found by Rubens and Kurlbaum for low radiation frequencies, but it is entirely wrong for high radiation frequencies. Yet if it is accepted that h has a very small but *finite* magnitude, large enough so that the quantity $h\nu/kT$ becomes appreciable in magnitude for part of the ν/T range, the equation retains its proper form.

For Planck there was no escape from an "act of desperation." The proportionality factor h, now known the world over as Planck's constant, *must* be assumed to have a finite magnitude. It must be conceded that it is *not* possible for a material resonator to absorb and emit energy in a continuous range. The resonators must gain and lose energy discontinuously, in small, absolutely indivisible units $\epsilon = h\nu$, which Planck called "energy quanta." This was a complete break with the principle of continuous change which had been fundamental to all nineteenth-century physics.

Planck's conservative nature did not allow him to take such a radical step easily. He wrote later, "I had already been struggling with the problem of the equilibrium of matter and radiation for six years without success; I knew that the problem is of fundamental significance for physics; I knew the formula that reproduces the energy distribution in the normal spectrum; a theoretical interpretation *had* to be found at any cost, no matter how high." On December 14, 1900, Planck delivered a paper entitled "On the Theory of the Energy Distribution Law in the Normal Spectrum" before the German Physical Society, and the quantum theory was born.

It would be nice if this history could now tell of the triumphant entry of Planck's quantum theory into an applauding and celebrating world of physics. But scientists, like most people, hold to the *status quo* with a grim attachment. To accept a change as profound as that proposed by Planck was something like adapting to life on another planet. Max Born, who was a student during these years, writes that ". . . during the first years of the new century very little happened. . . . I remember that Planck's idea was hardly mentioned in our lectures, and if so as a kind of preliminary 'working hypothesis' which ought of course to be eliminated." Planck was probably not surprised. In an earlier controversy he had learned what to expect: "A new scientific truth does not triumph by convincing its opponents and making them see the light, but rather because its opponents eventually die, and a new generation grows up that is familiar with it."

In the vanguard of the new generation was the junior patent examiner in Berne, who not only believed the quantum postulate but used it to formulate a theory so bold that Planck himself could not accept it for many years.

Albert Einstein

"You will never amount to anything, Einstein," was the judgment of one of his *Gymnasium* teachers. Another, who did not appreciate his disrespectful attitude, suggested that he leave school. Einstein was pleased to take this advice, and he spent a few happy months roaming around northern Italy. He next applied for admission to the Polytechnic Institute of Zurich and was refused. After a year of catching up on the *Gymnasium* subjects he finally entered the Institute, only to stay away from most of the classes and follow his own course of study in his rooms. With the considerable help of a friend, Marcel Grossmann, who had a talent for taking lecture notes, he managed to pass the examinations with average marks.

It is not easy to believe that about five years later this same Einstein was to make contributions to physics which rank with those of Galileo and Newton. How could such a mediocre student become a great creative thinker? To Einstein there was an inverse proportion between ability as a student and genuine creative ability. His successes, he felt, were achieved largely in spite of his formal education rather than because of it. His criticism of the educational system to which he was submitted makes it clear that not much has changed in seventy years: "This coercion had such a deterring effect that, after I had passed the final examinations, I found consideration of any scientific problems distasteful to me for an entire year. . . . It is, in fact, nothing short of a miracle that the modern methods of instruction have not yet entirely strangled the holy curiosity of inquiry; for this delicate little plant, aside from stimulation, stands mainly in need of freedom; without this it goes to wrack and ruin without fail."

When Einstein left the Polytechnic Institute his prospects were not brilliant. He was unable to get a permanent academic position even on the lowest rung of the ladder, and finally (after two years and further help from Marcel Grossmann) he found a position as a junior patent examiner in the Berne Patent Office. Not until he was almost thirty years old did he lay eyes on a genuine theoretical physicist. Thus was Albert Einstein barred by the scientific establishment, which was then, as it is today, dominated by the academic world.

To Einstein the years spent in the Patent Office came as "a kind of salvation." The work was interesting and not demanding, and, without the pressures of an academic job, he was free to exploit his marvelous ability "to scent out that which was able to lead to fundamentals and to turn aside from everything else, from the multitude of things which clutter up the mind and divert it from the essential." The university world offered no haven for the pursuit of such speculations: ". . . an academic career puts a young man into a kind of embarrassing position by requiring him to produce scientific publications in impressive quantity—a seduction into superficiality which only strong characters are able to withstand." For example, Einstein's great 1905 paper (described in the next section) would have done little to further an academic reputation; its arguments were so strange that they failed to impress the experts for almost twenty years.

Einstein spent seven years in the Berne Patent Office. In that dark, quiet corner of the scientific world he rewrote classical physics in his papers on relativity, greatly broadened Planck's quantum theory, and developed a system of statistical mechanics which he applied to molecular and radiation problems. His brilliance during those years has possibly never been surpassed. Inevitably recognition came, and suddenly, in just four years, he was raised to the very pinnacle of the academic world. In 1913, after he had been appointed to a succession of positions of increasingly higher rank, Planck invited him to come to the Kaiser Wilhelm Physical Institute in Berlin. Einstein first hesitated, then finally accepted, but for the rest of his life he had misgivings about the established ways of science. Shortly before his death he wrote, ". . . If I were a young

man again and had to decide how to make a living, I would not try
to become a scientist or scholar or teacher. I would rather choose to
be a plumber or a peddler, in the hope of finding that modest degree
of independence still available under present circumstances."

Particles of Radiation

In 1905, when he was twenty-four years old, happily employed in
the Patent Office, and had yet to make the acquaintance of a "real"
theoretical physicist, Einstein published three papers in the *Annalen
der Physik*. This was Volume 17 of that journal, and it is, as Max
Born writes, "one of the most remarkable volumes in the whole
scientific literature. It contains three papers by Einstein, each dealing with a different subject and each today acknowledged to be a
masterpiece, the source of a new branch of physics."

One of these papers provided the next step, and a giant step it
was, in the development of the quantum theory beyond Planck's
theory of the radiation formula. Planck had been very cautious about
the use and significance of the quantum concept. For good reasons,
considering its radical implications, he had hesitated to regard the
quantum as a real entity; it was to him more of a "formal assumption" necessary for the derivation of the radiation formula. Furthermore, Planck was careful not to infer anything concerning the structure of the radiation field; he restricted quantization to the behavior
of the material resonators. Einstein, in his 1905 paper, and in several
subsequent papers, took up the thesis that real quanta of energy
exist and that these are to be found, at least in certain experiments,
in the radiation field. He stated his position clearly:

> In accordance with the assumption to be considered here, the
> energy of a light ray spreading out from a point source is not
> continuously distributed over an increasing space but consists
> of a finite number of energy quanta which are localized at points
> in space, which move without dividing, and which can only be
> produced and absorbed as complete units.

Even more than Planck's work, Einstein's theory was developed
by reasoning from fundamental assumptions with very little experimental support. Such theories are frequently regarded with profound suspicion (or neglect) until the experimental support finally
appears, and then there is likely to be enthusiastic acceptance.

In the 1905 paper Einstein developed the concept of light quanta, or "photons" as they are designated in modern terminology,† using a variety of short and simple arguments. One of these takes a thermodynamic approach, with some similarities to Planck's method. Recall first that the total radiation energy density from all frequencies in a black body cavity is given by the integral

$$\int_0^\infty \rho(\nu,T)d\nu,$$

involving the energy (density) distribution function $\rho(\nu,T)$. Wien had shown earlier that another distribution function $\phi(\rho,\nu)$ can be used to form an integral

$$\int_0^\infty \phi(\rho,\nu)d\nu$$

to represent the total entropy density and that the two functions ϕ and ρ are related by the derivative $d\phi/d\rho = 1/T$, in close analogy with $dS/dE = 1/T$. The $d\phi/d\rho$ derivative is now applied to the case of low energy density, where Wien's radiation formula (3),

$$\rho = \alpha\nu^3 e^{-\beta\nu/T}, \qquad \text{or} \qquad -(1/\beta\nu)\ln(\rho/\alpha\nu^3) = 1/T,$$

applies, so that,

$$d\phi/d\rho = -(1/\beta\nu)\ln(\rho/\alpha\nu^3).$$

Integration of this, noticing that zero energy density ($\rho = 0$) implies zero entropy density ($\phi = 0$), proceeds as follows:

$$\int_0^\phi d\phi = -\left(\frac{1}{\beta\nu}\right)\int_0^\rho \ln\left(\frac{\rho}{\alpha\nu^3}\right)d\rho$$

$$\phi = -\left(\frac{1}{\beta\nu}\right)\left[\rho\ln\left(\frac{\rho}{\alpha\nu^3}\right) - \rho\right]\Big|_0^\rho$$

$$= -\left(\frac{\rho}{\beta\nu}\right)\left[\ln\left(\frac{\rho}{\alpha\nu^3}\right) - 1\right] \qquad (‡)$$

$$= -\left(\frac{\rho k}{h\nu}\right)\left[\ln\left(\frac{\rho}{\alpha\nu^3}\right) - 1\right]$$

† The term "photon" was introduced in 1926 by G. N. Lewis, who regarded this entity as an "important structural element within the atom." The name was suggested by the terms "electron" (named by Stoney in 1891) and "proton" (named by Rutherford in 1920).
‡ $\lim_{\rho\to 0}(\rho\ln\rho) = 0$.

In the last step $\beta = h/k$ has been used, † as is implied by Planck's radiation law (see page 17).

Now represent the total energy of the "monochromatic" radiation with frequencies in the range ν to $\nu + d\nu$ as $E(\nu)$ and write

$$E(\nu) = \rho v d\nu,$$

where v is the volume occupied by the radiation. Then the corresponding entropy in this frequency range,

$$S(\nu) = \phi v d\nu,$$

is written as follows, making use of the expressions just mentioned for ϕ and $E(\nu)$:

$$S(\nu) = -(\rho k/h\nu)[\ln (\rho/\alpha\nu^3) - 1]v d\nu$$
$$= -(\rho v d\nu k/h\nu)[\ln (\rho/\alpha\nu^3) - 1]$$
$$= -[E(\nu)k/h\nu][\ln (E(\nu)/v\alpha\nu^3 d\nu) - 1].$$

This is the total entropy of the monochromatic radiation with energy $E(\nu)$ occupying a volume v. If this same amount of radiation now squeezes itself into a smaller volume, v', there is a decrease in the entropy to

$$S'(\nu) = -[E(\nu)k/h\nu][\ln (E(\nu)/v'\alpha\nu^3 d\nu) - 1],$$

and the change in entropy is

$$S' - S = [E(\nu)k/h\nu] \ln (v'/v). \tag{9}$$

This bears a remarkable resemblance to the entropy decrease accompanying the contraction of n moles of an ideal gas from a larger volume v to a smaller volume, v',

$$S' - S = nR \ln (v'/v).$$

It also suggests the statistical calculation of the probability that N independent particles initially located in a volume v will be found by chance in a smaller volume v'. This probability is found to be

$$W = (v'/v)^N, \tag{10}$$

---

† This substitution was not made by Einstein in the 1905 paper. He showed a curious reluctance to use Planck's theory directly. Planck's constant, h, appears nowhere in the paper. In place of $h\nu$, for example, Einstein wrote $R\beta\nu/N_0$, where R is the gas constant and N_0 is Avogadro's number. It appears that in 1905 Einstein was unable to place the Planck radiation law in the framework of his own theory. In a later paper, the radiation law, and with it the constant h, became a part of the Einstein version of the quantum theory.

a calculation which assumes nothing concerning the structure of the particles or their laws of motion. The corresponding entropy decrease, according to the Boltzmann-Planck equation, is

$$S' - S = k \ln (v'/v)^N.$$

The "heuristic" viewpoint central to Einstein's paper is now displayed if (9) is rewritten in the Boltzmann-Planck form, so as to isolate a $k \ln W$ expression:

$$S' - S = k \ln (v'/v)^{E(\nu)/h\nu}.$$

A certain probability,

$$W = (v'/v)^{E(\nu)/h\nu}, \tag{11}$$

appears. Regard this as the probability that radiation of energy $E(\nu)$ and frequency ν will be found by accident in v', some part of the original volume v. The two probabilities, (10) and (11), are, of course, very similar. The implication is that (11), as well as (10), describes the behavior of independent particles and that these are, in some sense, particles of radiation. Since the particle viewpoint requires that the power to which the volume ratio v'/v is raised be the total number of particles N, it follows that

$$E(\nu)/h\nu = N, \qquad \text{or} \qquad E(\nu) = Nh\nu,$$

and, therefore, that the energy carried by each radiation particle is $h\nu$. Thus Einstein's argument suggests that the energy of a low-density radiation field (to which Wien's formula applies), like the energy of the material resonators in Planck's theory, is made up of small, indivisible quantum units.

The Photoelectric Effect

Aside from the black-body data analyzed by Planck, the experimental indications of quantum behavior available to Einstein in 1905 were rather meager. Nevertheless, he found three well known, but unexplained, effects which seemed to have quantum explanations according to his theory. One of these explanations, the most famous and important, concerned the photoelectric effect.

When a metal surface in a vacuum is illuminated with ultraviolet light an electric current is produced in direct proportion to the intensity of the light. A typical arrangement of the experiment is as follows:

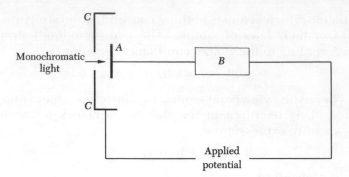

The photoelectric current is produced by illumination of the metal surface A, collected at the electrode C, and measured on the sensitive current-measuring device B. The potential between A and C, partly applied and partly the natural "contact" potential,† has a distinctive effect on the measured current:

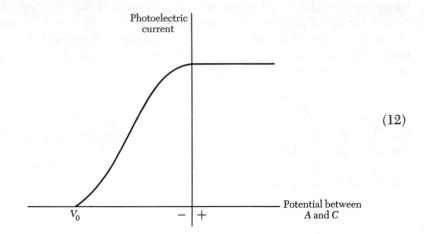

(12)

The current decreases sharply when "retarding" potentials are applied, making the collecting electrode negative with respect to the target electrode, and, at a definite retarding potential, marked as V_0 above, the photoelectric current stops entirely.

In 1899 Philipp Lenard had established that the current emitted

† The contact potential between two metals is the work required to move a charge (one coulomb if the potential is expressed in volts) from the interior of one metal to the interior of the other when there is no applied potential. The contact potential may either aid or retard the passage of charge between the metals, thus adding to or subtracting from the effect of the applied potential. A great deal of care was required to define the effect of contact potentials in photoelectric phenomena.

by the illuminated metal consists of electrons, making it clear that the electrical part of the experiment can be visualized as a simple particle phenomenon. Electrons leave the target metal with kinetic energy $mv^2/2$ and continuously lose this energy if they travel against a retarding negative potential between the target and collecting electrode. Electrons which are collected and contribute to the measured current must have had (when initially emitted) at least the energy

$$mv^2/2 = Ve,$$

where V is the total retarding voltage (including the effect of the contact potential) and e is the electronic charge.

The emitted electrons must acquire their kinetic energy from the light beam shining on the metal surface. If the classical viewpoint is taken, that the light waves beat on the metal surface like ocean waves, and the electrons are disturbed like pebbles on a beach, it seems necessary to assume that the electrons receive more energy when the illumination is made more intense, when the waves strike with more energy. This, however, is not what Lenard found; in 1902 he discovered that the electron energies, as measured by the retarding potentials, are entirely independent of the light intensity. Subsequent experiments have also demonstrated that, *whatever* the light intensity, there can be no more than a very small time lag (less than 3×10^{-9} second) between the time illumination is started and the time the photocurrent appears. This, too, does not seem to follow classical theory. When the light intensity is very weak many hours should be required for the region occupied by an atom to absorb, from the broad wave fronts of classical theory, sufficient energy to eject an electron. But this is not what happens.

Einstein, in another part of his 1905 paper, showed that these puzzling features of the photoelectric effect are quite comprehensible once the illuminating radiation field is understood as a collection of particles, or photons. If the photons can transfer their energy to the electrons of the target metal, a complete and very simple theory is easily stated:

> According to the concept that the incident light consists of energy quanta [photons] of magnitude $h\nu$, . . . one can conceive of the ejection of electrons by light in the following way. Energy quanta penetrate into the surface layer of the body [the target electrode], and their energy is transformed, at least in part, into kinetic energy of electrons. The simplest way to imagine this is

that a light quantum delivers its entire energy to a single electron; we shall assume that this is what happens. The possibility should not be excluded, however, that electrons might receive their energy only in part from the light quanta.

An electron to which kinetic energy has been imparted in the interior of the body [the target electrode] will have lost some of this energy by the time it reaches the surface. Furthermore, we shall assume that in leaving the body each electron must perform an amount of work P characteristic of the substance. The ejected electrons leaving the body with the largest normal velocity will be those that were [located exactly on] the surface. The kinetic energy of such electrons is given by $h\nu - P$.

If the body is charged to a positive potential V_0 and is surrounded by conductors at zero potential, and if V_0 is just large enough to prevent loss of electricity, it follows that

$$V_0 e = h\nu - P, \tag{13}$$

where e denotes the electronic charge. . . .

Each interaction leads to the same photon-electron energy transfer, regardless of the light intensity. The observation that electron energies do not respond to changes in light intensity is thus explained quite simply. Photoelectrons are produced almost immediately after illumination is started, since the particle-like photons impart their energy to highly localized regions; there is no spreading of photons on expanding wave fronts.

Einstein's equation (13) is written for the most energetic photoelectrons, those which leave in the normal direction and from near the surface of the illuminated metal. They correspond, then, to the maximum retarding potential, to the point marked V_0 where the photocurrent-potential curve (12) intercepts the potential axis. The kinetic energy of these electrons is

$$mv^2/2 = V_o e.$$

When the retarding potential is less than V_0 these surface photoelectrons are collected along with others that originate at points below the surface and have less than the maximum kinetic energy after they have worked their way to the surface. Therefore, as the retarding potential is decreased the photocurrent increases, and finally the photocurrent becomes constant when the retarding potential is zero or changed in sign to an accelerating potential.

It is clearly a consequence of (13) that the maximum retarding potential V_0 is a linear function of the frequency of the incident light. During the years 1912–1917, Robert Millikan, working in the Ryerson Laboratories at the University of Chicago, submitted the Einstein equation to this test. He used sodium as the target metal and illuminated it with light of various frequencies. Some of his results are plotted below (the potential V_0 does not take into account the contact potential between the target electrode and the collecting electrode):

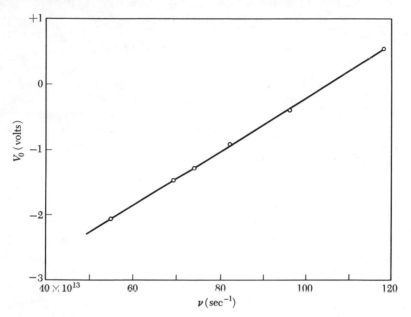

Unquestionably the V_0 versus ν relation is linear as required.

A further and particularly critical test is to use the slope of this line, which is h/e according to (13), to calculate Planck's constant. Millikan combined this slope measurement with a value for the electronic charge,

$$e = 4.774 \times 10^{-10} \text{ esu},$$

which he had measured himself, to arrive at

$$h = 6.56 \times 10^{-27} \text{ erg-sec}$$

for the most reliable value from his entire work. This is remarkably close to the result Planck obtained from black-body data:

$$h = 6.55 \times 10^{-27} \text{ erg-sec.}†$$

The precise agreement between these two calculations—which have nothing in common but the quantum postulates—is very impressive. Surely this is the strongest kind of evidence for the validity of the quantum theory in general, and for the Einstein photon concept in particular. But in 1915 it was not enough to establish any kind of general belief in photons. Even Millikan was skeptical. He admitted the empirical strength of the Einstein photoelectric equation —but no more: "I spent ten years of my life testing that 1905 equation of Einstein's, and, contrary to all my expectations, I was compelled in 1915 to assert its unambiguous experimental verification in spite of its unreasonableness. . . ." When Millikan described his results in 1916 he felt that the photon concept was hardly worthy of comment: "I shall not attempt to present the basis for such an assumption, for, as a matter of fact, it had almost none at the time." Nevertheless, he had to marvel at "the astonishing situation that these facts [the photoelectric equation] were correctly and exactly predicted nine years ago by a form of quantum theory which has now been pretty generally abandoned."

The Compton Effect

The story of the further trials of Einstein's quantum theory, and the accumulation of the mountain of evidence which finally brought photons into the world of physics, must be cut short for lack of space. We shall proceed to what was effectively the final episode in the story, the work of Arthur H. Compton on the scattering of X rays, first reported in 1923.

Compton's investigation concerned the "secondary radiation" produced by irradiating thin layers of such light elements as carbon with a "primary" beam formed in a conventional X-ray tube. Compton measured the wavelengths of the secondary, or scattered, radiation (using a Bragg crystal spectrometer) at various wavelengths of the primary radiation and at various angles with respect

† This calculation involves using the Planck distribution law (8) to derive an equation for the frequency ν_m or wavelength λ_m of maximum energy density and a theoretical version of the Stefan-Boltzmann equation (1). When measured values for ν_m and the Stefan constant σ are introduced into these two equations, two unknown quantities remain, h and the Boltzmann constant k. Planck's result for h is quoted; Planck obtained

$$k = 1.346 \times 10^{-16} \text{ erg deg}^{-1}.$$

to the direction of the primary beam. He found a difference in wavelength between the primary and secondary radiation. The difference was not large, but there was, unquestionably, a difference. The scattered wavelengths were always larger than those of the primary beam, and the magnitude of this wavelength was dependent only on the angle at which the secondary radiation was observed, and not at all on the scattering material or on the wavelength of the primary beam.

For some years before Compton's experiments it had been surmised that the scattering of X rays was due to interactions between the incident X rays and the electrons of the scattering material. A classical theory, based on the assumption that radiation was strictly wavelike, was available. However, when this theory was applied in a simple form to the X-ray–electron scattering interaction, it predicted that the primary and scattered radiation should have exactly the same wavelength, in direct disagreement with Compton's observations. After a futile attempt to elaborate the classical theory to fit the scattering data, Compton arrived at a highly successful quantum interpretation.

The central idea, as in Einstein's explanation of the photoelectric effect, is that the radiation beam (X rays, in this case) contains photons, each one of which carries an amount of energy $h\nu$. These are the same attractively simple radiation particles that Einstein had proposed, to no avail, almost twenty years earlier. If anything, the Compton concept of the photon is even simpler than that of Einstein. The photon-electron scattering interaction is, from the mechanical viewpoint, nothing more than a collision between two minute billiard balls. An electron belonging to an atom such as carbon is struck by an X-ray photon from the primary beam. Before the collision the electron is imagined to be stationary and free (actually it is bound by an atom, but the binding energy is negligible compared to the large energy which the photon brings to the collision), and the collision sets it in motion, billiard-ball fashion. To be sure, the electron, after the collision, is an exceedingly rapidly moving billiard ball. Its speed is so great that it must be described, from the relativistic viewpoint, as having a momentum of

$$m_0 v / \sqrt{1 - \beta^2} \quad \text{or} \quad m_0 \beta c / \sqrt{1 - \beta^2},$$

where m_0 is the electron's rest mass and β is v/c, the ratio between the electron's velocity v and the velocity of light c. The corresponding kinetic energy is $m_0 c^2 (1/\sqrt{1 - \beta^2} - 1)$. To represent the photon energy before and after the scattering collision, write $h\nu_1$ and $h\nu_2$, respectively; the corresponding momenta are $h\nu_1/c$ and $h\nu_2/c$.†

In Compton's words, the scattering event is "an X-ray particle colliding with an electron and bounding elastically from it with reduced energy, the lost energy appearing as the recoil energy of the electron." The momentum changes are shown with a vector diagram as follows:

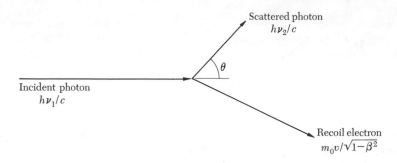

Conservation of momentum requires that the incident photon vector be equal to the vectors representing the scattered photon and the recoil electron:

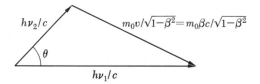

and this (with the law of cosines) leads to the equation

$$(m_0\beta c/\sqrt{1-\beta^2})^2 = (h\nu_1/c)^2 + (h\nu_2/c)^2 - 2(h\nu_1/c)(h\nu_2/c)\cos\theta.$$

Conservation of energy can also be stated, to the effect that the incident photon energy is equivalent to the total of the energy of

† That $h\nu/c$ is a measure of photon momentum can be seen by equating two Einstein equations for total energy, $E = h\nu$ and $E = mc^2$: $h\nu = mc^2$. The quantity on the left is the photon energy specified by Einstein's quantum theory and the quantity on the right is the total energy of any particle whose mass is m, as prescribed by Einstein's special theory of relativity. Since c is the velocity of the photon, mc is its momentum, and this, according to the above energy equation, is equivalent to $h\nu/c$. The situation is especially simple for the photon because it has no rest mass. For a particle with rest mass m_0 the momentum p is

$$p = \sqrt{(mc^2)^2 - (m_0 c^2)^2}/c$$
$$= (\sqrt{m^2 - m_0^2})c.$$

the scattered photon and the kinetic energy of the recoil electron:

$$h\nu_1 = h\nu_2 + m_0 c^2 (1/\sqrt{1 - \beta^2} - 1).$$

This can be rearranged as:

$$m_0 c^2 / \sqrt{1 - \beta^2} = h\nu_1 - h\nu_2 + m_0 c^2$$

$$m_0 c / \sqrt{1 - \beta^2} = h\nu_1/c - h\nu_2/c + m_0 c$$

$$(m_0 c / \sqrt{1 - \beta^2})^2 = (\quad)^2,$$

where ( ) has been written for the quantity $h\nu_1/c - h\nu_2/c + m_0 c$. The last equation can be solved for β^2:

$$\beta^2 = 1 - m_0^2 c^2 / (\quad)^2,$$

so that

$$\beta^2 (m_0 c / \sqrt{1 - \beta^2})^2 = (\quad)^2 - m_0^2 c^2$$

$$= (h\nu_1/c - h\nu_2/c + m_0 c)^2 - m_0^2 c^2$$

$$= (h\nu_1/c)^2 + (h\nu_2/c)^2 + 2m_0 c(h\nu_1/c)$$

$$- 2m_0 c(h\nu_2/c) - 2(h\nu_1/c)(h\nu_2/c).$$

When this is subtracted from the momentum-balance equation, and the result is whittled down, a simple equation in the two frequencies (before and after the collision) is derived:

$$\nu_1/\nu_2 = 1 + 2(h\nu_1/m_0 c^2) \sin^2(\theta/2).$$

Conversion to an equation in wavelength leads to †

$$\lambda_2/\lambda_1 = 1 + 2(h/m_0 c \lambda_1) \sin^2(\theta/2), \quad \text{or} \quad \lambda_2 = \lambda_1 + (2h/m_0 c) \sin^2(\theta/2).$$

The increase in wavelength $\lambda_2 - \lambda_1$ caused by the scattering of the primary X-ray beam at an angle of θ is therefore

$$(2h/m_0 c) \sin^2(\theta/2) \quad \text{or} \quad 0.0484 \sin^2(\theta/2)$$

when the wavelength is expressed in Angstroms (Å). For scattering at $\theta = 90°$ the theory calculates a wavelength increase of

$$(0.0484)/2 = 0.0242 \text{ Å},$$

regardless of the scattering material and the wavelength of the incident beam. Using X rays of wavelength 0.708 Å, Compton found an increase of 0.022 Å for the radiation scattered at 90°. When γ rays of

† Wavelength and frequency for any electromagnetic disturbance are related by $\lambda\nu = c$, where λ is the wavelength. Thus, $\lambda_1/c = 1/\nu_1$, $\lambda_2/c = 1/\nu_2$, and $\nu_1/\nu_2 = \lambda_2/\lambda_1$.

wavelength 0.022 Å were used the scattered wavelength at 90° was 0.043 Å, an increase of 0.021 Å. In spite of the large difference between the primary X-ray wavelength and the γ-ray wavelength, the scattered wavelengths are nearly the same amount longer in the two cases, and this wavelength increase agrees reasonably well with the theoretical calculation. Compton used his basic premise to derive several other equations which could be checked experimentally. In all aspects the theory was successful.

With the publication of Compton's work, resistance to the photon concept was at last struck a mortal blow. But death came slowly and painfully. Compton wrote that his "results . . . immediately became a subject of the most lively scientific controversy that I had ever known." The chief opponent was William Duane of Harvard University, who had been willing to accept photons in other X-ray phenomena, but curiously opposed any thought of photons in the scattering process. For some reason Duane was unable to repeat Compton's scattering experiments in his own laboratory. There was a formal confrontation at a meeting of the American Physical Society, in which Compton and Duane defended their results and interpretations. Compton diplomatically decided not to press his criticism: "I might have criticized his interpretation of his results on rather obvious grounds, but thought it would be wiser to let Duane himself find the answer." † Later, Compton visited Harvard and Duane's laboratory. This visit seems to have been the occasion for some intense discussions; late one afternoon Compton was seen "disheveled, unshaven and obviously overtired." Duane's difficulty was not found then, but a new series of experiments was started which eventually turned up some spurious effects and Duane at last found himself in agreement with Compton. Compton's matter-of-fact assessment of his own work seems a good closing remark for this final scene in the story of the Einstein photon: "It may be fair to say that these experiments were the first to give, at least to physicists in the United States, a conviction of the fundamental validity of the quantum theory."

---

† After another Compton-Duane encounter, at the 1924 meeting of the British Association for the Advancement of Science, the Indian physicist C. V. Raman expressed himself to Compton with the remark: "Compton, you are good debater, but the truth is not in you." This story is told by Compton with the opinion that this same discussion may have inspired Raman to begin the investigation which led to the discovery of the "Raman effect," a scattering phenomenon involving ordinary photons which is in many ways, as it turns out, similar to the Compton X-ray scattering.

Duality

To do them justice, the enemies of the photon were disturbed by much more than the simple idea of particles of radiation. The "corpuscular" theory of radiation had long been known in physics: it was originally proposed by Newton. The difficulty was that nine-teenth-century physics had very firmly established another, seem-ingly incompatible, theory of radiation. Such phenomena as refrac-tion and diffraction had been studied with great care and explained to everyone's satisfaction on the assumption that radiation forms, such as light and X rays, have a wave-like structure. Among other things, there was a need to explain "interference" effects, the mixing of radiation beams to give alternating light and dark bands. The two beams seem to cancel in one part of the pattern and to reinforce in another part. As anyone knows who has watched water waves, this sort of behavior is possible where two trains of waves come together. A wave theory gives a natural and easy explanation of interference. A particle theory, on the other hand, cannot, at least apparently, explain interference patterns unless it is assumed that the particles from the two beams annihilate each other in the dark bands and produce more particles in the light bands. Such a theory is very unattractive to the physicist, who finds it advantageous to insist on the principle of con-servation of energy with no complete annihilation processes and no creation of new particles.

So it was with nineteenth-century physics: a single picture, that of waves, sufficed to explain all the observed phenomena associated with radiation. Then came the quantum theory, Einstein's paper, and the unwelcome data on the photoelectric effect and X-ray scattering. Now there were observations which had simple *particle* explana-tions, and apparently no acceptable *wave* explanation. A strange duality had emerged: depending on how you looked at it, the same beam of light or X rays could seem to be either a shower of particles or a procession of waves. But which was it actually? Waves or parti-cles?

Like most of the other perplexing problems of modern physics, this one was first recognized and partially resolved in the mind of Albert Einstein. His remarks in 1909 prophesied exactly the way physics would turn in about fifteen years:

> It is undeniable that there is an extensive group of data concern-ing radiation which shows that light has certain fundamental properties that can be understood much more readily from the

standpoint of the Newton emission [particle] theory than from
the standpoint of the wave theory. It is my opinion, therefore,
that the next phase of the development of theoretical physics
will bring us a theory of light that can be interpreted as a kind
of fusion of the wave and emission theories.

In 1909 Einstein presented a theory which did indeed show a fusion of the wave and particle viewpoints. The central argument of
this theory dealt with the statistical calculation of energy fluctuations. The elements of the calculation lie outside the scope of this
chapter; it can only be said that Einstein's result showed two distinct kinds of fluctuations, one that could be traced to interference
between wave trains and another that reflected deviations of a type
familiar in collections of particles.†

The paradox of wave-particle duality, elaborated and extended in
many different ways, and finally resolved by completely uprooting
the great classical principle of determinism, became the dominant
theme of the quantum theory in the 1920's. Finally, when applied to
matter, that is, to electrons (which had previously been regarded
strictly as particles, but suddenly in 1925 emerged in a wave manifestation), it brought forth the present form of the quantum theory,
what is now known as "quantum mechanics." But that is a story for
other chapters.

† This analysis made use of the full Planck radiation law, unlike Einstein's argument
of the 1905 paper which was based on the Wien formula (3) and therefore restricted to
low energy densities.

2

The Bohr Era and Beyond

The whole history of its development [the quantum
theory] reminds me of the well-proved adage that "to
err is human." †

There are other directions to be followed now. Turn back—from the
physics of 1923, finally prepared to accept photons and wave-particle duality—to the primitive days of 1913. Max Planck had just proposed Albert Einstein for membership in the Prussian Academy, and
he found it necessary to make this remark: "That he may sometimes
have missed the target in his speculations, as for example, in his
hypothesis of light quanta [photons], cannot really be held against
him, for it is not possible to introduce fundamentally new ideas, even
in the most exact sciences, without occasionally taking a risk."
Robert Millikan was engaged in his thorough attempt to disprove the
photoelectric equation. The Planck postulates were more or less accepted, but they had been applied only a few times to atomic and
molecular problems. The quantum theory was contained in scattered, mostly misunderstood, papers. There had been no movement
toward the formulation of a general quantum physics.

In the summer of 1913 there appeared in the *Philosophical Magazine* the first of a series of papers which began to turn the tide. The
author was a twenty-eight-year-old Danish theoretical physicist,
with a rare personality, named Niels Bohr. Bohr's theory told of the
behavior of atoms, particularly the hydrogen atom, with a carefully
concocted mixture of Planck's postulates and classical mechanics.
The theory was applied by Bohr, with spectacular success, to the remarkable regularities of the hydrogen emission spectrum. This was,
to the physicists of fifty years ago, an almost incredible achievement.

† Max Planck, in an essay, "The Origin and Development of the Quantum Theory."

Spectroscopists had looked so long at the intricate patterns of atomic spectral series without benefit of a theory that they had despaired of ever finding one. Bohr's papers brought new light and hope for spectroscopy, and for the quantum theory as well.

To some extent Bohr's role in this was good fortune. Quantum physics was certainly coming, and it was inevitable that a quantum version of atomic physics would be proposed. Einstein remarked that he had had such ideas earlier, "but had no pluck to develop [them]." To be sure, it took skill and intuitive sense in large measure to devise a workable mixture of classical and quantum principles. To Einstein, Bohr's application of the "insecure and contradictory foundation" supplied by the quantum theory to the atomic problem was a marvel, "the highest form of musicality in the sphere of thought." Still the quantum theory loomed large enough after 1913 that its value to atomic physics could not have been overlooked much longer. Bohr was there, at the right time and the right place — and with just the right insights.

Physics owes a greater debt to Niels Bohr than to his theory of the atom, vital as it was. With an extraordinary combination of personal influence, simple tenacity, and stature as a Danish citizen, Bohr formed an institute in Copenhagen which became an international center for theoretical work in quantum physics. The Bohr Institute (officially, the Institute for Theoretical Physics) was dedicated on September 15, 1920, and it quickly attracted a most remarkable collection of young German, English, French, Russian, Dutch, Hungarian, Swedish, and American physicists. Bohr offered them a place to live and work at a time when academic positions were virtually unattainable and physicists, like artists, were poor.

Activities at the Institute were not always what one would expect from a learned gathering: ping-pong, girl-watching, and cowboy movies were favorite pastimes, along with poking elaborate fun at the chief. But a lot of strenuous and brilliant work was done in this seemingly easy atmosphere. Pauli, Dirac, Heisenberg, Landau, Bloch, Teller, Kramers, Gamov, and Heitler were all alumni of Bohr's institute: their names and accomplishments tell a large part of what happened in quantum physics during the crucial years of the 1920's and 1930's. Robert Oppenheimer wrote of this and Bohr's indispensable role in it: "It was a heroic time. It was not the doing of one man; it involved the collaboration of scores of scientists from many different lands, though from first to last the deep creative and critical spirit of Niels Bohr guided, restrained, deepened, and finally transmuted the enterprise."

What kind of a man was responsible for such incomparable leadership? Bohr had almost none of the characteristics expected of the man of influence. His lectures were likely to be "neither acoustically nor otherwise completely understandable." Despite prodigiously thorough effort, his papers and books are frequently repetitious and dense. Many an anecdote is told of his unembarrassed questions about matters of common knowledge. (Once, during a Princeton colloquium on nuclear isomers, Bohr became increasingly agitated, turning to his neighbor, who happened to be Abraham Pais, several times and whispering that it was all wrong. Finally he looked with "unhappy bewilderment" at Pais and asked: "What is an isomer?") His stock of jokes at any time was limited to about six and his own reaction to the punch line was likely to be more memorable than the joke itself. Yet his personality — without polish, erudition, eloquence, or fluency — was profoundly forceful and penetrating. Bohr spoke with a gentle directness and sincerity which impressed students and presidents alike. As Rosenfeld remarked of the stream of visitors to Copenhagen: "They come to the scientist, but they find the man, in the full sense of the word."

Bohr's energy and tenacity in all tasks, large and small, seemed beyond mortal capacity. When a Bohr paper or speech was in its final stages, the Institute, especially those of its occupants who were assisting in the preparations, had little rest for days, sometimes weeks and months. Every sentence and word, concept and equation, would be criticized until all arguments for and against had been precisely reviewed. After five or six drafts (the last one probably on the printer's page proofs), and still no end in sight, Bohr would retire to some deserted corner of Europe or England, accompanied by an unfortunate assistant, and the struggle would continue. Finally, unbelievably, Bohr would be satisfied. Pauli, who was frequently invited to Copenhagen for his valuable services as a critic, responded to one invitation with: "If the last proof is sent away, then I will come."

With his relentless insistence on clarity and vast gift for coaxing criticism from others, Bohr managed to penetrate some of the most tangled problems of quantum physics, especially those of a conceptual and philosophical nature. Bohr's arguments were not always as quick and brilliant as those of his younger colleagues, but they had daring and insight and, above all, a thoroughness which was impregnable. One of the most famous of Bohr's concepts, the principle of "complementarity," met with the friendly, but potent, opposition of Albert Einstein. Beginning in 1927, and continuing for twenty years, Bohr and Einstein carried on a perennial debate concerning the implications of complementarity. Einstein could not accept Bohr's conclusion that the physical world is fundamentally indeterminate, and did his best to break Bohr's defenses. But there was always an answer to Einstein's ingenious criticisms, and complementarity prevailed.

Bohr won a Nobel Prize. He occupied Carlsberg Castle, Denmark's "House of Honor" for its first citizen. He advised President Roosevelt and President Truman, entertained royalty, opposed the authority of Winston Churchill, and became known in every corner of the world of physics. His life and personality and supreme aspirations became legend. No scientist in this century, Einstein included, has reached such a position of eminence. But, before all else, his place was with the carefree—yet devoted and highly gifted—members of the Institute, teaching them, advising them, taking and using their criticism, and hugely enjoying their endless spoofing:

> Hail to Niels Bohr from the Worshipful Nations!
> You are the master by whom we are led,
> Awed by your cryptic and proud affirmations,
> Each of us, driven half out of his head,
> > Yet remains true to you,
> > Wouldn't say boo to you,
> Swallows your theories from alpha to zed,
> > Even if—(Drink to him
> > Tankards must clink to him!)
> None of us fathoms a word you have said!

Rutherford and the Nucleus

"All science is either physics or stamp collecting." †

It is no doubt significant that Niels Bohr began his career as a physicist in a laboratory "full of characters from all parts of the world working with joy under the energetic and inspiring influence of the great man." The "great man," known as "papa" to the inhabitants of the laboratory, was Ernest Rutherford.

Between 1907 and 1919 Rutherford brought together a research school at the Victoria University of Manchester which became internationally famous for its work on problems connected with radio-

† Rutherford's words of advice to a student.

activity. Under Rutherford, the "tribal leader," the physics laboratory at Manchester was alive with the activities, both serious and
humorous, of the young, talented—and frequently poor—members of
the staff. Presiding at all times, attending to any "gingering up"
needed when the work pace lagged, making the rounds of the laboratory "carolling 'Onward Christian Soldiers' (recognizable chiefly by
the words)," was the exuberant and genial Rutherford.

Rutherford was not inclined to indulge in undeserved modesty. A
friend once said to him enviously: "You are a lucky man . . . Always
riding on the crest of a wave." Rutherford's reply was, "Well, I made
the wave, didn't I?" One of his greatest achievements, certainly one
of the great "crests" in the history of physics, was the invention of
the nuclear model for the atom. The concept of the atomic nucleus in
Rutherford's extraordinarily fertile scientific imagination was at once
simple and capable of intricate predictions. The nucleus was to
Rutherford, and is to us today, a sphere of about 10^{-12} cm radius
which carries a positive charge and most of the mass of the atom and
is surrounded by negative electricity to a total radius of about
10^{-8} cm. With the classical theory of motion in a central force field
Rutherford drew from this model a clear description of how alpha
particles should be scattered by thin metallic foils. The predictions
were checked and corroborated completely in a monumental series
of experiments reported in 1913 by Hans Geiger and Ernest Mars-
den.

Bohr joined Rutherford and his "tribe" in 1912, just as the nuclear
atom was beginning to emerge. The Manchester laboratory and its
chief were very much to his liking: "Rutherford is a man you can rely
on; he comes regularly and enquires how things are going and talks
about the smallest details. . . . Rutherford is such an outstanding
man and really interested in the work of all the people who are
around him." Although Bohr showed signs of being a theoretician, a
breed of physicist not always welcome at Manchester, his talent, sincerity, and lack of pretension—and his previous fame as a soccer
player—seem to have impressed Rutherford immediately: "Bohr's
different. He's a football player!" was his judgment.

Bohr was fascinated by the nucleus concept of the atom, not only
by its impressive success in accounting for the scattering experiments, but also by its most conspicuous failure. It was obvious, to
Rutherford most of all, that no simple version of the nuclear atom
could ever be stable. It was natural to picture the negative electricity
surrounding the nucleus as electrons moving in planet-like orbits.
But electrons in orbits would continually change their velocity (at

least in direction); they would be accelerating and therefore, according to classical electrodynamics, would have to radiate energy all of the time. Thus the electrons in this atom would continually lose energy, and would gradually succumb to the attractive force of the nucleus. Eventually the electrons would collapse into the nucleus and the atom would be destroyed.

This was no challenge to the nucleus itself; the scattering experiments left no doubt about its characteristics. The problem to be solved, for which the scattering data offered no clues, concerned the status of the surrounding electrons.

The Atom According to Bohr

To Niels Bohr (and to several others who had thought about the problem before him, notably J. W. Nicholson) it was obvious that, however the electrons are disposed in the atom, they must obey laws which are predominantly nonclassical. Bohr noted in his first paper "On the Constitution of Atoms and Molecules" the "general acknowledgement of the inadequacy of the classical electrodynamics in describing the behavior of systems of atomic size." Why allow the classical theory to create a mystery concerning nonradiating electrons, when there is no reason to believe that the classical theory applies? Why assume that the electrons *should* radiate? Perhaps the greatest accomplishment of Bohr's theory was that it supplied and masterfully used the assumption that atomic electrons have "stationary states" or "waiting places" in which they do *not* radiate. This assumption, which Bohr restated and re-examined throughout five papers published between 1913 and 1915, finally emerged: †

> I. "An atomic system possesses a number of states in which no emission of energy radiation takes place, even if the particles are in motion relative to each other, and such an emission is to be expected in ordinary electrodynamics. The states are denoted as the 'stationary' states of the system under consideration."

† Bohr's arguments were not distinguished for their direct, straight lines. Postulates were likely to be worked out after the main conclusions had been reached. An impatient listener once interrupted a Bohr lecture for some clarification, bringing the angry response: "Of course you cannot understand what I try to say now; this may perhaps become understandable, but only after you have heard the story as a whole and have understood the end." De Broglie refers to Bohr, "with his predilection for 'obscure clarity,'" as the "Rembrandt of contemporary physics." The simple sketch of Bohr's theory presented here cannot, of course, do justice to the entire Bohr canvas.

How can electrons be described under the restrictions of a stationary state while they move around in the atom? Bohr, like Planck, felt that classical physics should be retained wherever possible. Although classical *electrodynamics* created difficulties (rotating electrons must radiate), there appeared to be no reason why classical *mechanics* should be entirely rejected. Bohr pictured the electron in a stationary state while it moved in circular or elliptical orbits according to Newton's laws. On the other hand, when the electron changed from one stationary state to another it appeared to make a nearly discontinuous "jump," *not* governed by classical mechanics. Bohr stated a second postulate:

> II. "The dynamical equilibrium of the systems in the stationary states is governed by the ordinary laws of mechanics, while these laws do not hold for the transition from one stationary state to another."

The rudiments of the classical mechanics of the Bohr atom can be demonstrated by writing the equations of motion for an electron of charge $-e$ and mass m, located by the polar coordinates r and θ and rotating around a nucleus of charge $+Ze$ in a circular orbit of radius a. The angular momentum l for an electron in this orbit is

$$l = ma^2\dot{\theta} \qquad (\dagger)$$

$$= 2\pi ma^2\omega,$$

where $\omega = \dot{\theta}/2\pi$ is the frequency of rotation, the number of circuits made by an electron in one second. The kinetic energy is

$$T = ma^2\dot{\theta}^2/2$$

$$= 2\pi^2 ma^2\omega^2 \qquad (1)$$

$$= l(\pi\omega). \qquad (2)$$

The nucleus exerts an attractive force of magnitude Ze^2/a^2 on the electron in the (negative) radial direction. Newton's second law of motion asserts that this force is equal to the mass of the electron times the radial component of its acceleration $a\dot{\theta}^2$:

$$Ze^2/a^2 = ma\dot{\theta}^2$$

$$= 4\pi^2 ma\omega^2,$$

or
$$Ze^2/a = 4\pi^2 ma^2\omega^2$$

$$= 2T,$$

† $\dot{\theta} = d\theta/dt$.

so that $\qquad\qquad\qquad T = Ze^2/2a.$

The potential energy due to the electron-nucleus electrostatic attraction is

$$V = -Ze^2/a.$$

The equations for the kinetic and potential energy can be combined to give the total energy A:

$$A = T + V$$

$$= -Ze^2/2a.$$

Both the potential energy and the total energy are always negative; they decrease (become more negative) as the electron and the nucleus approach each other, and increase as the electron moves away from the nucleus. Bohr represented the positive quantity

$$-A = Ze^2/2a$$

(the energy needed to take the electron entirely away from the influence of the nucleus—that is, the binding energy or ionization energy) with the symbol W:

$$W = Ze^2/2a. \qquad\qquad (3)$$

Notice that this is numerically identical to the kinetic energy,

$$W = T$$

$$= 2\pi^2 ma^2\omega^2. \qquad\qquad (4)$$

An equation containing only the binding energy W and the rotation frequency ω is derived by combining (3) and (4):

$$\omega^2 = 2W^3/\pi^2 me^4 Z^2. \qquad\qquad (5)$$

The above derivations assume a stationary nucleus. In fact, the nucleus has a slight rotational motion; both the nucleus and the electron rotate around the atom's center of mass. When this is taken into account the simple electron mass m is replaced in the above equations with $mM/(m + M)$, where M is the mass of the nucleus; the quantity $mM/(m + M)$ is the so-called "reduced mass" of the electron-nucleus system. Assume in what follows that the symbol m represents the reduced mass instead of the simple electron mass.

As yet no condition has been provided for recognition of the various possible stationary states. Bohr approached this problem by forming a suitable adaptation of Planck's theory. He formulated two postulates, concerning two processes, the binding of an electron to a nucleus and the transition of an atom from a higher stationary state to a lower one. Bohr assumed that as each process occurred there was an emission of "homogeneous radiation"—that is, a single quantum of energy. Changes in the opposite direction, the ionization process in which an electron escapes from a nucleus, and an "upward" transition from a lower to a higher stationary state, proceeded with the *absorption* of a single energy quantum. In all cases the energy of the quantum was taken to be equivalent to Planck's constant multiplied by an appropriate frequency factor.

The postulate dealing with transitions between stationary states was this:

> III. "Any emission or absorption of energy radiation will correspond to the transition between two stationary states. The radiation emitted during such a transition is homogeneous and the frequency ν is determined by the relation
>
> $$h\nu = A_1 - A_2,$$
>
> where h is Planck's constant and A_1 and A_2 are the energies of the system in the two stationary states."

The binding-energy postulate was developed with the following rather detailed argument.† When an atom forms a stationary state by the binding of an electron to a nucleus the system loses an amount of energy W, and this must be different for each of the various possible stationary states. Bohr assumed the connection $W \propto h\omega$ between the binding energy W and the fundamental "vibration" frequency of the electron, its rotation frequency ω. He pictured two different stationary states forming with energies which differed by whole-number multiples of $h\omega$; for a particular stationary state, say the nth one, the binding energy was therefore written $W_n \propto nh\omega$, where n is a "quantum number" with only whole-number values: $n = 1, 2, 3, \ldots$. Thus Bohr related atomic energy quanta to electron rotation frequencies in much the same way Planck had related resonator energy quanta to the resonator vibration frequencies. The above proportionality is made into an equality by inserting a constant α (to be evaluated in the subsequent argument): $W_n = \alpha nh\omega$. By substituting this expression for W into (5) and then solving for ω, an equa-

---

† This is one of several derivations presented by Bohr to justify the binding-energy postulate. The others, though simpler, are less complete and seem somewhat less convincing.

tion is obtained which contains only the quantum number n and the fundamental constants h, e, and m:

$$\omega_n = \pi^2 m e^4 Z^2 / 2\alpha^3 n^3 h^3. \tag{6}$$

An equation for the binding energy is derived by multiplying (6) by $\alpha n h$:

$$W_n = \pi^2 m e^4 Z^2 / 2\alpha^2 n^2 h^2.$$

The total energy A_n for the electron-nucleus system is the negative of the expression for W_n:

$$A_n = -W_n$$
$$= -\pi^2 m e^4 Z^2 / 2\alpha^2 n^2 h^2. \tag{7}$$

But what value can be assigned to α? It might be surmised from Planck's theory that $\alpha = 1$. However, Planck and Bohr used quite different procedures and dealt with different dynamical systems (atoms are not simple harmonic resonators); the value of α must be obtained without any further use of the Planck theory. Bohr's solution was to consider the situation in which the quantum number n becomes very large, forming orbits of large radius and low rotation frequency. In this way a region is defined where the quantum laws merge into the classical laws. Since the latter are well known it proves possible to evaluate α for the classical case, but α, a true constant, must have the same value elsewhere, particularly for the "nonclassical" orbits which place the electron closer to the nucleus.

The device of making the quantum laws "correspond" to the classical laws was one of Bohr's most important contributions and one in which he took particular pride (in a letter to Rutherford he mentions ". . . a beautiful analogy between the old electrodynamics and the considerations used in my paper . . ."). This "correspondence principle" was used by Bohr throughout much of his work in quantum physics and it finally became the basis for the new quantum mechanics invented by Heisenberg. Although the correspondence principle became increasingly elaborate in later work, it was always based on one simple concept: that when the scale is suitably adjusted, classical physics and quantum physics must merge.

Consider a transition from the $(n + 1)$th to the nth stationary state in this "correspondence region." From (7) and Postulate III it follows that the frequency of the quantum emitted in this transition is

$$\nu = \left(\frac{\pi^2 m e^4 Z^2}{2\alpha^2 h^3}\right)\left[\frac{1}{n^2} - \frac{1}{(n+1)^2}\right]$$
$$= \left(\frac{\pi^2 m e^4 Z^2}{2\alpha^2 h^3}\right)\left[\frac{(2n+1)}{n^2(n+1)^2}\right].$$

If n is very large, as it should be if the correspondence argument is to apply, it follows that $2n \gg 1$, $n \gg 1$, and that

$$\nu = (\pi^2 m e^4 Z^2 / 2\alpha^2 h^3)(2/n^3)$$

is a good approximation. According to classical electrodynamics, which must also have validity in the correspondence region, the frequency ν of the radiation emitted by the rotating electron is equivalent to the electron rotation frequency ω. Before the transition, the latter from (6) is

$$\omega = \pi^2 m e^4 Z^2 / 2\alpha^3 n^3 h^3,$$

and, within the approximation used ($n \rightarrow \infty$), the frequency after the transition is the same. When the two frequencies ω and ν are equated, the requirement $\alpha = \frac{1}{2}$ is established, equations (6) and (7) are completed, and

$$\omega_n = 4\pi^2 m e^4 Z^2 / n^3 h^3, \tag{6a}$$

$$A_n = -2\pi^2 m e^4 Z^2 / n^2 h^2, \tag{7a}$$

and the original assumption for the binding energy is now

$$W = n h \omega / 2. \tag{8}$$

This last equation must now be incorporated into the theory as a postulate. Rather than use the binding energy W for this statement Bohr preferred to use its equivalent, the kinetic energy T:

> IV. "The various possible stationary states of a system consisting of an electron rotating around a positive nucleus are determined by the relation $T = n h \omega / 2$, where T is the mean value of the kinetic energy of the system, ω the frequency of rotation, and n a whole number."

To Bohr's critics this postulate was hard to accept, apparently because of the factor $\alpha = \frac{1}{2}$. The correspondence argument, powerful as it was, seemed to them little more than a contrivance to force the right conclusion. Richard Courant, who defended Bohr against these critics (becoming "a martyr to Bohr's model"), recalls Carl Runge, a well-known Göttingen spectroscopist, saying: "Niels, it is true, has made a nice enough impression, but he obviously has done a strange if not crazy stunt with that paper . . . ." Others, who were able to penetrate Bohr's arguments beyond his unconventional postulates, found that the theory had some very impressive applications. As early as 1913 James Jeans remarked to a meeting of the British Association for the Advancement of Science: ". . . Dr. Bohr has arrived at a most ingenious and suggestive, and I think I must add convincing, explanation of the laws of the spectral series." Jeans could not object to the unorthodox postulates: their justification was "the very weighty one of success."

What impressed Jeans, and a considerable representation of the rest of the world of physics, was the ease with which Bohr's theory explained two well-known but mysterious empirical rules of spectroscopy. The first of these had been discovered thirty years earlier by Johann Jakob Balmer, a Swiss schoolteacher and accomplished numerologist, who found that the lines of the hydrogen emission spectrum could be expressed by the formula

$$\lambda = Am^2/(m^2 - n^2),$$

where m and n are both integers (and $m > n$), λ is the wavelength of the emitted line, and A is a constant. The hydrogen lines known in Balmer's time fit the formula with $n = 2$ and $m = 3, 4, 5, 6, \ldots$. Balmer also conjectured that other "orders" of hydrogen lines might be found in which n would have other integer values.

A more general form of the Balmer equation was found by Janne Rydberg, who inverted and modified it slightly to calculate the inverse wavelength $1/\lambda$, or "wave number." As it is written in modern usage, the Rydberg version of the equation is

$$\tilde{\nu} = \frac{1}{\lambda} = R \left(\frac{1}{n^2} - \frac{1}{m^2} \right), \tag{9a}$$

in which $\tilde{\nu}$ (read this "nu tilde") represents the wave number (usually in units of cm^{-1}) and R is another constant, known today as the "Rydberg constant." An equation for the emitted frequency ν is formed when the general wavelength-frequency equation, $\lambda \nu = c$ (c = velocity of light), is used:

$$\nu = R' \left(\frac{1}{n^2} - \frac{1}{m^2} \right), \tag{9b}$$

where R' is another version of the Rydberg constant, related to the first one by the factor c: $R' = Rc$.

The Rydberg formula suggests that the frequency of a spectral line can be expressed, at least mathematically, as a difference between two "spectral terms," one being Rc/n^2 and the other Rc/m^2. Formally, then, one can write $\nu = T_n - T_m$, where T_n and T_m represent the two spectral terms. This way of writing the spectral frequencies raises an important possibility. If, for example, a spectrum contains two lines which can be labeled $\nu_a = T_3 - T_1$ and $\nu_b = T_2 - T_1$, then if there is a line in the spectrum corresponding to the term difference $T_3 - T_2$ it must have the frequency

$$T_3 - T_2 = (T_3 - T_1) - (T_2 - T_1)$$
$$= \nu_a - \nu_b.$$

On the other hand, if the frequencies ν_a and ν_b have the different term labels $\nu_a = T_2 - T_1$ and $\nu_b = T_3 - T_2$, the line for $T_3 - T_1$, if it occurs, must be

$$T_3 - T_1 = (T_2 - T_1) + (T_3 - T_2)$$
$$= \nu_a + \nu_b.$$

These relationships can be seen diagrammatically, with a vertical scale representing the relative position of each term. The three terms T_1, T_2, T_3 might, for example, be located as follows:

The second term relation described above is then represented

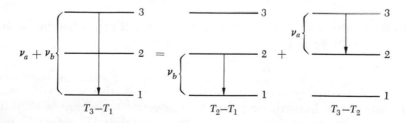

This implies that there may be certain "combination" relations among the frequencies of a spectrum: if the frequencies ν_a and ν_b

occur in the spectrum, the combination frequencies $\nu_a + \nu_b$ and $\nu_a - \nu_b$ may also occur. Such combinations are, in fact, found with great regularity and precision, not only in the hydrogen spectrum but in all other spectra as well; and they are efficiently represented and predicted with term formulas. This mode of spectrum analysis was first recognized by Rydberg and first used explicitly by Walther Ritz. The method, in all of its aspects, is known as the "Rydberg-Ritz combination principle."

Incredibly, these various rules of spectroscopy had been known for years without arousing any suspicion that they contained simple clues concerning the structure of the atom. Bohr once remarked that the Balmer formula and the Rydberg version of it were regarded in the same light "as the lovely patterns on the wings of butterflies; their beauty can be admired, but they are not supposed to reveal any fundamental biological laws."

The "lovely patterns" of spectroscopy are the very substance of Bohr's theory. The Balmer-Rydberg formula for the hydrogen spectral series emerges directly when Postulate III and (7a) are used to evaluate the energies of the two stationary states involved in a transition ($Z = 1$ for hydrogen):

$$\nu = (1/h)(A_1 - A_2)$$
$$= (2\pi^2 me^4/h^3)(1/n_2{}^2 - 1/n_1{}^2). \tag{10}$$

This applies to a transition between the n_1th and the n_2th stationary state ($n_1 > n_2$: an emission). The equation derived has the same form as the empirical Balmer-Rydberg equation (9b) and, in fact, agrees with it exactly if the theoretical factor $2\pi^2 me^4/h^3$ has the same numerical value as the measured constant R'. Using the values for e, m, and h that were available in 1914, Bohr calculated

$$2\pi^2 me^4/h^3 = 3.26 \times 10^{15} \text{ sec}^{-1}.$$

He found this to be in excellent agreement with the observed value for the Rydberg constant,

$$R' = 3.29 \times 10^{15} \text{ sec}^{-1}.$$

The Rydberg-Ritz combination principle is also a simple consequence of the Bohr theory. The Ritz spectral terms are simply the energies of the various stationary states. Postulate III naturally associates two such energy terms with each line of the spectrum. If A_n and A_m are two stationary-state energy levels ($A_n > A_m$), then the

$n \to m$ transition results in emission of a quantum whose energy is $A_n - A_m$ and whose frequency is

$$\nu(n,m) = (A_n - A_m)/h.$$

Frequency combinations are easily derived. If, for instance, $\nu(n,k)$ and $\nu(k,m)$ are the frequencies emitted in $n \to k$ and $k \to m$ transitions, then

$$\nu(n,k) = (A_n - A_k)/h \qquad \text{and} \qquad \nu(k,m) = (A_k - A_m)/h,$$

and

$$\nu(n,m) = (A_n - A_m)/h$$

$$= \nu(n,k) + \nu(k,m) \tag{11}$$

is the frequency emitted in the $n \to m$ transition. As the combination rule requires, it is predicted that if the frequencies $\nu(n,k)$ and $\nu(k,m)$ occur in a spectrum then the sum of these $\nu(n,k) + \nu(k,m)$ can also occur.

Term diagrams in the Bohr theory become diagrams of energy levels. The three energies, A_n, A_k, A_m, can, for example, be placed on a vertical energy scale,

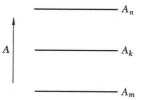

The three transitions, $n \to m$, $n \to k$, $k \to m$, which give rise to the three frequencies $\nu(n,m)$, $\nu(n,k)$, $\nu(k,m)$, are pictured as follows:

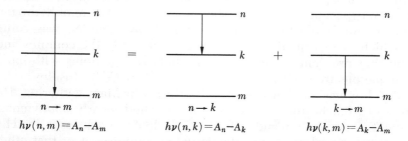

The entire atomic hydrogen emission spectrum as we know it today is expressed by Bohr's equation (10). It happened, however, that at the time Bohr presented his first paper there were three spectral

series ascribed to hydrogen which were *not* of the type specified by
(10), since they required that both n_1 and n_2 take on half-integral
values. One of these series had been discovered by E. C. Pickering
in the spectrum of a star and the other two had been observed by Alfred Fowler in mixtures of hydrogen and helium. With considerable
courage and confidence in his theory Bohr asserted that all series of
the half-integral type were due to helium. Postulate III and (7a) applied to a helium nucleus ($Z = 2$) bound to one electron (e.g. the ion
He$^+$) lead to

$$\nu = \left(\frac{8\pi^2 me^4}{h^3}\right)\left(\frac{1}{n_2{}^2} - \frac{1}{n_1{}^2}\right)$$

or

$$\nu = \left(\frac{2\pi^2 me^4}{h^3}\right)\left[\frac{1}{(n_2/2)^2} - \frac{1}{(n_1/2)^2}\right].$$

This formula (with $n_2 = 4$ and $n_1 = 5, 6, 7, \ldots$) seemed to account for
the Pickering series, but did not, to Fowler's satisfaction, agree
precisely enough with the observed frequencies of the other two
series. This prompted Bohr to correct his equation by replacing the
simple electronic mass with the reduced mass, something he had
neglected to do in his first paper. At about this same time Bohr's
viewpoint was corroborated experimentally, when E. J. Evans reported that the Fowler series had been observed in pure helium but
could not be found in pure hydrogen. Bohr also predicted that the
lithium ion Li^{++} (for which $Z = 3$) and the beryllium ion Be^{+++} ($Z = 4$)
should form a series of spectral lines. Subsequently, series of these
types were found in star spectra.

Moseley and Many-electron Atoms

While Bohr's papers were bringing new life to theoretical atomic
physics, especially to an understanding of the structure of hydrogen
with its single electron, an experimental investigation was going
on which made equally dramatic contributions to the complex and
confusing problem of sorting out the behavior of atoms with more
than one electron. This was the work of Henry G. J. Moseley.

Moseley was another one of Rutherford's brilliant gathering. He
came to Manchester after an undistinguished, nearly anonymous,
student career at Eton and Oxford. His lack of promise, as judged by
the conventional academic standards, is reminiscent of that other
unsuccessful student, Albert Einstein.† To Rutherford's discerning

---

† Moseley remarked that at the time of his graduation from Oxford his mind was so
"full of cobwebs" he could not think intelligently of a research problem.

eye, however, there was clearly a spark. Moseley was hired as a "lecturer and demonstrator" with an annual salary of £140, and he began work on the problem of characterizing the β particles emitted by radium. This work, which Moseley completed when he was only twenty-five, was masterfully done and drew the attention of the President of the Royal Society.

In 1913 Moseley began his famous work on X rays. His purpose was to measure the characteristic X-ray spectra of series of elements. Unlike the optical spectra, the lines of the X-ray spectra of elements adjacent in the periodic arrangement are similar, there being a continuous and predictable increase in the characteristic frequencies along a series toward higher atomic masses. These predictable wavelength changes were first investigated and accurately characterized by Moseley. His approach was to measure the frequency of the "K_α" and other lines produced when the element investigated is used as the target in an X-ray tube, and then to correlate this frequency with the element's supposed atomic number, the number that designates its position in the periodic table.

Before the application of X-ray spectra to the problem of determining atomic numbers, the elements were listed in the periodic table largely in the order of increasing atomic mass, and placement in series and groups was determined by chemical similarities. The atomic number was then decided by the position of the element in this sequence. In a few cases the chemical criteria and the arrangement strictly according to atomic mass were in conflict; for example, if argon and potassium are listed with potassium first (atomic mass = 39.10) and argon next (atomic mass = 39.94) potassium falls in the group of inert gases and argon falls in the alkali metal group. This is, of course, chemically absurd, and so these elements were placed with the atomic masses in reverse order. Two other such pairs of elements are tellurium and iodine, and cobalt and nickel.

Vagueness of the chemical evidence left the "rare-earth" part of the periodic table almost hopelessly confused. The rare-earth series was known to begin with lanthanum (atomic number = 57) and end before tantalum, but estimates on the number of elements lying between varied from fourteen to twenty-three. Atomic number assignments within the rare earths and thereafter were entirely speculative.

Moseley first worked with the series of metals lying between calcium and zinc. For these elements he found a precise and beautiful correlation between the K_α frequency ν and the atomic number Z. When the frequency is divided by $(3/4)R'$, where R' is the Rydberg constant, a number is obtained whose square root is very nearly one less than the atomic number:

$$Z - 1 = \sqrt{\nu/(3R'/4)}, \qquad \text{or} \qquad \nu = R'(Z-1)^2(3/4). \qquad (12)$$

Whereas the number $\sqrt{\nu/(3R'/4)}$ increases in a regular way from one element to the adjacent one in the series, the atomic masses vary in a much less uniform way. In fact, the anomalous pair cobalt and nickel happened to be included in the metals investigated; their order as predicted by (12) is the reverse of the order of their atomic masses.

Continuing and extending the technique originated with the calcium-zinc series, Moseley observed X-ray spectra (not only the K_α-line but four others as well) for thirty-nine of the sixty-seven elements between aluminum and gold. Besides verifying the necessity for listing some elements out of order in the mass sequence, Moseley's unambiguous evaluation of the atomic numbers also showed gaps where there was a number, but no known element that matched it. Four such elements were indicated, for numbers 43, 61, 72, and 75, and they were eventually found, the last one some thirty-four years later. Each element, as Moseley remarked, was put "into its right pigeon hole," even those that had never been seen.

Moseley had arrived at a physical method for determining the atomic number of an element which was entirely independent of the element's chemical properties. He could give a definite assignment of the atomic number and the appropriate place in the periodic table, a task incomparably more difficult when done by chemical means. The French chemist Georges Urbain, who supplied Moseley with samples of rare earth compounds, wrote to Rutherford of his amazement with Moseley and what he could do:

> I was most surprised to find a very young man capable of doing such remarkable work. . . . Moseley's law, for the end as well as for the beginning of the group of rare earths, has established in a few days the conclusions of my efforts of 20 years of patient work. However, it is not only that which makes me admire Moseley's work. His law replaced the somewhat imaginative classification of Mendeleyev with one which was scientifically precise. It brought something definite into a period of the hesitant research on the elements. It ended one of the finest chapters in the history of science.

The simplicity of Moseley's formula (12) raises the intriguing question of its theoretical significance. A theory which explains this equation also explains physically the atomic number Z. It happened that Bohr was evolving a theory of many-electron atoms at the same time the remarkable X-ray data were being collected, and Moseley used Bohr's theory to derive an equation almost identical in form to (12). Neither Bohr's theory nor Moseley's use of it has survived the more sophisticated theories which came later; but the major conclusion derived from Moseley's interpretation, that an element's atomic number and the nuclear charge of its atoms (measured in electronic units) are identical, remains an indispensable landmark. Among other things, it defines exactly the contents and limits of the periodic table. Since the nuclear charge must be an integral number of electronic units $+e$ (fractions of e are not known), so must the atomic number be an integer. Once an element is found for each possible whole number the list of elements must be considered closed and complete.

Moseley's X-ray work, a highly distinguished effort if it had required a lifetime, was completed and published in less than a year (this included time for a move from Manchester to Oxford and a complete rebuilding of the apparatus with the dubious services of a technician who was "a thorn in the flesh"). When England entered the war in 1914 Moseley quickly volunteered his services. He was commissioned in the Royal Engineers and became a signals officer. In June of 1915 his brigade was sent to the Dardanelles. Two months later a confused action took place in which the brigade was led, deliberately or mistakenly, by two guides who later disappeared, to a position in front of the British lines. The men slept during the night and awoke to recognize their mistake in the daylight, but by that time the Turks had started an attack. Sometime during the morning Moseley was shot through the head.

The colossal evil of that bullet and the war that caused it to be fired was expressed by Robert Millikan: "In a research which is destined to rank as one of the dozen most brilliant in the history of science a young man twenty-eight years old threw open the windows through which we can glimpse the sub-atomic world with a definiteness and certainty never dreamt of before. Had the European War had no other result than the snuffing out of this young life, that alone would make it one of the most hideous and irreparable crimes in history . . . ."

Franck and Hertz

Bohr's first paper expressed clearly the hypothesis of atomic stationary states and, as outlined earlier, it made superb use of this concept by explaining atomic emission spectra. However, the implications of the stationary state postulate reach considerably beyond emission processes involving radiation. The reverse process, absorption of energy from a radiation field so as to excite the atom to higher states and form dark lines of an "absorption spectrum," can also be analyzed with the Bohr postulate. There is the implication, too, that the energy of each stationary state is an intrinsic property of the atom, having nothing to do with the way in which the energy is acquired. Thus the Bohr theory says that energy supplied to the atom in other than radiation forms should also be accepted by the atom in absorption "lines." In 1913, when Bohr's paper appeared, there was available an experimental method for supplying non-radiation energy to an atom in an acceptable form: bombardment with a beam of electrons that has been accelerated to the required energy. The electron bombardment experiment suggested by Bohr's paper was actually performed by James Franck and Gustav Hertz of the Kaiser Wilhelm Institute in Berlin. They reported the results in 1914.

But the ways of scientific progress are imperfect: Franck and Hertz had not seen Bohr's paper, and if they had read it before collecting their own results, they apparently would not have believed it. Franck's candid remarks on the attitude in Berlin show how dim the light can be that shines on major discoveries:

> It might interest you that when we made the experiments that we did not know Bohr's theory. We had neither read nor heard about it. We had not read it because we were negligent to read the literature well enough — and you know how that happens. On the other hand, one would think that other people would have told us about it. For instance we had a colloquium at that time in Berlin at which all the important papers were discussed. Nobody discussed Bohr's paper. Why not? The reason is that fifty years ago one was so convinced that nobody would, with the state of knowledge we had at that time, understand spectral line emission, so that if somebody published a paper about it, one assumed, "probably it is not right." So we did not know it . . . .†

† From an interview given by Franck in 1961. See the Notes and Comment section.

The apparatus used by Franck and Hertz is illustrated schematically, and in cross section, below:

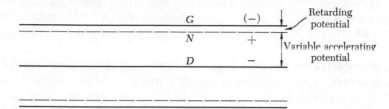

A thin platinum wire D is heated to incandescence electrically so that it emits electrons whose energies are increased by a variable potential applied between D and N; the latter is a cylindrical wire mesh electrode located several centimeters from the hot wire. After they have passed through a small retarding potential the electrons are collected on the concentric platinum foil electrode G and measured on a galvanometer. The three electrode elements are held and enclosed by a glass tube. The measurements to be described were made with mercury admitted to the tube to a vapor pressure of about 1 mm, a high enough pressure so that, in passing between D and N, electrons collide many times with mercury atoms. When the accelerating potential on the mesh electrode is increased the galvanometer displays a peculiar rising and falling behavior:

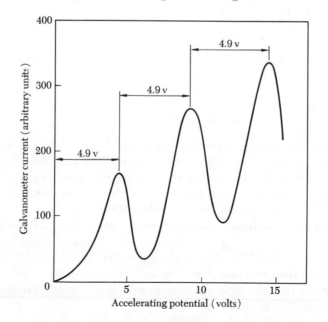

As the Bohr theory views this experiment, low accelerating potentials supply the electrons with less than the full quantum of
energy required to promote a mercury atom from one stationary state
to another. Collisions with the mercury atoms are "elastic," of the
billiard-ball type, and little energy is lost by the electrons even in
many collisions. A "critical potential" is reached at 4.9 volts, and
here the measured current drops abruptly. Electrons accelerated to
this potential apparently have exactly the energy of one quantum,
and all of this can be lost in a single collision. The mercury atoms
can receive this energy because it is just enough to cause a transition
between two stationary states. After such an "inelastic" collision,
an electron is left with insufficient energy to move against the retarding potential; it is turned back to the mesh electrode and not
measured on the galvanometer. Inelastic collisions are numerous
enough to reduce the current sharply.

At higher accelerating potentials the collided electrons have sufficient energy to overcome the retarding electrode potential and be
collected. The current increases again until *twice* the critical potential (9.8 volts) is reached, where it is possible for electrons to
lose all of their kinetic energy in *two* inelastic collisions. The current drops as before. The same behavior is seen at three times the
critical potential, and so on.

The kinetic energy of an electron after it has been accelerated
through V volts is $E = eV$, where

$$e = 1.602 \times 10^{-19} \text{ coulomb,}$$

the electronic charge, so that acceleration through the critical potential $V = 4.9$ volts gives the electron the energy

$$E = (1.602 \times 10^{-19})(4.9) \text{ joule}$$

$$= 7.84 \times 10^{-12} \text{ erg.}$$

This is the size of one quantum of energy. It is somewhat more conveniently expressed as 4.9 electron volts. The natural origin of the
electron volt unit is seen in these experiments where energy is
supplied by an accelerating potential: the numerical value of the
potential is simply translated directly into energy units.

The electron-collision data of Franck and Hertz are entirely in
agreement with optical data. A line appears in the emission spectrum
of mercury at 2537 Å; this corresponds to an energy of 4.89 ev.
Franck and Hertz found that this same emission line makes an appearance in the electron bombardment experiment when the first
critical potential is reached.

Franck and Hertz had no doubt that their results showed the quantum theory at work, but in their ignorance of Bohr's hypothesis they interpreted the 4.9 ev as an *ionization* energy, not as the energy required for a transition between two stationary states. Furthermore, they supplied evidence that ionization actually took place. To Bohr, with his theory as a basis for estimates, it was obvious that 4.9 ev was too small for an ionization energy. He felt that the ionization must have been due to a photoelectric effect on the electrodes of the apparatus. Bohr and a Manchester colleague, W. Makower, designed an "intricate quartz apparatus with various electrodes and grids" to trace the source of the ionization current. Unfortunately the apparatus caught fire, was ruined, and could not be repaired. It was wartime and the German glassblower who was responsible for its construction had been interned. His temper, "not uncommon for artisans in his field . . . released itself in violent superpatriotic utterances" which were too much for the British authorities. For several more years Franck and Hertz continued to speak of their critical potentials as ionization energies until 1917, when Bohr's assertion was proved correct; the ionization was shown to have a secondary origin, not in the primary electron-mercury-atom collisions.

Aside from misinterpretations of the results, the Franck-Hertz work gave a direct and impressive demonstration of the two Bohr stationary-state postulates I and III. This was evidence completely independent of the spectral data, yet entirely in agreement with it. Like most other episodes in this story this one ends with a Nobel Prize. Franck and Hertz shared a Prize in 1925.

De Broglie's Wave Theory

There is a story told by F. J. Dyson about a visit to the United States by Wolfgang Pauli, who had come with what he thought was a substantially new theory of elementary particles. The theory was presented formally to an audience that included Niels Bohr. After the talk the discussion became heavily critical of Pauli's viewpoint, and finally Bohr gave this remarkable evaluation: "We are all agreed that your theory is crazy. The question which divides us is whether it is crazy enough to have a chance of being correct. My own feeling is that it is not crazy enough." †

For sheer craziness the theory which occupies this section has

† Remember Runge's comment: "he [Bohr] obviously has done a strange if not crazy stunt with that paper."

rarely, if ever, been equaled. This theory follows to a strange conclusion the duality argument which Einstein had started in 1909. Remember that Einstein's analysis concerned the particle and wave nature of radiation. The astounding idea, put forward in 1924 by a French aristocrat, Prince Louis-Victor de Broglie, was that nature had a fundamental symmetry, requiring that matter, as well as radiation, have a wave-particle duality. In other words, the particles of matter, particularly electrons, should exhibit wave behavior, even though, to the time of de Broglie's theory, they had been known strictly as particles. "I was convinced," wrote de Broglie, "that the wave-particle duality discovered by Einstein in his theory of light quanta was absolutely general and extended to all of the physical world, and it seemed certain to me, therefore, that the propagation of a wave is associated with the motion of a particle of any sort—photon, electron, proton or any other."

Even more than Einstein, de Broglie was inclined to reason purely from general principles with little—in fact, no—recourse to experimental evidence. Unlike the Einstein photon paper, however, the de Broglie paper met with a more tolerant reception, at least in the minds of an influential minority. This was partly because Einstein himself became de Broglie's spokesman. The paper, which de Broglie had originally written as a doctoral thesis, was sent to Einstein, who announced, in customary Einsteinian eloquence, that de Broglie had "lifted a corner of the great veil." Einstein immediately took up the cause of the new "wave mechanics"; he found a way to present the wave-particle concept for material systems using the same energy-fluctuation framework applied earlier to the radiation problem. The benefit to de Broglie was immeasurable: "The scientific world of the time hung on every one of Einstein's words, for he was then at the peak of his fame. By stressing the importance of wave mechanics, the illustrious scientist had done a great deal to hasten its development." Einstein's influence was certainly helpful, but so many strange things had happened since Planck's paper in 1900 it also seems that science, for a few moments in its history, had lost some of its natural resistance to radical (that is, crazy) innovations.

De Broglie's argument begins with the supposition that "The basic idea of quantum theory is . . . the impossibility of considering an isolated fragment of energy without assigning a certain frequency to it"; such is the content of the Einstein equation, energy $= h \times$ frequency. It is difficult to understand precisely the physical sense of this frequency but it apparently describes a certain internal "periodic process."

Quanta of light had, of course, already been treated in this manner; but de Broglie saw no reason why particles of matter, since they, too, are "isolated fragments of energy," should not also have an associated internal periodic process. When the particle is at rest the frequency of the internal process is ν_0 and the energy of the particle is $h\nu_0$, following the Einstein equation. Another Einstein energy equation can also be applied to the particle at rest,

$$E = m_0 c^2$$

(m_0 is the particle's rest mass), this one being derived from the theory of special relativity. When the two energies are equated the rest frequency of the internal periodic process is found to be

$$\nu_0 = m_0 c^2 / h.$$

The frequency ν_0 follows the internal process according to the particle's "own clock." A fixed observer, who sees the particle moving with velocity $v = \beta c$ ($\beta = v/c$), finds a different frequency ν_1, which must be less than ν_0 by the factor $\sqrt{1 - \beta^2}$,

$$\nu_1 = \nu_0 \sqrt{1 - \beta^2}$$
$$= (m_0 c^2 / h) \sqrt{1 - \beta^2},$$

due to the relativistic "dilation" of time intervals.† This, however, is not the frequency which the quantum theory associates with a moving particle. Write the quantum theory frequency as ν, so that, according to the two Einstein equations above, the particle's energy is either $h\nu$ or

$$m_0 c^2 / \sqrt{1 - \beta^2} \qquad (\ddagger)$$

to the fixed observer who sees the particle moving with velocity $v = \beta c$. Equating these two energies leads to

$$\nu = m_0 c^2 / h \sqrt{1 - \beta^2}, \qquad (13)$$

---

† One cycle of an internal periodic process which requires time τ_0 sec when the particle is seen at rest seems to require a longer time,

$$\tau_1 = \tau_0 / \sqrt{1 - \beta^2} \text{ sec,}$$

when the particle is moving (with respect to the fixed observer) at a velocity $v = \beta c$. Thus the frequency of this periodic change,

$$\nu_1 = 1/\tau_1 = (1/\tau_0)(\sqrt{1 - \beta^2})$$
$$= \nu_0 \sqrt{1 - \beta^2},$$

is decreased by the factor $\sqrt{1 - \beta^2}$ for the moving particle.

‡ In addition to the time-dilation effect, special relativity also asserts that a moving particle has a total energy which is larger than $m_0 c^2$ by the factor $1/\sqrt{1 - \beta^2}$.

a frequency distinctly different from ν_1 for velocities large enough to make β appreciable.

The problem of reconciling the frequencies ν and ν_1 was central to de Broglie's investigation. It determined the "whole trend" of his work. He solved the problem in a formal way by assigning the frequency ν not directly to the internal periodic behavior of the particle, but to a *wave* which accompanies the particle through space and time in such a way that it is always in phase with the internal process. This is, then, a traveling wave whose phase at time t and at the point x where the particle is located is (assuming linear motion)

$$\phi = 2\pi\nu(t - x/u),$$

in which u is the "phase velocity" of the wave (the velocity of a particular wave crest). At the same time the phase of the internal periodic process whose frequency is ν_1 is simply

$$\phi_1 = 2\pi\nu_1 t.$$

The phase velocity u is now evaluated by making the two phases the same:

$$\phi = \phi_1$$

$$2\pi\nu(t - x/u) = 2\pi\nu_1 t$$

$$(m_0 c^2/h\sqrt{1 - \beta^2})(t - x/u) = (m_0 c^2\sqrt{1 - \beta^2}/h)t$$

$$u = (x/t)(1/\beta^2).$$

If the particle moves linearly and starts at the origin ($x = 0$ when $t = 0$) x/t is simply the particle's velocity v and

$$u = v/\beta^2$$

$$= c^2/v. \tag{14}$$

Two properties of de Broglie's particle waves have been determined, the frequency ν and phase velocity u. A third property, the wavelength λ, can be related to these two with

$$\lambda\nu = u, \tag{15}$$

an equation common to all wave motion.

The real strength of de Broglie's argument lies in the various simple and highly suggestive uses he found for his particle waves. One of these develops a remarkable "wave equation" for the particle momentum. Begin with the relativistic equation for the momentum, $p = m_0 v/\sqrt{1 - \beta^2}$, and transform it to wave language as follows:

$$p = m_0 v / \sqrt{1 - \beta^2} \qquad (16)$$

$$= m_0 c^2 / u \sqrt{1 - \beta^2}$$

$$= (h/u)(m_0 c^2 / h \sqrt{1 - \beta^2})$$

$$= h\nu / u \qquad (\dagger)$$

$$= h/\lambda \qquad (\ddagger)$$

$$= h\tilde{\nu}. \qquad (17)$$

The symbol $\tilde{\nu}$, as before, represents the wave number. A momentum equation, $p = h\tilde{\nu}$, known to the world as the "de Broglie equation," has been brought forth with a mathematical and physical appearance very close to the Einstein energy equation $E = h\nu$. The two equations $E = h\nu$ and $p = h\tilde{\nu}$ put in a particularly acute form the difficulties of the wave-particle duality. Each equation has a "particle quantity" on the left, a "wave quantity" on the right and the ever-present Planck's constant standing between.

The phase velocity of the de Broglie particle waves has the seemingly impossible property that it is greater than the velocity of light (the particle velocity v is always less than c, so that $u = c^2 / v > c$). How can the motion of these mysterious waves possibly relate to the actual motion of a particle? De Broglie demonstrated that the physically significant wave velocity is not the phase velocity but the "group velocity," the velocity of the reinforcement regions formed when many waves are superimposed. The value of the group velocity w is calculated from the change in the frequency ν per unit of change in the wave number $\tilde{\nu}$,

$$w = d\nu / d\tilde{\nu},$$

in the region where a reinforcement crest forms. Both the frequency and wave number are available as functions of the velocity variable β:

$$\nu = m_0 c^2 / h \sqrt{1 - \beta^2} \qquad (18)$$

$$\tilde{\nu} = p/h$$

$$= (m_0 v / h) / \sqrt{1 - \beta^2} \qquad (\S)$$

$$= (m_0 c / h)(\beta / \sqrt{1 - \beta^2}).$$

The group velocity derivative is evaluated as follows:

† Evaluate ν using (13).
‡ $\nu / u = 1/\lambda$ according to (15).
§ $p = m_0 v / \sqrt{1 - \beta^2}$, according to (16).

$$dv/d\tilde{v} = (dv/d\beta)/(d\tilde{v}/d\beta)$$
$$= [(m_0c^2/h)\beta/(1 - \beta^2)^{3/2}]/[(m_0c/h)/(1 - \beta^2)^{3/2}]$$
$$= c\beta$$
$$= v.$$

A reinforcement region therefore moves with the same velocity v that was said before to describe the motion of a "particle." Indeed, a reinforcement crest shows all the mechanical properties associated with the particle, an energy

$$E = m_0c^2/\sqrt{1 - \beta^2}$$

and a momentum

$$p = m_0v/\sqrt{1 - \beta^2}.$$

Thus, to a certain extent, de Broglie made it clear that a wave-particle entity, something that has an underlying wave structure and yet follows the laws of particle mechanics, could exist.

But what *are* these particle waves? The waves are waves of *what*? De Broglie was well aware that his theory could not provide detailed answers to these questions. The particle waves ("phase waves" in de Broglie's terminology) and the internal periodic process were deliberately left as formal concepts: "The definitions of the phase wave and the periodic process were purposely left somewhat vague . . . so that the present theory may be considered a formal scheme whose physical content is not yet fully determined, rather than a full-fledged definite doctrine." De Broglie's intuitive under-standing of the waves was perhaps better than he realized. When members of the committee examining him on his doctoral thesis expressed skepticism concerning the reality of the waves, de Broglie replied that the waves might be observable in crystal diffraction experiments such as those already familiar in X-ray work, and it appears that he tried unsuccessfully to persuade a colleague to try some electron-diffraction experiments (the colleague preferred to experiment with television). Three years later electron-diffraction phenomena were reported in the United States and England.

In spite of its limitations the de Broglie theory had turned an ex-tremely important key. Just a year after de Broglie's thesis was published, Erwin Schrödinger presented a much broader wave mechanics which encompassed a wide range of atomic and molecular problems. Schrödinger drew his inspiration largely from de Broglie's wave analysis and from the various comments made by Einstein on the duality problem. "My theory," wrote Schrödinger, "was stimulated by de Broglie's thesis and by short but infinitely far-seeing remarks by Einstein." Eventually the Schrödinger theory, and a reinterpretation of it by Born, provided a clue to the identity of the mysterious waves. The Schrödinger theory and its implications will be introduced in the next chapter.

The Experiments of Davisson and Germer

The supporting experimental evidence, so marvelously waived in the original acceptance of the de Broglie-Schrödinger wave mechanics, finally appeared in 1927. In that year electron waves were reported and unmistakably characterized by Clinton J. Davisson and Lester H. Germer in the United States, and by George P. Thomson † in England. Davisson's earlier work (with C. H. Kunsman) had shown anomalous maxima in the distribution of electrons scattered from a metal plate. It occurred to Max Born and James Franck that these peaks might originate in simple diffraction effects. This possibility was explored by a Göttingen research student, Walter Elsasser, who made use of the rather rough Davisson-Kunsman data. Elsasser's estimates showed that a diffraction interpretation was feasible. The later, more refined, and much more definitive Davisson-Germer experiments will be outlined here.

The essentials of the apparatus used by Davisson and Germer are shown below:

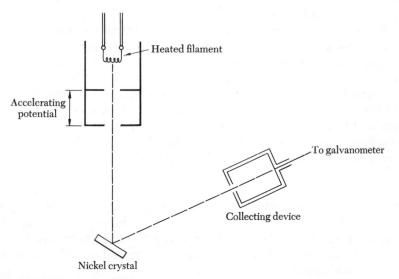

† The only son of J. J. Thomson, who had demonstrated thirty years earlier that electrons have *particle* properties.

Electrons are produced on a heated tungsten filament and formed into a narrow beam of well-defined energy by an accelerating electrostatic field. The beam is directed at a specially prepared face of a nickel crystal and electrons reflected by the crystal are collected and then measured on a galvanometer. The collector can be moved so that it gathers electrons reflected at various angles. The entire apparatus is degassed and kept in a high vacuum.

Experiments with this apparatus first showed that when a single crystal of nickel is used a definite selective reflectivity of the beam appears. Electrons are not found scattered uniformly in *all* directions. Instead, under certain conditions a sharply defined stream of emitted electrons is observed in a direction for which the angle of incidence is equal to the angle of reflection.

If, to the electrons, the nickel surface were entirely smooth and flat, this result would not be particularly surprising: throw a rubber ball at a smooth wall and it always bounces off at an angle equal to the angle of incidence. But to the particle-like electrons the nickel surface cannot conceivably be smooth. Remember that electrons in the shape of particles must be much smaller and less massive than the nickel atoms. The reflection of electron particles from a nickel surface is, in the apt description of Lester Germer, "like imagining a handful of bird shot being regularly reflected by a pile of large cannon balls." The difficulty is that "a surface made up of cannon balls is much too coarse-grained to serve as a regular reflector for particles as small as bird shot."

The bird-shot image for electrons is evidently not appropriate. What explanation can be given, then, for the regular reflection? Davisson and Germer successfully analyzed this experiment, as well as many others, by regarding the stream of electrons in the same sense as a beam of X rays (displaying its wave manifestation), and the nickel surface as if it were a diffraction grating. It is well known that X rays incident at a certain angle on a crystal face are reflected with peaks of relatively high intensity when the wavelength has certain values given by a formula due to Bragg:

$$\lambda = 2d \cos \theta / n,$$

where θ is the angle of incidence (measured with respect to a line drawn *normal* to the crystal surface), d is the perpendicular distance between the crystal planes causing the reflection, and n is an integer. If the first peak in the intensity of the reflected beam occurs for the wave number

$$1/\lambda = 1/2d \cos \theta,$$

then higher-order reflections are found at integral multiples of this wave number, $2/\lambda$, $3/\lambda$, $4/\lambda$, ...

The electron waves in the Davisson-Germer experiment are pictured in the same way. Their wavelength, calculated by the de Broglie relation, is $\lambda = h/p$, and their kinetic energy (shifting to the particle viewpoint) is $E = p^2/2m$. This same energy, as determined by the accelerating potential V, is $E = Ve$, or $E = Ve/300$, with V given in volts. Consequently,

$$\lambda = \sqrt{150h^2/meV} \qquad \text{and} \qquad 1/\lambda = V^{1/2}\sqrt{me/150\ h^2}$$

or, with the constants evaluated,

$$1/\lambda = V^{1/2}/12.25. \tag{19}$$

If an electron beam of potential V_1 and wave number

$$1/\lambda_1 = V_1^{1/2}/12.25$$

shows an intensity peak for the beam reflected at a certain angle, it follows from the X-ray analogy that peaks should also occur at integer multiples of this wave number. If V_1 gives a "first-order" reflection peak ($n = 1$ in the Bragg equation) then, at this same angle of incidence, there should be a "second-order" reflection peak when an acceleration potential V_2 produces electrons of wave number

$$V_2^{1/2}/12.25 = 2/\lambda_1 = 2V_1^{1/2}/12.25, \qquad \text{or} \qquad V_2^{1/2} = 2V_1^{1/2}.$$

"Third-order" and "fourth-order" peaks are found for $V_3^{1/2} = 3V_1^{1/2}$ and $V_4^{1/2} = 4V_1^{1/2}$, and so forth. When $V^{1/2}$ vs reflected intensity (at a certain angle) was plotted from the Davisson-Germer data this effect was displayed in a series of peaks with nearly regular spacings:

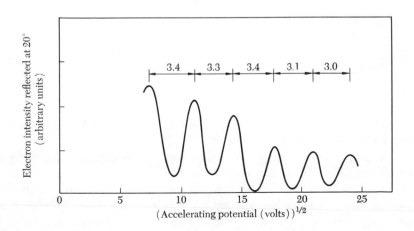

Davisson and Germer found it possible to analyze "diffraction" data as well as the reflection data just described. Here the scattered beam leaves the crystal at an angle other than the angle of incidence. Intensity peaks form in much the same way as in the reflection process. In fact, the physical principles are just those upon which the Bragg equation is based. An example of a diffraction beam is shown below and compared with a simple reflection beam.

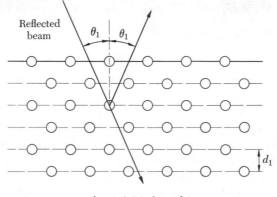

$$\lambda = (1/n)(2d_1 \cos \theta_1)$$

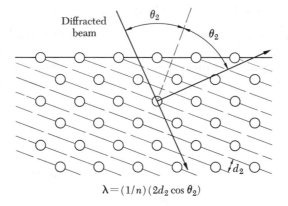

$$\lambda = (1/n)(2d_2 \cos \theta_2)$$

The technique used by Davisson and Germer to gather diffraction data will not be described in detail. The main point is that the wavelengths and angles predicted by a simple analysis of these data turned out to be quite different from those actually measured.

All was brought into order, however, by simply assuming that the electron beam is *refracted* by the crystal. Suppose that the electron beam behaves in the same manner as a light ray; its direction is changed (the refraction process) when it passes from one medium to another. Picture an electron beam, or ray, entering a crystal along a direction normal to the crystal surface (such a beam is not refracted), being reflected by one of the crystal's planes and leaving the crystal with its direction changed by refraction at the crystal boundary.

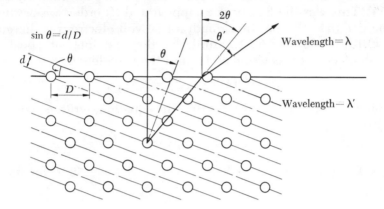

The refraction causes the beam, as it leaves the crystal medium, to change its direction relative to the normal from 2θ to θ'. The index of refraction μ is related to these two angles by

$$\mu = \sin \theta'/\sin 2\theta,$$

and is also related to the two wavelengths λ' and λ, inside and outside the crystal medium, $\mu = \lambda/\lambda'$. When there is an intensity peak the inside wavelength satisfies Bragg's law:

$$\lambda' = 2d \cos \theta/n,$$

where d is the perpendicular distance between the reflecting planes. A useful equation for the electron wavelength can now be derived:

$$\lambda/\lambda' = \sin \theta'/\sin 2\theta$$

$$\lambda = \lambda'(\sin \theta'/\sin 2\theta)$$

$$= \lambda'(\sin \theta'/2 \sin \theta \cos \theta)$$

$$= (2d \cos \theta/n)(\sin \theta'/2 \sin \theta \cos \theta)$$

$$= (1/n)(d/\sin \theta)(\sin \theta')$$

$$= (1/n)(D \sin \theta'),$$

where $D = d/\sin\theta$ is the distance between adjacent atoms on the surface of the crystal (consult the diagram above).

The derived equation is similar to the Bragg equation and is just as easily applied, since the angle θ' is measurable and, for the nickel crystal used by Davisson and Germer, the distance D was known from X-ray measurements to be 2.15 Å. For example, electrons accelerated through 54 volts were found to give an intensity peak at 50°. This was the first peak to appear and its order was assumed to be one ($n = 1$). The wavelength for 54-volt electrons is therefore $\lambda = (2.15)(\sin 50°) = 1.65$ Å. Similarly, the first intensity peak for 65-volt electrons was found at 44° and the wavelength is

$$\lambda = (2.15)(\sin 44°) = 1.50 \text{ Å}.$$

A simple application of the de Broglie equation, written according to (19),

$$\lambda = 12.25/V^{1/2},$$

gives $\lambda = 1.67$ Å for 54-volt electrons and $\lambda = 1.52$ Å for 65-volt electrons.

So once more the two worlds of physics, experimental and theoretical, meet in perfect harmony, and the quantum theory, or wave theory, as it seems from the de Broglie-Schrödinger viewpoint, takes a great step forward. But here, as in the Franck-Hertz confirmation of the Bohr theory, the meeting of theory and experiment seems to have been arranged as much by accident as by design. Davisson and Germer did not read de Broglie's paper and then set out on a systematic search for electron waves: these experiments had their origin in a famous patent suit.

The principal parties in the suit were the General Electric and Western Electric companies. General Electric had applied for a basic patent on a three-element vacuum tube which was quite similar to a design already owned by Western Electric. It was the contention of General Electric that theirs was a high vacuum device, whereas the Western Electric tube required appreciable air for its operation. The General Electric argument claimed that emission of electrons from the cathode of the tube was caused by bombardment of the oxide covering of the cathode by positive ions formed from air molecules. To support their case Western Electric started a series of investigations of the effects of positive-ion bombardment on oxide coatings. This work was started by Germer under Davisson's direction in the Western Electric Laboratories (now the Bell Telephone

Laboratories). The General Electric claim was conclusively disproved and the suit was eventually decided in Western Electric's favor.

The bombardment experiments were continued after the settlement of the suit and extended to include bare metal surfaces from which the oxide coating was mostly removed. As Germer remarks, it was also possible, "by changing a few potentials on some of the electrodes, to measure electron emission under electron bombardment." The work that finally led to the measurement of the electron wavelength was "undertaken as a sort of sideline." These studies continued over several years (for a time the experiments were done by C. H. Kunsman), and the data revealed an increasingly complex and mysterious pattern. A major clue was found accidentally, when the evacuated tube holding the nickel metal target burst. To reconstruct the experiment it was necessary to clean the nickel surface by heating it to a high temperature. This had the unforseen effect of forming a few large crystals not present in the original polycrystalline sample. The complexities were now traced to the large crystals and experiments were started with a *single* nickel crystal whose planes and orientations could be controlled.

Up to this time (it was now 1926) Davisson and Germer were unaware of the de Broglie electron waves. At a meeting of the British Association in Oxford Davisson heard of the new wave theories and came to the realization that the pattern of the bombardment results, which he and Germer had already found similar to X-ray diffraction data, actually told a story of wave behavior. "The experiments were at once guided by the theory," writes Germer, "and were quickly successful." Davisson shared a Nobel Prize with the other discoverer of electron waves, G. P. Thomson, in 1937.

Why must physics proceed in this apparently erratic manner, turning on mere accidents? Thomson tells us that the inspiration for his electron diffraction work came while watching an experiment which later proved to give results that were "quite erroneous and entirely instrumental in origin." The truth is that the accidents and errors are, in the words of the science historian Gerald Holton, "triggering events" which generally lead nowhere unless they are preceded by "half a lifetime of preparing oneself" and are succeeded by "half a lifetime of following up." Davisson and Germer had, with the years of earlier work on the patent case (started in 1919), developed a highly unusual and difficult experimental technique. The magnitude of their achievement is not to be found in their publications, but it has been assessed by Thomson: "It is not, I think, always realized nowadays what a supreme experimental feat these early experiments were. Slow electrons [less than about 100 ev] are most difficult to control, and if the result is to be of value, the vacuum has to be what would still be considered a pretty good vacuum and what was then quite outstanding. In fact, very few people since that time have succeeded in this field of slow electron diffraction . . . ."

These "accidents" that earn Nobel Prizes are more than they seem. They are accidents served by long preparation, great talent, and incomparable technique. Laboratory accidents with mysterious consequences are, perhaps, happening all the time, but people who have the perception to be ready for the accident and the courage and freedom to follow it wherever it might lead are rarer even than Nobel Prizes.

3

The New Mechanics

This chapter begins with the description of an experiment which is, perhaps, more perplexing and more of a strain on the imagination than anything else brought into the world by quantum physics.

It is possible to develop light sources so weak that only a few photons are emitted per second. A source of this kind was used by G. I. Taylor in 1909 to illuminate a single- and double-slit diaphragm arrangement as in Young's interference experiment:

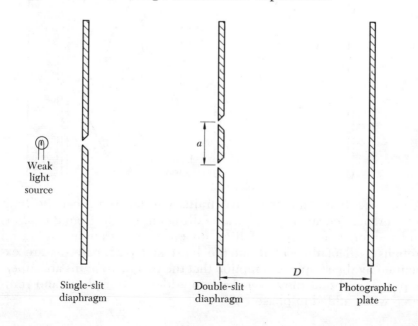

When very long time exposures are made in these experiments
there appears on the photographic plate a pattern of light and dark
bands. If the wavelength λ of the light is small compared with the
distance a between the two slits, adjacent light bands are separated
by a distance which is approximately $D\lambda/a$, where D is the distance
between the double slit and the plate. The image on the plate forms
very slowly and is comprised of a large number of tiny bright spots,
these spots being concentrated in certain areas to form the band
pattern.

The spots strongly suggest that the image on the plate is formed
as it is bombarded by photons, but where do the light and dark bands
come from? Throughout the nineteenth century, and, for that matter,
to the present day, the appearance of light and dark "interference"
patterns has been taken as unmistakable evidence for wave phenomena of some kind. Consider the light to fall on the double slit
as a train of waves and to be split into two diffracted wave trains by
the double slit:

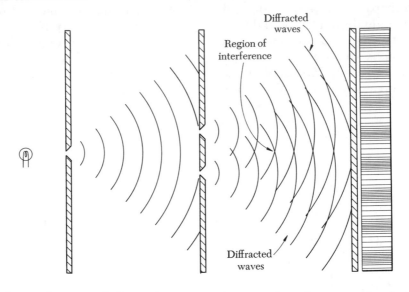

Where the two diffracted wave trains overlap there can be both
interference (crests from one train falling on troughs from the other)
and reinforcement (crests falling on crests and troughs falling on
troughs). All of the details of the light and dark patterns are explained by the simple assumption that the two wave trains are superimposed, and that they cancel when added out of phase and reinforce when added in phase.

Any attempt to explain interference patterns with the incident light regarded entirely as a shower of particles makes little physical sense. The dark bands must be regions where photons come together and annihilate each other; the light bands must be regions where photons interact to form more photons. Aside from the difficulty in explaining the patterns of the bands, the necessity for assuming that energy is created and destroyed has no appeal to the physicist who has built most of his science on the principle that energy is conserved. Besides, in Taylor's experiment only *one photon at a time* passes through the slit system. Even in a world accustomed to *non*conservation of energy, a photon could hardly destroy *itself* or spontaneously divide into two photons.

Nevertheless, the interference image forms in minute spots, so it seems advisable to retain *some* of the features of the particle picture. For how can a broad wave front suddenly collapse when it strikes the photographic plate to expose one of the spots? The photons are there, apparently, but we must realize that great care must be taken in describing where a photon goes and how it moves between the time it leaves the light source and the time it arrives at the plate and forms one of the spots.

It is most natural to picture a photon traveling between the light source and the photographic plate along a path which takes it through one or the other of the slits, a path such as this one:

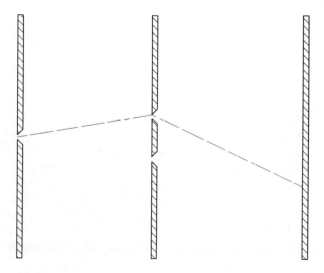

But in Taylor's experiment, which allows only one photon in the slit system at a time, is it conceivable that a *single photon* passing through a *single slit* can in any way generate an interference pattern? The most basic necessity for the interference effect, even more important than the wave assumption, is that *something* must come out of *both* slits. Something must always interfere with something else. With the single slit there cannot be the "something else." That this is the case can be proved by experiment: closing one of the slits destroys the interference pattern. Whatever the actual situation may be, it makes no physical sense to think that a photon travels a definite path between the source and the photographic plate, necessarily through only one of the slits. Our mental image of the photon and its motion must be blurred somewhat, at least to the extent that we accept an uncertainty in where the photon passes through the double-slit diaphragm, a position uncertainty which amounts to a, the distance between the two slits. And, most important of all, we must abandon the concept of a precise path for the photon.

Does this imply that a photon spreads itself over the double slit, with two fragments emerging on the other side to interfere with each other? This, like the simple wave picture, is hard to reconcile with photons small enough to form the minute spots of the photographic image. Remember the photons of the photoelectric and Compton effects which must be small enough to interact with the region occupied by an atom. Furthermore, photons are apparently indivisible: no evidence has ever been found that they can be split.

The double-slit experiment can also be conducted with a beam of electrons replacing the photons. An electron source (e.g. a heated tungsten wire) replaces the light source. The electrons (one at a time if necessary) are formed into an homogeneous beam by using an accelerating electrostatic field. They are directed at a two-slit arrangement and their presence is observed beyond the slits with a sensitive detector, such as a screen covered with a phosphor. As might be expected from the electron wave properties mentioned in Chapter 2, diffraction maxima and minima that are similar qualitatively to those in the photon experiment are observed in the pattern of the data collected by the screen. The conceptual problems connected with the behavior of electrons are therefore as difficult as those connected with photons. The wave-particle paradox is no easier with electrons: all of the perplexing questions asked about photons in the two-slit apparatus must be asked again about electrons.

As it happens, the *answers* to these questions take a fundamentally different form in the electron and photon cases, even though the questions are the same. Since the story told here is concerned more with electrons than photons, the subsequent discussion will refer mostly to electron particles.

Still the paradox remains. How can a beam passing through the diaphragm arrangement, a single (electron or photon) particle at a time, conceivably generate an interference pattern? We have abandoned the concept of a particle following a definite path through a single slit, and also the concept of one particle passing through both slits. Two possibilities that *cannot* produce interference have been eliminated. But that brings us no closer to an explanation of what actually happens. If the particle itself does not pass through the double slit and spread out on the other side in two fields which overlap and produce regions of cancellation and reinforcement, then what does?

Rescue from this enigma is not going to be easy. The full depth of the mystery is hard to appreciate: it even seems to have demolished ordinary modes of logic. One would ordinarily expect to say that if there are two slits in a diaphragm, and a particle passes through the diaphragm, it must pass through one slit or the other: there is no third possibility. But the appearance of an interference pattern requires that in some sense there *must be* a third possibility.

The Observed and the Unobserved

A useful clue in the strange matter of accounting for the behavior of electrons (or photons) is uncovered by noticing that all the difficulties arise when statements are made about what happens *when the electron is not under direct observation.* When an electron arrives at the detector, we know the electron is definitely located in the region of the detector at the time the detector registers its presence. The events in question are those that take place between the time an electron leaves the source (an event which also can be observed) and the time the detector shows an electron arrival. Our language and logic seem to be adequate when they apply to the results of direct observation. But there are profound difficulties, even in the rudiments of our logic, when we attempt to describe what is *not* observed. This is a pattern that persists throughout quantum physics: the observed and the unobserved seem to be in different realms.

In the remainder of this chapter, and in Chapter 4 and Chapter 5, a general theory will be developed that accounts in a satisfactory way for (i.e. predicts) the results of direct observations. These will be,

for example, measurements that locate particles such as electrons in space and time, showing not only their position, but also their momentum and energy. The instruments visualized as being applied to the measurements will be laboratory equipment of ordinary design.†
The pattern of the measurements, as revealed by the theory, will frequently be strange, but the language that describes this pattern must be the language of the measuring instruments, a language adjusted to the scale of the laboratory and to such familiar concepts as wave and particle motion: it is, in other words, a language of "classical" words and variables. That quantum physics, or any other physics, would be difficult to construct in another way is a point that has been made especially by Bohr:

> However far [quantum] phenomena transcend the scope of classical physical explanation, the account of all evidence must be expressed in classical terms. The argument is that simply by the word "experiment" we refer to a situation where we can tell others what we have done and what we have learned and that, therefore, the account of the experimental arrangement and of the results of the observations must be expressed in unambiguous language with suitable applications of the terminology of classical physics.

Bohr's words point the way for the development of a theory. Primarily, we hope to be able to predict the results of measurements on particles, and these measurements are to concern such classical properties as the space-time position, the momentum, and the energy. This will be a theory concerned as much as possible with observables and what we observe. An account of a phenomenon will consist entirely of what we see in isolated observations. What happens in the world that lies beneath the world of observations must remain largely outside the theory. When a particle is observed first in one place and then in another place, we can allow no inference from the theory concerning how the particle travels between the two points. In particular, we cannot assume that the particle traverses a definite path. The difficulties raised by the definite-path assumption in the double-slit experiment have already been mentioned. The same limitation holds throughout quantum physics.

All this may come as a surprise and a disappointment. We have

---

† "Ordinary" at least in principle. A crucial argument presented originally by Heisenberg visualizes a "gamma-ray microscope" which has never been constructed, but, nevertheless, shows the uncertainties limiting instruments of the same design which *have* been constructed. This remarkable microscope will be the subject of a later section.

learned to expect more from physics, because the familiar classical theory seems to tell a much more complete story. Once an object is located in space and time and its initial velocity is established, the classical equations of motion (which include any applied forces) predict precisely the trajectory the object will follow for the rest of time. And its trajectory has physical reality whether the object is under observation or not. The classical viewpoint will, of course, probably persist for phenomena occurring on a macroscopic scale. We have no expectations that classical physics applied to laboratory events, as it always has been, will ever fail us. But quantum physics forces the conclusion that classical methods, especially the calculation of unobserved trajectories, are not admissible in the microscopic realm of photons, electrons, and atoms. The quantum theory as it now stands concerns itself with prediction of the patterns of observations. What lies beyond the observations is always obscure and sometimes entirely uncertain.

Werner Heisenberg

One of the first to recognize the need for an atomic physics built strictly on observations and observables was Werner Heisenberg, a "second-generation" quantum physicist, who was born in 1901, a year after Planck's paper on black-body radiation was published.†
Heisenberg, like Planck, Bohr, Moseley, and Pauli, came from an academic family. His father was a professor at the University of Munich and devoted to a life of culture. Heisenberg had a strong interest in music, mathematics, and the classics, all developed by the atmosphere of his home and the influence of the *Gymnasium.* When he studied science, he found the Greek philosopher-scientists better reading than his textbooks. Immediately after leaving the *Gymnasium,* when he was nineteen years old, Heisenberg presented himself to Arnold Sommerfeld (a professor at Munich and one of the foremost atomic physicists of his time) as a prospective student in theoretical physics. He was allowed to attend Sommerfeld's seminars, but was also requested to begin the standard physics curriculum. Whatever delay this may have caused was temporary: only six semesters after entering the University Heisenberg finished his

† One might fancy that the appearance of Planck's paper was a signal for the birth of a whole crop of brilliant physicists: Pauli and Joliot in 1900; Fermi, Lawrence, Pauling, and Heisenberg in 1901; Dirac and Condon in 1902; Gamov and Oppenheimer in 1904.

work at Munich and received his doctorate, at the age of twenty-two.

The high point of Heisenberg's education in physics came during his fourth semester, when Sommerfeld took his brilliant pupil to the University of Göttingen to attend a series of lectures given by Niels Bohr, an occasion known to the students as the "Bohr Festival." Heisenberg's impression of Bohr was vivid and fascinating: "He spoke softly and with some hesitation, but behind every carefully chosen word one could discern a long chain of thought, which eventually faded somewhere in the background into a philosophical viewpoint . . . ." Young as he was, Heisenberg did not hesitate to speak with Bohr and even argue against some of the work Bohr had reported in his lectures. One discussion was so absorbing it took the two physicists out of Göttingen and into the mountains near by. Heisenberg was struck by Bohr's immense insight, "not a result of a mathematical analysis of the basic assumptions, but rather an intense occupation with the actual phenomena, such that it was possible for him to sense a relationship intuitively rather than derive it formally."

About a year later Heisenberg visited the Bohr Institute in Copenhagen and found its occupants awesomely gregarious and full of atomic physics. He soon felt at home, however, and for a few weeks resumed the long, "infinitely instructive" talks and walking tours with Bohr.

Heisenberg's first academic position was at the University of Göttingen. In 1923 he became assistant to Max Born, who had established Göttingen as a center for research in theoretical physics which rivaled the Copenhagen Institute. Two years later Heisenberg returned to Copenhagen and began a three-year collaboration with Bohr. Heisenberg's papers, which he wrote both alone and in collaboration with Bohr, Born, and Jordan during this five-year Göttingen-Copenhagen period, brought a new era to quantum physics.

Heisenberg, like Bohr ten years earlier, started his career in atomic physics at a critical time "when the difficulties in quantum theory became more and more embarrassing, its internal contradictions seemed to become worse and worse, and to force us into a crisis which by an almost dramatic series of surprising discoveries in the course of a few years led to a solution of the fundamental problems." The Bohr theory and its numerous variations (known today as the "old" quantum theory) could reach no further. In the words of Max Jammer, the historian of physics, the quantum theory prior to 1925 "was, from the methodological point of view, a lamentable hodgepodge of hypotheses, principles, theorems and computational recipes rather than a logical consistent theory." Most problems were solved initially with the methods of classical physics and then translated into the language of quantum theory by clever use of the correspondence principle. Frequently the translation process required more "skillful guessing and intuition . . . than . . . systematic reasoning." It was apparent, to Bohr most of all, that an entirely new method was needed.

Matrix Mechanics

Werner Heisenberg was privileged to make the first step in a new direction. While working under Born at Göttingen, Heisenberg put together the beginnings of a mechanics which started with one of Bohr's axioms, the correspondence principle, but worked with a strange new method. In spite of, or perhaps because of, its peculiarities, this method did much more than the Bohr theory and with much less trouble. Gone was the need for "skillful guessing and intuition." Heisenberg had brought forth a genuine "quantum mechanics." The Bohr theory, with its admixture of classical mechanics, could never rightly be described as such.

The roots of Heisenberg's mechanics grow from a long-established mathematical method in classical physics known as Fourier analysis. To see the patterns of the Fourier procedure, consider the problem of a particle moving back and forth in a periodic way across an equilibrium position $x = 0$, it being held there by an attraction force. The equation of motion for this situation is

$$\ddot{x} + \omega_0^2 x = 0,$$

where ω_0^2 is a constant that depends on the strength of the restoring force and on the mass of the oscillating particle. The total energy (potential and kinetic) of the system is

$$E = m\dot{x}^2/2 + m\omega_0^2 x^2/2.$$

These equations describe the "simple harmonic oscillator." Among other things, the simple harmonic oscillator can serve as the model for the atomic "resonators" visualized by Planck as the active constituents in the walls of the black-body cavity. The equation of motion has the particular solution

$$x = a_1 \cos 2\pi\nu t,$$

where ν is the frequency of the motion and a_1 is its amplitude. This can also be written in the complex exponential form

$$x = (a_1/2)e^{2\pi i\nu t} + (a_1/2)e^{-2\pi i\nu t}. \qquad (\dagger)$$

More complicated kinds of motion cannot be expressed this easily, but these simple expressions for the coordinate variable can be extended into series to cope with a wide variety of situations. Take, for example, a complication on the harmonic oscillator, in which a small x^2-term is added to the linear term, creating the "anharmonic oscillator" equation of motion:

$$\ddot{x} + \omega_0^2 x + \lambda x^2 = 0,$$

where λ is a small constant. It is assumed that this equation can be solved with solutions written in the form of a converging infinite series:

$$x = a_1 \cos 2\pi\nu t + a_0\lambda + \lambda a_2 \cos 4\pi\nu t + \lambda^2 a_3 \cos 6\pi\nu t + \cdots.$$

The small "correction terms" with the factors λ, λ^2, ... have been added in the expectation that this series will allow a solution with any accuracy desired, depending on how many of the increasingly smaller factors λ, λ^2, ... are used. To see if this is possible the series must be substituted into the equation of motion. The algebra of the substitution is simplified somewhat by writing the infinite series in its equivalent exponential form:

$$x = [\lambda a_0 + (a_1/2)e^{2\pi i\nu t} + (a_1/2)e^{-2\pi i\nu t} + (\lambda a_2/2)e^{4\pi i\nu t}$$

$$+ (\lambda a_2/2)e^{-4\pi i\nu t} + (\lambda^2 a_3/2)e^{6\pi i\nu t} + (\lambda^2 a_3/2)e^{-6\pi i\nu t} + \cdots].$$

When this is used to express x, x^2, and $\ddot{x}$, and the series expressions are returned to the equation of motion, it is found that the frequency of oscillation ν is simply related to the constant ω_0, $2\pi\nu = \omega_0$, and a collection of simultaneous algebraic equations in the a's is derived:

$$a_0 = -a_1^2/2\omega_0^2$$

$$a_2 = a_1^2/6\omega_0^2$$

$$a_3 = a_1^3/48\omega_0^4$$

.

.

.

† According to the Euler relation a complex exponential function can be expanded in simple trigonometric functions:

$$e^{2\pi i\nu t} = \cos(2\pi\nu t) + i \sin(2\pi\nu t).$$

For a derivation of this equation see page 144.

This solves the equation in terms of the constants ω_0 and a_1, the latter being determined by the initial conditions of the problem.

Many other kinds of complex periodic motion can be handled in this same way, with x always expressed as an infinite series of the form

$$x = \sum_\alpha a(\alpha)e^{2\pi i \alpha \nu t}.$$

The symbol $\sum_\alpha$ stands for the summation operation $\sum_{\alpha=-\infty}^{\alpha=+\infty}$. The $a(\alpha)$'s are expansion coefficients, or "Fourier amplitudes." Notice that x must be real in the physical problem and that this is assured by the condition $a(\alpha) = a(-\alpha)$. The frequencies $\alpha\nu$ in the exponents are all seen to be harmonics of the fundamental frequency ν. A general Fourier series has been written for x; each term $a(\alpha)e^{2\pi i \alpha \nu t}$ is a "Fourier component" of the periodic motion.

To cope with events occurring on the atomic scale this description must in some sense be quantized. A preliminary attempt at this involves saying that there are various discrete values possible for the frequency ν, one for each stationary state. The nth of these frequencies is written $\nu(n)$. Each stationary state has its Fourier series, the terms of which for the nth stationary state are

$$a(n,\alpha)e^{2\pi i \alpha \nu(n)t},$$

where $a(n,\alpha)$ is the Fourier amplitude for the αth term. To write the Fourier terms closer to what is needed for the quantum description, the frequency $\alpha\nu(n)$ of the αth term is written in a special way:

$$\alpha\nu(n) - \nu(n,\alpha).$$

The point of this will soon be apparent. The entire Fourier series for the nth stationary state is

$$x(n) = \sum_\alpha a(n,\alpha)e^{2\pi i \nu(n,\alpha)t}. \tag{1}$$

Heisenberg set out to build a quantum theory from the pattern of this classical method, with full faith in the correspondence concept that each classical element must have a parallel element in the quantum realm. He also adhered tenaciously and brilliantly to the principle that no quantum mechanics should be allowed to use quantities that are not directly observable. Such things as electron orbital paths must be discarded. Nevertheless, the *form* of dynamic equations, such as

$$\ddot{x} + \omega_0^2 x = 0$$

for the harmonic oscillator, was to be retained. There was no need, Heisenberg felt, to change the underlying *dynamics*. He was concerned with a change in the *kinematics:* "the problem has nothing to do with electrodynamics but rather—and this seems to be particularly important—is of a purely kinematic nature." The crucial problem, as Heisenberg remarked, is almost as simple as the question: what do x and x^2 mean in the quantum realm?

To adapt (1) to a quantum description, an interpretation for the frequencies $\nu(n,\alpha)$ must first be found. In the Fourier series $\nu(n,\alpha)$ is the αth harmonic of the fundamental frequency $\nu(n)$ (for the nth stationary state): $\nu(n,\alpha) = \alpha\nu(n)$. Harmonics seem to have no place in the quantum description, but there is, nevertheless, a quantum frequency which is apparently a legitimate replacement for the classical harmonic frequency. Consider the frequency emitted by an atomic system that makes a transition from the nth state to the upper or lower $(n - \alpha)$th state (α is a positive or negative integer). This frequency, written $\nu(n,n - \alpha)$, is, according to the Bohr rule (equation (10) in Chapter 2):

$$\nu(n,n - \alpha) = (1/h)[A(n) - A(n - \alpha)].$$

The Bohr rule can be converted to classical circumstances by making n very large and α small in comparison with it. Some time before Heisenberg's work, Bohr and others had made it clear that, when classical conditions prevail, the frequency of the light emitted in the $n \rightarrow n - \alpha$ transition is simply $\alpha\nu(n) = \nu(n,\alpha)$, the αth harmonic of the fundamental frequency $\nu(n)$. Thus the classical-to-quantum conversion we are seeking evidently involves replacing the harmonic frequencies $\nu(n,\alpha)$ with the transition frequencies $\nu(n,n - \alpha)$.

There is also the related and highly important question of frequency combination rules. Classically, all frequencies are harmonics of a set of fundamental frequencies $\nu(n)$. Two different harmonics of the same fundamental can therefore be combined by simple addition:

$$\nu(n,\alpha) + \nu(n,\beta) = \alpha\nu(n) + \beta\nu(n)$$

$$= (\alpha + \beta)\nu(n)$$

$$= \nu(n,\alpha + \beta). \tag{2}$$

The quantum frequency combination rule has an entirely different appearance. Its form is specified by the Rydberg-Ritz combination principle, mentioned in Chapter 2 (see (11) on page 49). In the notation used here

$$\nu(n,n-\alpha) + \nu(n-\alpha, n-\alpha-\beta) = \nu(n,n-\alpha-\beta) \qquad (3)$$

expresses combination of the frequencies for the $n \to n - \alpha$ and the $n - \alpha \to n - \alpha - \beta$ transitions.

The argument has so far produced an intelligible quantum replacement for the classical fundamental frequency $\nu(n)$ and its harmonics $\nu(n,\alpha)$. But how is the Fourier amplitude $a(n,\alpha)$ to be translated into a suitable quantum version? Symbolically, the quantum amplitudes should evidently be written $a(n,n - \alpha)$, so that they correspond to the same transition $(n \to n - \alpha)$ for which the frequencies $\nu(n,n - \alpha)$ are written. But what is their physical significance, and how are they measured? (Remember that Heisenberg was insistent that his quantum mechanics be built on nothing but observable quantities.) The quantum amplitudes $a(n,n - \alpha)$, or "transition amplitudes" as they are called, were understood (somewhat vaguely at first) to be proportional in magnitude to the probability that a given transition will occur. If $|a(n,n - \alpha)|$ is large, the transition has a relatively high probability for occurrence. If

$$|a(n,n - \alpha)| = 0,$$

the transition does not occur at all.

These various clues can now be used to attempt a revision of (1) which will work in the quantum realm. The basic rules to be used for converting the classical terms to quantum terms are:

1. Replace $\nu(n,\alpha)$ with $\nu(n,n - \alpha)$.
2. Replace $a(n,\alpha)$ with $a(n,n - \alpha)$.
3. Replace the terms $a(n,\alpha)e^{2\pi i\nu(n,\alpha)t}$ with
    $a(n,n - \alpha)e^{2\pi i\nu(n,n-\alpha)t}$.

Can the quantum terms formed in this way be used to write a Fourier series analogous to (1)? Heisenberg was concerned that the summation loses its physical meaning in the quantum realm because the term-labeling indices n and $n - \alpha$ have almost equal status in the quantum interpretation: either or both could be designated as the summation index. Nevertheless, he felt that the individual Fourier-like components

$$a(n,n - \alpha)e^{2\pi i\nu(n, n-\alpha)t}$$

could be assembled in some other meaningful way. Leaving open the question of how this assembling process should be done, Heisenberg considered the form the terms should take in order to fit dynamical equations such as $\ddot{x} + \omega_0^2 x + \lambda x^2 = 0$.

Terms that appropriately represent $\ddot{x}$ are not hard to obtain. A simple differentiation of the x-terms seems to be all that is required. A single $\ddot{x}$-term should evidently have this appearance:

$$- 4\pi^2\nu^2(n,n - \alpha)a(n,n - \alpha)e^{2\pi i\nu(n,\, n-\alpha)t}.$$

Dealing with the quantum representation for x^2 proves to be a more formidable task, however. Return once more to the classical Fourier series:

$$x(n) = \sum_{\alpha} a(n,\alpha)e^{2\pi i\nu(n,\, \alpha)t}.$$

Multiply this by itself, omitting the n-indices temporarily to simplify the writing:

$$x^2 = \left(\sum_{\alpha} a(\alpha)e^{2\pi i\nu(\alpha)t}\right) \left(\sum_{\beta} a(\beta)e^{2\pi i\nu(\beta)t}\right).$$

Two different summation indices α and β are used to distinguish the two factors. To proceed expand the factors:

$$x^2 = [a(0) + a(1)e^{2\pi i\nu(1)t} + a(-1)e^{2\pi i\nu(-1)t} + \cdots]$$
$$\times [a(0) + a(1)e^{2\pi i\nu(1)t} + a(-1)e^{2\pi i\nu(-1)t} + \cdots].$$

The multiplication is now carried out term by term. Each product term formed involves two factors, one from the α-summation and one from the β-summation. Thus each such term can be labeled with a value of $\alpha + \beta$. To organize the x^2-series, first collect together all of the terms for which $\alpha + \beta = 0$. These are

$$[a(0)a(0)e^{2\pi i\nu(0)t}e^{2\pi i\nu(0)t} + a(1)a(-1)e^{2\pi i\nu(1)t}e^{2\pi i\nu(-1)t} + \cdots]. \qquad (\dagger)$$

The terms for which $\alpha + \beta = 1$ are

$$[2a(0)a(1)e^{2\pi i\nu(0)t}e^{2\pi i\nu(1)t} + 2a(-1)a(2)e^{2\pi i\nu(-1)t}e^{2\pi i\nu(2)t} + \cdots],$$

and the terms for which $\alpha + \beta = -1$ are

$$[2a(0)a(-1)e^{2\pi i\nu(0)t}e^{2\pi i\nu(-1)t} + 2a(-2)a(1)e^{2\pi i\nu(-2)t}e^{2\pi i\nu(1)t} + \cdots].$$

Terms are found in this same way for

$$\alpha + \beta = \pm 2, \pm 3, \ldots$$

and the x^2-series is completely defined in this way. The terms collected into brackets obviously express a summation themselves. They are all of the form

$\dagger\ \nu(0) = 0\nu = 0.$

$$a(\tau')a(\tau - \tau')e^{2\pi i \nu(\tau')t}e^{2\pi i \nu(\tau - \tau')t},$$

where $\tau = \alpha + \beta$ and τ' is another positive or negative summation index.

The entire x^2-series can therefore be written

$$x^2 = \sum_{\tau}\left(\sum_{\tau'} a(\tau')a(\tau - \tau')e^{2\pi i \nu(\tau')t}e^{2\pi i \nu(\tau - \tau')t}\right).$$

This expression is actually simpler than it looks, since the frequencies in the exponents can be added according to the classical combination rule (2), rewritten slightly to fit the τ-indices:

$$\nu(\tau') + \nu(\tau - \tau') = \nu(\tau).$$

Then

$$x^2 = \sum_{\tau}\left(\sum_{\tau'} a(\tau')a(\tau - \tau')\right)e^{2\pi i \nu(\tau)t},$$

or, with the ns restored,

$$x^2(n) = \sum_{\tau}\left(\sum_{\tau'} a(n,\tau')a(n,\tau - \tau')\right)e^{2\pi i \nu(n,\tau)t}$$

$$= \sum_{\tau} a^2(n,\tau)e^{2\pi i \nu(n,\tau)t}.$$

The symbol $a^2(n,\tau)$ in the last line stands for the τth Fourier amplitude of x^2:

$$a^2(n,\tau) = \sum_{\tau'} a(n,\tau')a(n,\tau - \tau').$$

Notice that the series for $x^2(n)$ contains no frequencies other than those of the original series for $x(n)$; they are all harmonics of the fundamental frequency $\nu(n)$. This condition, which is necessary for the physical description, is assured by the use of the frequency combination rule.

A single $x^2(n)$-term in the classical realm has been shown to be

$$a^2(n,\tau)e^{2\pi i \nu(n,\tau)t}$$

The prescriptions previously worked out for the classical-to-quantum conversion, $\nu(n,\tau)$ replaced by $\nu(n,n-\tau)$ and $a(n,\tau)$ replaced by $a(n,n-\tau)$, suggest that an $x^2(n)$-term in the quantum realm should look something like

$$a^2(n,n-\tau)e^{2\pi i \nu(n,n-\tau)t}.$$

The frequencies $\nu(n,n-\tau)$ involved in these terms all derive from transitions which start at the nth stationary state. This is the same set of frequencies that occurs in the terms used to express $x(n)$, as it should be. As mentioned before, these frequencies can be expressed as a combination of two other frequencies according to the Rydberg-Ritz rule (3) (written with the τ-indices):

$$\nu(n,n-\tau) = \nu(n,n-\tau') + \nu(n-\tau',n-\tau).$$

From this point the argument can be developed by tracing the classical derivation backward and following along with the parallel quantum equivalents. The "almost necessary consequence" of these simple manipulations is perhaps the most vital part of Heisenberg's analysis. The classical $x^2(n)$-terms are

$$a^2(n,\tau)e^{2\pi i\nu(n,\tau)t}.$$

This is actually a contraction of a more complicated expression. Each $a^2(n,\tau)$-factor stands for an expansion

$$a^2(n,\tau) = \sum_{\tau'} a(n,\tau')a(n,\tau-\tau'),$$

and each frequency $\nu(n,\tau)$ is obtained as one of the classical combinations

$$\nu(n,\tau) = \nu(n,\tau') + \nu(n,\tau-\tau').$$

When the classical $x^2(n)$-term is fully expanded it is

$$\sum_{\tau'} a(n,\tau')a(n,\tau-\tau')e^{2\pi i\nu(n,\tau')t}e^{2\pi i\nu(n,\tau-\tau')t}.$$

The parallel quantum formulation for the contracted $x^2(n)$-term is

$$a^2(n,n-\tau)e^{2\pi i\nu(n,n-\tau)t}.$$

The appropriate quantum frequency combination rule is

$$\nu(n,n-\tau) = \nu(n,n-\tau') + \nu(n-\tau',n-\tau),$$

which splits the exponential part of the x^2-term into two factors:

$$a^2(n,n-\tau)e^{2\pi i\nu(n,n-\tau')t}e^{2\pi i\nu(n-\tau',n-\tau)t}.$$

Writing this apparently also determines the form of the equation for a^2, since the classical argument shows us that the a-indices match the ν-indices. Following this lead we arrive at

$$\sum_{\tau'} a(n,n-\tau')a(n-\tau',n-\tau)e^{2\pi i\nu(n,n-\tau')t}e^{2\pi i\nu(n-\tau',n-\tau)t}$$

for a single $x^2(n)$-term. Having worked out the details, we can return to the contracted way of writing, with $a^2(n,n-\tau)$ now understood to be

$$a^2(n,n-\tau) = \sum_{\tau'} a(n,n-\tau')a(n-\tau',n-\tau).$$

Further aspects of the calculation procedures in the new mechanics are easier to follow if, as was done later, the sets of quantum terms are put into two-dimensional arrays. The x-components $a(n,n-\tau)e^{2\pi i\nu(n,n-\tau)t}$ are written

$$x = \begin{pmatrix} a(0,0)e^{2\pi i\nu(0,0)t} & a(0,1)e^{2\pi i\nu(0,1)t} \dots \\ a(1,0)e^{2\pi i\nu(1,0)t} & a(1,1)e^{2\pi i\nu(1,1)t} \dots \\ \cdot & \cdot \\ \cdot & \cdot \\ \cdot & \cdot \end{pmatrix}$$

with $n-\tau$ increasing along the rows and n increasing down the columns (n and $n-\tau$ are both positive). Notice that this way of writing, unlike the Fourier summations, leaves the labeling indices with equal status. The x^2-terms

$$a^2(n,n-\tau)e^{2\pi i\nu(n,n-\tau)t}$$

are written into an array of the same size and shape and with the same frequencies and exponential factors:

$$x^2 = \begin{pmatrix} a^2(0,0)e^{2\pi i\nu(0,0)t} & a^2(0,1)e^{2\pi i\nu(0,1)t} \dots \\ a^2(1,0)e^{2\pi i\nu(1,0)t} & a^2(1,1)e^{2\pi i\nu(1,1)t} \dots \\ \cdot & \cdot \\ \cdot & \cdot \\ \cdot & \cdot \end{pmatrix}$$

where

$$a^2(n,m) = \sum_k a(n,k)a(k,m)$$

as indicated by the quantum formula for the expansion of the a^2-coefficients. The procedure for calculating the $a^2(n,m)$-factors is to multiply the a-factors of the nth row of an x-array term by term with the a-factors of the mth column of another x-array and add all of the individual products. For example, take $n = 1$ and $m = 2$; the sum that defines $a^2(1,2)$ is

$$a^2(1,2) = a(1,0)a(0,2) + a(1,1)a(1,2) + a(1,2)a(2,2) + \cdots.$$

The first factors in the terms on the right are taken in order from the second row of an x-array and the second factors are taken from the third column of another x-array.

Products between two different quantities, say x and y, are formed similarly. The elements $xy(n,m)$ of an xy-array are defined as

$$xy(n,m) = \sum_k x(n,k)y(k,m).$$

Since the rows and columns of the x-array are not the same as those of the y-array this last rule leads to the curious conclusion that the algebra of x's and y's in Heisenberg's quantum kinematics is "noncommutative": $xy \neq yx$. In fact, Heisenberg found it necessary to make one such statement of noncommutation, that for the product of the coordinate x and the corresponding momentum component p_x, a fundamental part of his theory. This equation ultimately took the form

$$\sum_k [x(n,k)p_x(k,n) - p_x(n,k)x(k,n)] = ih/2\pi.$$

The first term in the brackets is the nn-element of the xp_x array; it is located along the upper-left-to-lower-right diagonal of the array. The second term in the summation is similar except that it belongs to the $p_x x$-array. Commutation (or, better, noncommutation) relations such as this one are known as "quantum conditions." They are found throughout the theorems and calculational procedures of quantum mechanics. The version of quantum mechanics seen in Chapters 5 and 6, quite different in many ways from the Heisenberg mechanics, makes abundant use of commutation relations recognizably similar to the $xp_x - p_x x$ equation.

The principal ingredients of Heisenberg's kinematics, the array representations, the symbolic multiplication rule, and the quantum conditions, have been assembled. The way is now clear to develop the accompanying dynamics. Even for simple problems this task involves somewhat lengthy algebraic manipulations, but the underlying principles are straightforward and familiar. The equations of the new mechanics are nothing more than those already known in classical mechanics. The harmonic oscillator is still described by

$$\ddot{x} + \omega_0^2 x = 0,$$

and its energy is still

$$E = m\dot{x}^2/2 + m\omega_0^2 x^2/2,$$

The equations for the anharmonic oscillator are also as before:

$$\ddot{x} + \omega_0^2 x + \lambda x^2 = 0$$

$$E = m\dot{x}^2/2 + m\omega_0^2 x^2/2 + m\lambda x^4/4.$$

The arrays for $\ddot{x}$, $\dot{x}$, x^2, and x are placed in these equations and a set of simultaneous algebraic equations in the various a's emerges.[†] These equations are solved in much the same way as those derived in the classical Fourier analysis. The results are useful primarily for calculating the total energy E. Heisenberg obtained energy expressions in this way for the anharmonic oscillator and a simple rotating system. The results were entirely in accord with previous observations and calculations.

In spite of these successes Heisenberg was uneasy about the peculiarities of the algebra: ". . . the fact that xy was not equal to yx was very disagreeable to me. I felt that this was the only point of difficulty in the whole scheme, otherwise I would be perfectly happy." Most of his theory was formulated by June 1925, when he received an invitation to lecture at the Cavendish Laboratory in Cambridge. The choice, as it seemed to Heisenberg, was to complete the work quickly or "throw it into the flames." Pauli, the invaluable critic, was asked to read the paper and comment: his reaction was favorable. Heisenberg was sufficiently encouraged to place his paper before Born, but in his Cambridge lectures he said nothing of his recent efforts.[‡]

Born was more enthusiastic. He immediately sent the paper to the editor of the *Zeitschrift für Physik*. To Born it was clear that a new quantum mechanics was at hand, and he set about the task of developing a full mathematical statement of the theory. He was particu-

---

† The details of this calculation are too lengthy to fit the limited space available in this chapter. For several reading references in which this work is described see Notes and Comment, page 230.

‡ Present at those lectures was Paul Adrien Maurice Dirac, who was to find in Heisenberg's method, when he saw a printer's proof of the paper several months later, "the key to the problem of quantum mechanics." This decisive opinion came, however, only after several weeks of meditation. At first he saw "nothing useful" in the method. Some of Dirac's story is told in Chapter 6.

larly intrigued by the multiplication rule: "Heisenberg's symbolic multiplication rule did not give me any rest, and after days of concentrated thinking and testing I recalled an algebraic theory which I had learnt from my teacher . . . in Breslau." The "algebraic theory" concerned "matrices," mathematical array-like entities, whose algebra had been formulated by Arthur Cayley, with mathematician's foresight, some seventy years earlier. The "row times column" rule prescribes the matrix multiplication process; the Heisenberg arrays are formally identifiable as matrices in this way, and in all other respects as well. Once this clue was recognized the way was cleared for the development of a comprehensive and rigorous "matrix mechanics." This work was done by Born with Heisenberg and a young matrix expert, Pascual Jordan, who overheard Born discussing matrix theory with a colleague on a train, and promptly offered his services.

Physics had hardly managed to become slightly acquainted with matrix mechanics before another mechanics made its appearance in a four-part paper published by Erwin Schrödinger in the *Annalen der Physik* of 1926. Conceptually, mathematically, and, in a sense, physically, Schrödinger's mechanics was altogether different from Heisenberg's mechanics. Where Heisenberg's method is algebraic, Schrödinger's method begins with a differential equation. The Heisenberg mechanics builds on discrete and discontinuous quantities (the elements of the matrices), whereas Schrödinger's mechanics is based on a quantity which is continuous. On the wave-particle question the Heisenberg procedure seems to side with the particle viewpoint, since it calculates momenta and coordinates; the Schrödinger differential equation is plainly a "wave equation."

As might be expected, Heisenberg and Schrödinger had difficulty accepting the validity of each other's theories. Heisenberg wrote to Pauli: "The more I ponder about the physical part of Schrödinger's theory the more disgusting it appears to me." And Schrödinger, who soon found a formal mathematical correspondence between his and Heisenberg's theory, nevertheless had doubts about the physical qualifications of matrix mechanics: ". . . I was discouraged, if not repelled, by what appeared to me a rather difficult method of transcendental algebra, defying any visualization." One is reminded of Brahms and Tchaikovsky criticizing each other's symphonic music.

As mentioned in Chapter 2, Schrödinger was led to his theory by Einstein's remarks on wave-particle duality and by de Broglie's version of "wave mechanics." He was also helped considerably by a remarkable statement of the laws of mechanics invented almost one hundred years earlier.

Hamilton's Analogy

Perhaps it is a mistake to say that quantum physics originated with Planck's paper on heat radiation in 1900. Twenty-five years before Planck was born, Sir William Rowan Hamilton, the great Irish mathematician and astronomer, developed a theory of mechanics which profoundly influenced Schrödinger, and de Broglie as well.

Hamilton's intention, largely realized, was to find a single law which describes both the motion of particles and the propagation of light. He was inspired particularly by the principle of Fermat, that a light ray passes from one point to another along a path which minimizes the time of passage. If the light is propagated in a homogeneous medium, this path is simply a straight line; but if the medium is variable, the path is curved. Fermat's principle makes it possible to calculate the correct path by expressing the minimum time condition in a variational form,

$$\delta \int_A^B dt = 0,$$

where A and B are the two points between which the light ray passes. So that the integral applies to the elements of the path ds, write for the "velocity" of the ray (actually the "phase velocity" of the waves which comprise the ray)

$$u = ds/dt \qquad \text{and} \qquad dt = ds/u,$$

and

$$\delta \int_A^B ds/u = 0. \tag{4}$$

This "trivial quintessence" of the wave theory of light, as Schrödinger was to call it, became a fundamental part of Hamilton's restatement of the laws of mechanics for particle motion. Hamilton found that the laws of motion can be recast in a variational form resembling (4). A statement of "Hamilton's principle," for a particle of constant energy, is

$$\delta \int_A^B 2T dt = 0,$$

where T is the particle's kinetic energy. This does not specify that the particle travels a path of minimum time, as (4) does for the light ray, but it has a mathematical form very close to (4). This is particularly evident if the integrand is rearranged, using $T = mv^2/2$ and

$T = E - V$ for the kinetic energy, where $v = ds/dt$ is the particle velocity, E is the (constant) total energy, and V is the potential energy:

$$2Tdt = 2T(ds/v)$$
$$= \sqrt{2mT}\ ds$$
$$= \sqrt{2m(E - V)}\ ds.$$

Thus the particle variational statement that is analogous to (4) for the light ray is

$$\delta \int_A^B \sqrt{2m(E - V)}\ ds = 0. \tag{5}$$

Schrödinger concentrated on probing the analogy between (4) and (5) further than Hamilton could carry it in the 1830's. The two equations become identical if a phase velocity

$$u = C/\sqrt{2m(E - V)}$$

is introduced; C is a constant which may depend on the particle's energy (assumed to be a constant). But what kind of a velocity is this from the viewpoint of the particle? Obviously it is not the actual particle velocity, for this is

$$v = \sqrt{2m(E - V)}/m.$$

To answer this question Schrödinger introduced the idea that, in some sense, the particle consists of a group of waves. The velocity u, just calculated, is the phase velocity of these waves, and the velocity of the wave group as a whole, the "group velocity," is identified with the particle velocity v.[†] The theory of wave motion specifies that the group velocity is $w = d\nu/d\tilde{\nu}$, $\tilde{\nu}$ being the wave number and ν the frequency. This is also $w = d\nu/d(\nu/u)$, where $\nu/u = 1/\lambda$ [‡] is used in place of the wave number. The particle velocity, now equivalent to the group velocity, is written

$$v = w = d\nu/d(\nu/u).$$

The derivative is rewritten, with the energy replacing the frequency, by introducing Einstein's energy-frequency equation:

† Remember that de Broglie had developed a similar correspondence between particle velocities and group velocities. See pages 61–62.
‡ The frequency ν, wavelength λ, and phase velocity u of all wave phenomena are related by the equation $\lambda\nu = u$.

$$v = dE/d(E/u)$$
$$= dE/d[E\sqrt{2m(E-V)}/C].$$

Since v is the particle velocity, it is also

$$v = \sqrt{2m(E-V)}/m$$
$$= dE/d[\sqrt{2m(E-V)}].$$

The conclusion implied by these two equations for the particle velocity is that

$$d[E\sqrt{2m(E-V)}/C]/dE = d[\sqrt{2m(E-V)}]/dE,$$

that

$$d[(E/C - 1)\sqrt{2m(E-V)}]/dE = 0,$$

and, therefore, that the quantity $[(E/C-1)\sqrt{2m(E-V)}]$ is independent of E. This is the case only if the factor $(E/C - 1)$ vanishes: †
$(E/C - 1) = 0$ and $C = E$. The phase velocity is therefore

$$u = E/\sqrt{2m(E-V)}. \tag{6}$$

From this a wavelength can be calculated by introducing the fundamental wave relationship $u = \lambda v$ and the Einstein equation $E = hv$:

$$\lambda = (E/v)/\sqrt{2m(E-V)}$$
$$= h/\sqrt{2m(E-V)}$$
$$= h/p.$$

It is noted in the last step that $\sqrt{2m(E-V)}$ is simply the particle momentum p. The final equation is, of course, just the de Broglie equation, derived here as a consequence of Hamilton's analogy and Einstein's energy-frequency relation.

Thus Schrödinger's interpretation of Hamilton's analogy presents a picture of a particle moving with an associated concentration of waves whose group velocity is the same as the particle velocity. In the language of optics, which should be just as appropriate to this discussion as the particle language, the mechanical paths can be regarded as "rays" and the moving particles as "light signals." This is clearly a kind of "wave mechanics" with important implications for the wave-particle question. Remember that this is an argument based mostly on the principles of classical mechanics and optics.

† If $(E/C - 1) \neq 0$, the quantity in the brackets must be dependent on E, because the factor $\sqrt{2m(E-V)}$ necessarily depends on E.

Classical physics needs only to be prompted by the Einstein $E = h\nu$
equation and it brings forth a wave-particle duality argument, complete with the companion to the Einstein equation, the de Broglie
relation $p = h/\lambda = h\tilde{\nu}$.

Schrödinger's Analogy

What Schrödinger found in Hamilton's analogy is a wave mechanics
in the sense that it draws a parallel between the classical mechanics
of particles and the physics of light rays. The wave-particle duality
theme is not unique to quantum physics: classical mechanics speaks
in this vein also. But, as Herbert Goldstein remarks, the classical
duality argument does not give equal importance to particle and
wave: ". . . the particle is the senior partner, and the wave has no
opportunity to display its unique characteristics."

Light, as we know, is more than a bundle of isolated rays. The rays
have a wavelike "fine structure," which leads to such important
phenomena as diffraction and interference. Ray optics ("geometrical
optics") says nothing about these effects; it is simply an approximation of a broader and more refined theory of optics. The more complete theory, known as "wave optics," gives a clear picture of the
wave structure, accounts for diffraction and interference effects, and
shows that the rays are fictitious constructions perpendicular to the
wave fronts. The fundamental differential equation in wave optics
is, for wave propagation in one dimension,

$$\partial^2\rho/\partial x^2 - (1/u^2)\partial^2\rho/\partial t^2 = 0,$$

where ρ and u are, respectively, the wave's amplitude and phase
velocity.

With analogy as his principal—perhaps his only—justification,
Schrödinger reasoned that the mechanics-optics parallel should hold
at all levels, that if geometrical or ray optics is an approximate form
of wave optics, then classical mechanics, the analogue of geometrical optics, must be an approximation for a more fundamental mechanics, a new wave mechanics:

ordinary mechanics : wave mechanics

= geometrical optics : wave optics.

If wave optics reveals the fine structure of rays and light-signals, the new mechanics should show the fine structure of particles such as electrons.

Mathematically, the Schrödinger analogy postulates that the basic differential equation in the new wave mechanics is similar in form to the equation of wave optics just quoted: replace the optical wave amplitude p by some kind of a mechanical wave amplitude Ψ and use (6) to express the phase velocity. The result, for one dimension, is

$$\partial^2\Psi/\partial x^2 - [2m(E - V)/E^2]\partial^2\Psi/\partial t^2 = 0,$$

or $\qquad [E^2/2m(E - V)]\partial^2\Psi/\partial x^2 - \partial^2\Psi/\partial t^2 = 0.$

The conventional procedure for solving partial differential equations of this kind is to try a solution which places the two independent variables into separate factors: write

$$\Psi(x,t) = \psi(x)\phi(t),$$

where $\psi(x)$ and $\phi(t)$ depend only on the variables indicated, and convert the wave equation to

$$[E^2/2m(E - V)]\phi d^2\psi/dx^2 - \psi d^2\phi/dt^2 = 0,$$

or $\qquad [E^2/2m(E - V)](1/\psi)(d^2\psi/dx^2) = (1/\phi)(d^2\phi/dt^2).$

This accomplishes a separation of the equation into a part (the left side) which depends only on x (V is assumed to be independent of time) and a part (the right side) which depends only on t. These two parts are equivalent and must therefore both be equal to a constant, say $-\alpha^2$: †

$$[E^2/2m(E - V)](1/\psi)(d^2\psi/dx^2) = -\alpha^2$$

$$(1/\phi)(d^2\phi/dt^2) = -\alpha^2.$$

The equation in t has solutions such as $\phi = \phi_0 \sin \alpha t$, which are periodic in time and go through a complete cycle when αt increases from 0 to 2π. If τ is the time required for a complete cycle, the so-called "period," then

$$\alpha\tau = 2\pi \qquad \text{and} \qquad \alpha = 2\pi/\tau = 2\pi\nu,$$

where ν is the number of cycles completed per unit of time, that is,

---

† α^2 cannot contain t because it is equal to a function of x only, nor can it contain x because it also equals a function of t only. Therefore it contains neither x not t: it is a constant. A negative constant is chosen because a positive constant ($+\alpha^2$ in place of $-\alpha^2$) does not give solutions that are wavelike.

the frequency. Substitute this evaluation of α into the equation for x,

$$[E^2/2m(E - V)](1/\psi)(d^2\psi/dx^2) = -4\pi^2\nu^2,$$

and simplify, using the $E = h\nu$ relation:

$$[h^2/2m(E - V)](1/\psi)(d^2\psi/dx^2) = -4\pi^2,$$

or $$-(h^2/8\pi^2m)(d^2\psi/dx^2) + V\psi = E\psi,$$

or $$-(\hbar^2/2m)(d^2\psi/dx^2) + V\psi = E\psi, \tag{7}$$

where the symbol $\hbar$ (read this "cut-h") stands for $h/2\pi$. Schrödinger found a three-dimensional version of the last equation to be very useful and powerful. Among other things, he applied it to the hydrogen atom by substituting for V a simple electrostatic potential energy function; $V = -e^2/r$, where e is the electronic charge and r is the electron-nucleus distance. Discrete energy values,

$$E = -2\pi^2me^4/n^2h^2,$$

are obtained, just as in the Bohr theory. (See (7a) in Chapter 2.) Applications were also made to the harmonic oscillator problem and to the hydrogen atom subject to an electric field; the results agreed completely with those of Heisenberg's matrix methods.

Schrödinger was particularly pleased that his equation "automatically selects" quantized energy values, what are known in the mathematics terminology as energy "eigenvalues." † Nothing like Bohr's stationary-state postulate is needed and there is no mention of atomic systems "jumping" from one stationary state to another: ". . . whatever the waves may mean physically, the theory furnishes a method of quantization which is absolutely free from arbitrary postulates that this or that quantity must be an integer." The concept of "quantum jumps," always unacceptable to Schrödinger, seems to be erased entirely from the theory.

It was Schrödinger's hope that his theory would restore to atomic physics the great classical principle of continuity of change which had been losing ground steadily since Planck's paper was published in 1900. Schrödinger's equation (7) and the classical wave equation are clearly related mathematically; perhaps they are related physically as well. This possibility appealed not only to Schrödinger but also to Einstein, Planck, de Broglie, and Sommerfeld. They were

† The half-German words "eigenfunction" and "eigenvalue" seem to have come into the mathematical vocabulary through the influence of quantum physics. The more genuine mathematical terms are "characteristic function" and "characteristic value."

skeptical, as Einstein wrote, "that one has to solve the quanta by giving up the continuum."

The crux of the problem is the wave mechanical amplitude function ψ, usually known simply as the "wave function." If this function can be interpreted in a continuous and essentially classical manner, then quantum physics is no-longer quantum physics: it merges with classical physics. To this end Schrödinger introduced the concept, mentioned earlier, that electrons and other particles consist of wave groups, each one of the component waves being described by a wave function ψ. The wave function takes on a sort of electromagnetic meaning; among other things it can be used to calculate the charge density associated with a wave group and therefore account for the distribution of the electronic charge. But electrons constructed of wave groups prove difficult to hold together: especially in scattering and collision processes they tend to spread rapidly over a broad region, an effect which must be reversed instantaneously when the electron is found at a certain location. Schrödinger's wave group concept was opposed, and finally replaced, with an interpretation that places the waves in a "guiding" role. The waves determine where the electron is likely to be found or not to be found, but no more fundamental understanding of the waves is sought, or even considered possible. This "statistical" interpretation will be seen in the next chapter, which deals especially with the enigma of the electron and the two slits.

Aside from matters of interpretation, the Schrödinger theory, particularly equation (7) and a time-dependent version which will appear in Chapter 5, has been supremely successful in all kinds of atomic and molecular problems. The Schrödinger 1926 paper was, in the words of the physics historian, Max Jammer, ". . . undoubtedly one of the most influential contributions ever made in the history of science. . . . In fact, the subsequent development of nonrelativistic quantum theory was to no small extent merely an elaboration and application of Schrödinger's work."

No less unique and profound than the theory was the man whose genius was responsible for it.

Erwin Schrödinger

Where riddles led me on to further riddles,
To *them* the truth was quite precisely known.

These lines of the Austrian dramatic poet Franz Grillparzer introduce Schrödinger's last book of essays, completed a few months before he died. They stand as a memorial to Schrödinger's life and achievements. He found riddles and answered them with a brilliance matched by few scientists in history, but he sought much more.

> What, then, is in your opinion the value of natural science? I answer: Its scope, aim and value is the same as that of any other branch of human knowledge. Nay, none of them alone, only the union of them all, has any scope or value at all, and that is simply enough described: . . . in the brief, impressive rhetoric of Plotinus, "And we, who are we anyhow?"

Schrödinger was one of the most eloquent spokesmen of his time for humanism in science. To the conceits that physics was nonexistent before Newton and that the concepts of quantum physics are unique and new he answered: ". . . quantum theory dates 24 centuries further back, to Leucippus and Democritus. They invented the first discontinuity—isolated atoms in empty space," and "physical science in its present form . . . is the direct offspring, the uninterrupted continuation of ancient science . . . ." He feared that physicists were beginning to talk to themselves:

> A theoretical science, unaware that those of its constructs considered relevant and momentous are destined eventually to be framed in concepts and words that have a grip on the educated community and become part and parcel of the general world picture—a theoretical science, I say, where this is forgotten, and where the initiated continue musing to each other in terms that are, at best, understood by a small group of close fellow travellers, will necessarily be cut off from the rest of cultural mankind; in the long run it is bound to atrophy and ossify . . . .

These uncompromising words appeared in a paper arguing against the idea of discontinuous quantum jumps. The "easy pictures" made available by Bohr's stationary-state concept, with atoms and molecules leaping rapidly, practically instantaneously, between them, "swallowing and respewing whole energy parcels," form a useful and reliable shorthand for the thoughts of the practicing physicist, but should they be taken literally? For one thing, the wave train produced by a single quantum "transition" is demonstrably one or two feet long; † the time an atom requires to radiate this wave train is about the same as the lifetime of an excited state. How, then, can the atom find time to exist in the stationary states so intricately described by the theory?

The physicist uses his theories in the daily tasks of organizing data and planning experiments. A theory "works" for him if it answers his peculiar needs, but to the world outside the physics journals, and, even worse, to the world and culture of another era, the preoccupied "musings" of the professional physicist may seem to be written in hieroglyphics. "Would it mean setting ourselves too high and proud a goal, if we occasionally thought of what will become of our scientific papers 2000 years hence? . . . Will there be anybody to grasp our meaning, as we grasp the meaning of Archimedes?"

Schrödinger's scientific work was extremely broad. One of his earliest projects concerned a theory of color perception. At one time or another he dealt with nearly all aspects of modern physics: statistical mechanics, X-ray diffraction, general relativity, the theory of specific heats and field theory, as well as his more familiar work in atomic theory. In 1944 he published a book entitled *What Is Life?* This was one of the first excursions into the realm of molecular biology, perhaps the dominant field in present-day science.‡

Schrödinger was born in Vienna, and his family, like Heisenberg's, had many intellectual interests. His formal education began at the *Akademische Gymnasium*, where ancient languages and literature were major subjects (much the same grammar school influence as Heisenberg's). He entered the University of Vienna shortly after the death of Ludwig Boltzmann and felt Boltzmann's vast influence very strongly: "His line of thought may be called my first love in science. No other has ever thus enraptured me or will ever do so again." Significantly, Schrödinger's university studies dealt extensively with the physics of continuous media, where vibrational phenomena lead to wave equations and eigenvalue representations.

In 1918, after World War I, Schrödinger looked forward to a career as a part-time physics teacher and full-time philosopher. A chair in theoretical physics at the University of Czernowitz seemed imminent. "I was prepared to do a good job lecturing in theoretical

† For more on this see Notes and Comment, page 231.
‡ Francis Crick, of the famous team of Watson and Crick, tells us that Schrödinger's book was largely responsible for his conversion from physics to molecular biology.

physics . . . but for the rest, to devote myself to philosophy . . . ."
Suddenly Czernowitz no longer belonged to Austria. "My guardian
angel intervened. . . . I had to stick to theoretical physics, and, to my
astonishment, something occasionally emerged from it."

For several years Schrödinger followed the kind of itinerant academic career common in German university life; after short stays
in Jena, Stuttgart, and Breslau, he finally settled for six years at the
University of Zurich (where Einstein had been one of his predeces-
sors). This was the most active period of his life, when the great work
on wave mechanics was completed. In 1927 Schrödinger became
Planck's successor in the Chair of Theoretical Physics at the University of Berlin. For a time life was pleasant in Berlin: Planck and
Einstein and von Laue were there, and Berlin was a major center
for research in theoretical physics. But gradually the Nazi nightmare
descended, and Schrödinger did not hesitate to show his opposition. In one incident he interfered with Storm Trooper operations
in a Jewish ghetto and would have been beaten to death had he not
been recognized.

To escape further horrors Schrödinger left Germany. After some
wandering he eventually settled in Rome. While there he was approached by Eamon De Valera, a mathematician and scientist, who
happened also to be Prime Minister of Ireland. An Institute for
Advanced Studies (modeled after the one in Princeton) was to be
established in Dublin. Funds were short; studies at first were to
be confined to two "paper and pencil" schools, a School of Celtic
Studies, and a School of Theoretical Physics which Schrödinger was
invited to direct. He accepted, and in neutral Ireland he found life
peaceful and productive once more. He was a popular lecturer in
Dublin, endearing himself to the Irish with his knowledge of Irish
music, Celtic design, and Gaelic. The Irish weather, however, did
not suit him. In 1956 failing health and a longing for his native
Austria brought him back to the University of Vienna. But his health
continued to decline.

Schrödinger died in 1961 and was buried in Alpbach, a small
Tirolean village. Few memorial papers, no biographies, and no
books of photographs and reminiscences were written at the time of
his death. His life never had been given the attention paid other
scientists, who were more gregarious. Schrödinger worked alone;
only two or three of his ninety papers were written with another
author. No more than the novelist, the composer, or the painter could
Erwin Schrödinger work as part of a "team." In many ways he approached science as an artist; with sensitivity, imagination, and
individual taste.

The Bohr-Schrödinger Encounter

Erwin Schrödinger and Niels Bohr, the two principal characters of the story told in this book, could hardly have been more different in their temperaments and methods of working. Schrödinger appears as the lonely, eloquent critic, a man with immense resources, but lacking the ability to impress his ideas, when they were controversial, on his colleagues. Bohr, on the other hand, had in almost unbelievable measure the persuasive ability which Schrödinger lacked. The immense gulf between the two physicists, both intellectual and personal, is shown in a story told by Heisenberg of a visit Schrödinger made to Copenhagen in 1926, shortly after his wave mechanics paper had appeared. Schrödinger was asked to come for seminar appearances and also for participation in the informal discussions, frequently of marathon length, which had become a specialty in Copenhagen. Bohr was particularly anxious to deal with the semi-classical interpretation Schrödinger had attached to his wave mechanics.

As Heisenberg tells it: "As far as I can remember these discussions took place in Copenhagen around September, 1926, and in particular they left me with a very strong opinion of Bohr's personality. For though Bohr was an unusually considerate and obliging person, he was able in such a discussion, which concerned epistemological problems which he considered to be of vital importance, to insist fanatically and with almost terrifying relentlessness on complete clarity in all arguments. He would not give up, even after hours of struggling, before Schrödinger had admitted that [his] interpretation was insufficient, and could not even explain Planck's law."

The clash developed over Schrödinger's unshakable faith in the fundamental continuity of nature and Bohr's slightly *more* unshakable insistence that somewhere, somehow, there must be quantum jumps. The discussions went on, with Schrödinger losing by inches, "point by point in infinitely laborious discussions." After a few days Schrödinger, whose capacity for this kind of thing was not equal to Bohr's, found himself in bed, "perhaps from overexertion." But this, as far as Bohr was concerned, was no reason to end the discussions: ". . . it was hard to get Bohr away from Schrödinger's bed and the phrase, 'But, Schrödinger, you must at least admit that . . .' could be heard again and again." Finally there came a desperate burst from Schrödinger: "If we are going to stick to this damned quantum-jumping, then I regret that I ever had anything to do with quantum theory." To this Bohr replied gently: "But the rest of us are thankful that you did, because you have contributed so much to the clarification of the quantum theory." When Schrödinger finally left Copenhagen he was, according to Heisenberg, "rather discouraged."

Bohr must have realized that his victory over the Schrödinger interpretation was somewhat less than complete, for neither he nor anyone else in Copenhagen could offer a better solution. Two useful computational methods, the Heisenberg-Born-Jordan matrix mechanics and the Schrödinger wave mechanics, had appeared. The way was open for applications of these methods to extensive atomic and molecular problems; the equations were available, and the many possibilities for their use were rapidly becoming apparent. But no physicist in 1926 could honestly say that he "understood" matrix mechanics and wave mechanics.

It was obvious that some fundamental changes in meaning would be necessary before a rational interpretation of the new "quantum mechanics" could possibly be formulated. For example, where in the new equations was anything recognizable said about the vital concepts of "position" and "velocity"? What meaning was to be attached to the Schrödinger Ψ-function? And what about the old, and still unanswered, question of the wave-particle duality?

Around the time of Schrödinger's visit, and no doubt prompted by it, Bohr and his colleagues, particularly Heisenberg (who had just taken up residence in Copenhagen), became committed to the formidable task of sorting out a coherent interpretation of quantum physics. In the best Copenhagen style, the problem was attacked in "discussions," day and night, week after week and month after month. Gradually Bohr and Heisenberg began to take different positions. In the end, their two interpretations were to be brought together into a single "Copenhagen Interpretation," but we shall at first see their separate contributions, more or less as they evolved.

The Uncertainty Principle

To Heisenberg the difficulties presented by the quantum theory suggested the problems of special relativity solved by Einstein in his famous analysis of the concepts of space and time. In a nearly parallel manner Heisenberg focused his attention on the space (i.e. position) and momentum concepts.

Heisenberg found, as had several others before him, that the mathematical formalism of the quantum theory seems to imply that certain physical variables cannot be known perfectly at the same time. This behavior is particularly prominent with the momentum p and the corresponding coordinate variable x. The theory reveals that if x is precisely known, then *any* value is possible for p. More generally, if x is known with the uncertainty Δx, then p can be determined no better than with the uncertainty

$$\Delta p = h/2\pi\Delta x.$$

The product of the two uncertainties is $h/2\pi$ or something larger:

$$\Delta p\Delta x \geqslant h/2\pi.$$

To Heisenberg, with his insistence that all physical arguments must be reduced to observable quantities, this theoretical argument alone was not sufficiently convincing. The $\Delta p\Delta x$ inequality might be something of an artefact introduced by the mathematical apparatus. He therefore advocated a much more elementary approach. On the question of the coordinate variable: "If one wants to clarify what is meant by 'position of an object,' for example, of an electron, he has to describe an experiment by which 'position of an electron' can be measured; otherwise this term has no meaning at all."

The electron-locating experiment which Heisenberg described is a rather fantastic one; it makes use of a "gamma-ray microscope" which is not likely ever to be built. Nevertheless, it is based on the ordinary principles of optics and, were it not for the extreme practical difficulty of handling the gamma-ray "light" which the microscope uses, this device could probably be made. The microscope is simple in principle; it consists of a single lens and a photographic plate to record the image:

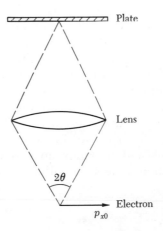

Imagine that an electron whose momentum in the x-direction is p_{x0} comes into the field of the microscope, as shown. When light of wavelength λ illuminates the microscope field the resolution of the microscope in the x-direction is, according to the laws of optics,

$$\Delta x = \sim \lambda/2 \sin \theta, \qquad (8)$$

where θ is one half the angle subtended by the lens, the so-called angular "aperture" of the microscope. This tells us that the electron-locating abilities of the microscope improve as the lens is made larger and as light of shorter wavelength is used, particularly the latter. If the light has the wavelength 10^{-9} cm, then $\Delta x < 10^{-9}$ cm, and the microscope is capable of looking inside atoms and locating electrons there, since atomic diameters are generally more than 10^{-8} cm.

But a beam of light with the wavelength 10^{-9} cm is really a beam of X rays, whose photon energies are about 124,000 ev:

$$h\nu = hc/\lambda = 1.24 \times 10^{5} \text{ ev.}$$

When these photons "shine" on the electron located in the microscope field they will seem to be scattered elastically in the manner described by Compton (see page 30). If the scattering process sends a photon toward the lens it is collected and an image forms on the plate. But the scattering also has an effect on the electron: it must recoil from the collision. Thus the process of locating the electron disturbs it, an effect which can be drastic if the illuminating photons are very energetic. The 10^{-9} cm photons mentioned can transfer tens of thousands of electron volts, easily enough to remove an electron completely from any atom in which it might be located. Any attempt to eliminate or reduce this effect by using less energetic photons is futile, because these photons, if they are sufficiently "soft" to leave the electron mostly undisturbed, have wavelengths much larger than 10^{-9} cm, and the microscope, according to (8), has insufficient resolution to be useful in locating the electron.

Even more damaging to the fundamental concepts of mechanics is the fact that the additional momentum the electron receives when it is struck by a photon cannot be known with certainty. This state of affairs is unavoidable, because the microscope collects photons from many directions and provides no way of telling one photon from another. The photon-electron collision may scatter the photon forward,

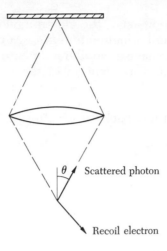

or backward,

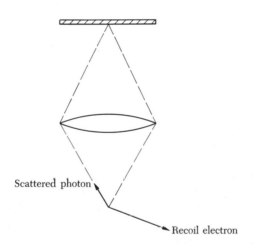

or in any direction between. All of these scattered photons are collected by the microscope lens, and they all make exactly the same
kind of contribution to the electron's image, even though they dis-
turb the electron in different ways. Not only does the position
measurement change the electron's motion, it does so in an in-
definite way.

To assess the extent of the momentum uncertainty after the photon-
electron collision, this being necessary for the position measurement,
a simple momentum conservation calculation can be made. Consider

that the photon approaches the electron (along the x-direction) with a wavelength λ_0 and a momentum h/λ_0. At the same time, the electron is assumed to have a parallel momentum p_{x0}. Thus initially the total electron-photon momentum in the x-direction is $(h/\lambda_0) + p_{x0}$. After it collides with the electron, the photon has a wavelength somewhere between λ_1 (in the extreme forward scattering situation) and λ_2 (in the extreme backward scattering direction):

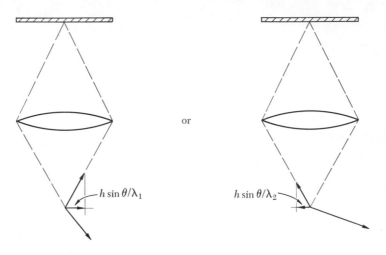

or

The momentum in the x-direction lies between $+h \sin \theta/\lambda_1$ and $-h \sin \theta/\lambda_2$. In order of magnitude it can be said that these two momenta are $+h \sin \theta/\lambda_0$ and $-h \sin \theta/\lambda_0$, where λ_0 is the photon wavelength before the collision. If the x-components of the electron momentum are p_x and p_x' for the maximum forward and backward scattering, the order of magnitude of the electron-photon momentum after the collision lies between $p_x + h \sin \theta/\lambda_0$ and $p_x' - h \sin \theta/\lambda_0$. Since momentum is conserved, and in any case the electron-photon momentum before the collision is $(h/\lambda_0) + p_{x0}$, it is concluded that

$$p_x + h \sin \theta/\lambda_0 = \sim (h/\lambda_0) + p_{x0}$$

$$p_x' - h \sin \theta/\lambda_0 = \sim (h/\lambda_0) + p_{x0},$$

and that

$$p_x' - p_x = \sim 2h \sin \theta/\lambda_0.$$

The last equation gives the difference between the maximum and minimum possible values for the electron's momentum in the x-direction after the measurement. This is the momentum uncertainty created by the measurement; it is usually written Δp_x:

$$\Delta p_x = \sim 2h \sin \theta / \lambda.$$

Use the momentum uncertainty now to form a product with the position uncertainty (8) created by the resolution limitation of the microscope:

$$\Delta x \Delta p_x = \sim h. \tag{9}$$

It is well to remark again that this is an order of magnitude statement; it will be put in a more precise and more general form in Chapter 6.

The calculation just made shows mathematically what the picture of the gamma-ray microscope shows physically, that it is impossible to use a microscope to make a simple, isolated position measurement. Whether we want it to or not, a position measurement made on an electron leaves the electron with uncertain momentum after the measurement, and the momentum uncertainly is related to the position uncertainty (the microscope resolution) in the simple reciprocal way shown by equation (9).

The "uncertainty relation" (9) is not peculiar to microscopes. As Heisenberg and others have discovered, any kind of position-measuring device has an inherent position-momentum limitation expressed by

$$\Delta p_x \Delta x = \sim h.$$

Furthermore, if experiments are invented to accomplish various kinds of energy measurements, they lead to an uncertainty relation of the same form as (9) but involving energy and time:

$$\Delta E \Delta t = \sim h. \tag{10}$$

Any attempt to make a precise energy measurement requires a finite length of time Δt, which is related in a reciprocal manner to the energy uncertainty ΔE inherent in the measurement.

The implications of Heisenberg's uncertainty relations extend to almost every corner of quantum physics. No wonder that when Pauli saw Heisenberg's paper his reply was, "Now it becomes day in quantum mechanics." One of the general rules implied in these relations is that certain pairs of variables are "incompatible." When one such variable is measured, nothing can prevent an effect on the other variable. Momentum and position, and energy and time, are examples of incompatible variables; other such pairs will appear later. All kinds of dodges can be and have been tried in "thought experiments," but no device based on real physical principles shows any promise of avoiding these effects and the resulting uncertainty limitations. The uncertainties are not due to any coarseness of the instruments and the experiments. More than anything else they are due to the inevitable interaction between that which is measured and that which does the measuring. Matter and radiation being what they are, all real measuring devices must have some kind of interfering effect. Quantum physics is thoroughly committed to the description of just those quantities whose measurement can be defined. The inherent uncertainties which are now revealed in these measurements must be regarded as no less basic.

The conclusions forced by the uncertainty relations are not always easy to accept or to understand. For example, if the physical conditions imply that there is complete certainty in the momentum and energy of an electron (not an uncommon situation), then *nothing* is known about where the electron is located in space and time. We must give up all hope of tracing the electron's progress from one definite space-time point to another, as is customary in classical physics. To be sure, a measurement can be made with the Heisenberg gamma-ray microscope, which precisely locates the electron at one instant, but the direction it takes in the *next* instant must be blurred to the extent of the momentum uncertainty specified by (9). The unwelcome conclusion is that, no matter how cleverly we try, no measuring device can be found which makes it possible to define continuously the path of a particle as small as an electron. Remember that, in a much different kind of a discussion, the peculiarities of the two-slit diffraction of a single photon (page 74) also forced the abandonment of the definite-path concept.

But why cling so doggedly to measuring devices, diffraction experiments, and the like, when they seem to do just what is not wanted, when they interfere with and seriously confuse the physical entities we want to describe? Might there not be a world of precise, continuous electron paths beneath this world of clumsy physical measurements? This raises again (see page 75) the issue of how much, if anything, can be said about an object when it is not under observation. As before, the best answer appears to be that no *physical* description can be attempted unless it can, at least in principle, *be verified by actual measurements*. As Alfred Landé writes, ". . . it is unphysical to accept the idea that there are particles possessing definite positions and momenta at any given time, and then to concede that these data can never be confirmed experimentally, as though by a malicious whim of nature."

This point of view has still another shattering implication. Not only are we to abandon the concept that small particles such as electrons have definite trajectories, but the conclusion is inescapable that electrons and other particles have no discernible *individuality*. Put a number of electrons in a box, for example; what possibility is there that the electrons can be followed individually as they move around the box? No microscope will do: microscope measurements of position precise enough to follow a particular electron from one point to another must inevitably have drastic effects on the electron's energy and momentum, not to mention possible collision effects on the other electrons. A system of electrons which must, by the requirements of most problems, have well-defined physical characteristics, is thoroughly disrupted by the process of locating and following electrons as individuals. Here, as elsewhere, we only know what we see. If position and other kinds of measurements allow no way of following the progress of individual electrons, then the physical theory cannot even allow the *concept* of individuality. Particles are identifiable as electrons, photons, protons, etc., but not as *individuals* of these species. In a sense atomic particles, for example, the electrons in an atom, can be *counted,* but the counting procedure is more involved and indirect than putting labels on single electrons.

This is a denial of the ancient, but no longer durable, concept that atomic particles are single, individual, and permanent specks of material. We must somehow attempt to cope with atomic particles that have no continuous history in the classical sense and no existence as individuals. *"We must not admit the possibility of continuous observation,"* wrote Schrödinger. "Observations are to be regarded as discrete, disconnected events. Between there are gaps which we cannot fill in. There are cases where we should upset everything if we admitted the possibility of continuous observation. That is why . . . it is better to regard a particle not as a permanent entity but as an instantaneous event. Sometimes these events form chains that give the illusion of permanent beings — but only in particular circumstances and only for an extremely short period of time in every single case."

4

An Emergency Exit

Electron-watching is, as Henry Margenau remarks, very much like sitting out on a summer evening and watching fireflies. There is a firefly flash here, a flash there, and a flash somewhere else. We know that a lampyrid species is located wherever a flash appears, but we have no way of being sure that the individual causing one flash is the same one that caused a flash seen a few minutes before, and the appearance of one flash reveals almost no information concerning where to look for another flash. That there actually is a firefly path between flashes we know, of course, from watching fireflies in daylight. Electron events also appear here and there in disconnected "flashes," but in a way that is unfortunately different: "There is no daytime in which the electron's path could be watched."

Nevertheless, a lot can be learned about fireflies on dark summer nights by watching a great many flashes and recording their pattern. Many details of the fireflies' behavior, including (so we are told) their sex life, can be read from a careful analysis of the apparently chaotic blinking that fills the summer night. This picture says nothing of the continuous behavior of any single firefly, but it tells an informative story concerning fireflies *collectively*.

To change the analogy and also point the way to a useful computational procedure, note that the information supplied by firefly blinkings, and also by disconnected electron events, is of a *statistical* type collected and used to great advantage by insurance companies. Statistical data on car-owners, for example, predicts nothing with certainty concerning what will happen to an individual, but it makes precisely clear how often the *average* car-owner wrecks his car. Now

110

the individual car-owner has no expectation of wrecking his car in the average length of time, for he does not live in a world of average behavior. But the insurance executive does, and he becomes very adept at inventing profitable schemes out of averages calculated by making many observations.

The modern atomic physicist has found, not always happily, that he must handle his business in somewhat the same way the insurance executive handles his.† His physics is written entirely for the average behavior of atomic particles. The laws of this physics are derived by imagining that many measurements of a certain type are made on a number of like particles, all of which are in the same state before the measurement. This leads, for example, to a calculation of the average position of the electrons found in unexcited hydrogen atoms. Like the insurance company data, this approach also tells how all of the measurements are distributed around the average, and how much fluctuation there is above and below the average. In this way a procedure is developed for calculating the average position and spatial distribution (something like the firefly's habitat) for electrons of a certain kind. Once this is clear, then judicious use of Schrödinger's equation ‡ and the patterns of classical mechanics (by way of the correspondence principle) tell us how to calculate other average quantities such as the momentum and the energy.

Just as a psychologist may wonder whether insurance company studies constitute a complete science of human behavior, some physicists have wondered whether a genuine physics can allow nothing but a statistical interpretation. If it is not possible (not even in principle) to show what a single electron "actually" does between observations, if all our knowledge of atomic particles must take the form of statistical tables, do we have a physics worthy of the name? Whatever the answer may be to this question, there is no better procedure now available to account for the behavior of electrons and other atomic particles. What has evolved may be a "makeshift," or an "emergency exit," as Schrödinger was inclined to think, but there is no denying that an exit has been found which success-

† There is one basic difference between atomic and insurance company statistics. The insurance executive *can*, if he wants to, and has the time, follow continuously the progress of an individual policyholder. The physicist, unfortunately, does not have this alternative. Single, isolated atomic particles are beyond his reach, if they exist at all.

‡ Equation (7), in Chapter 3.

fully escapes an extremely difficult and complex situation. Though "fundamentally an expedient," the statistical method in quantum physics is, in Planck's words, "absolutely indispensable in practical physics. A renunciation of it would involve the abandonment of the most important of the more recent advances of physical science."

The author of this ingenious and highly effective theory is a man who prefers to regard himself as a "dilettante."

Max Born

One might say, with pardonable exaggeration, that half of the story told in these chapters was written in Copenhagen, under the guidance of Niels Bohr. The "other half" of the story, it might be said with no greater exaggeration, was written in Göttingen, where the guiding inspiration was largely that of Max Born.†

The Georgia Augusta University in the Prussian town of Göttingen became a major center for research in mathematics and theoretical physics in the mid-nineteenth century, during the tenure of Karl Friedrich Gauss, the "prince of mathematicians." Gauss's successor was Felix Klein, who, like Gauss, worked with and encouraged physical and technological applications of mathematics. In spite of his devotion to applied mathematics, Klein brought to Göttingen two mathematicians, David Hilbert and Hermann Minkowski, who were intolerant, even disdainful, of the wasted efforts of the "technicians." Nevertheless, as the new physics grew and penetrated more and more the realm of "pure" mathematics, both men applied their mathematical talents to the enrichment of the "intellectually poverty-stricken" physicists.

Minkowski and his work on relativity first brought Max Born to teach in Göttingen in 1908. Minkowski's sudden death in 1909 changed Born's immediate plans, but he stayed on in Göttingen for five years and began the major lines of his research in physics. In 1915, just as war broke out, he moved to the University of Berlin where he was to relieve Planck of his teaching duties. The dismal days of wartime intervened; but chaotic as the war and postwar conditions were in Germany the intellectual life of the country was not extinguished. Born tells of the consolation of evenings spent with friends from the academic community, of long political and scientific discussions and violin sonatas played with Einstein. After

† But don't forget the third half, written by Schrödinger.

the military defeat, many of the German universities managed to resume as vigorously and productively as ever. Born's first position after the war was at the University of Frankfurt (Born went to Frankfurt in a remarkable "trading" arrangement: he took the place of Max von Laue at Frankfurt and von Laue took his place in Berlin).

In 1921 Born returned once more to Göttingen (for the third time. he had been a student there under Hilbert) to direct the Second Physics Institute. He soon displayed his genius for organization and getting his own way by maneuvering the Prussian Minister of Education into dividing the Institute into two divisions: one experimental and the other theoretical. Born directed the theoretical institute and James Franck, an old friend from student days, was called to direct the experimental institute.

Born writes of his first move to Göttingen as a student: ". . . the mecca of German mathematics was Göttingen and three prophets lived there, Felix Klein, David Hilbert and Hermann Minkowski. So I decided to make the pilgrimage." Fifteen years later Göttingen became a mecca for the burgeoning world of quantum physics, and the three prophets were Hilbert, the mathematician and now esteemed mathematical physicist; Franck, the experimentalist; and Born, the theoretician. The pilgrims came from all over the world: Pauli and Heisenberg were Born's first two assistants; Heitler, Hückel, Rosenfeld, and Stern also were assistants; Hund, Maria Goeppert-Mayer, Jordan, and Oppenheimer were doctoral students; Condon, Dirac, Fermi, Pauling, Teller, and Wigner were some of the visitors. As in Copenhagen, the 1920's and early 1930's were "beautiful years" in Göttingen. The student inscription in a Ratskeller, *extra Gottingam non est vita*, must have seemed quite natural.

Hitler and the Nazis brought an end to all of this. The Nazis began to attack the "Jewish physics" of Einstein and Bohr. Göttingen was purged of its influential non-Aryans, including Born and Franck. They were replaced by representatives of a dubious something called "German physics." In the space of a few weeks Göttingen was brought down from the rank of a great university to a second-rate provincial school. The new Minister of Education asked Hilbert if the Physics Institute had suffered from "the departure of the Jews and their friends." "Suffered? No, it didn't suffer, Herr Minister," replied Hilbert. "It just doesn't exist any more!"

When the purge was ordered, Born first went to Cambridge and then to the University of Edinburgh, where he remained for seventeen years. While Schrödinger was taking refuge in Ireland, Born found a peaceful haven in Scotland. He returned to his work, but carefully avoided an activity which was beginning to occupy many of his former collaborators, assistants and students. The research and development work on nuclear weapons had started in England, the United States, and Germany. Born remarks that he was not qualified to participate in nuclear research because he had "never learned nuclear physics properly." But it appears that something more than an inadequate course in radioactivity dictated his lack of enthusiasm for weapons research: More quickly and courageously than most of his colleagues he saw the ghastly consequences of nuclear weapons and "balance of terror" politics, and he found it impossible to contribute.

"I never liked being a specialist," he writes, "and have always remained a dilettante, even in what were considered my own subjects." One wonders how a "dilettante" could have invented several major theories, earned a Nobel Prize, and directed an internationally famous school of physics. But he means what he says. To Max Born science is a pastime. He has, in a sense, remained an amateur; like Einstein, Schrödinger, Bohr, and most of the other contributors mentioned in this story, he has an enthusiastic and profound *appreciation* for science.

To our vast benefit Max Born, perhaps more than any other major scientist of this century, has the ability to write of this appreciation in both textbook and general styles. This brief sample says more about a simple physical fact and the human predicament it implies than many an 800-page tome: "There is no longer any doubt: all matter is unstable. If this were not true, the stars would not shine, there would be no heat and light from the sun, no life on earth. Stability and life are incompatible. Thus life is necessarily a dangerous adventure which may have a happy ending or a bad one."

The Statistical Interpretation

It has been mentioned that Schrödinger originally regarded the waves of his theory as the fundamental constituents of matter. Electrons and other atomic entities were groups of waves represented mathematically by combining a number of amplitude functions, each one being a solution of the wave equation (7), in Chapter 3. Particle properties of electrons, if they had any physical reality at all, were less fundamental than wave properties. For those who knew the ways of electrons in the laboratory this was a difficult position to accept. Electron *detecting* devices are particularly clear in suggesting that electrons are fundamentally particles. Max Born began to think along these lines very soon after he saw Schrödinger's wave mechanics paper. "To us in Göttingen Schrödinger's interpretation appeared unacceptable in the face of experimental facts. At the time it was already possible to count particles by means of scintillations or with the Geiger counter and to photograph their tracks with the help of the Wilson cloud chamber."

But how is a wave equation to be converted, at least partially, into a particle equation? The interpretation that Born developed was inspired by a concept Einstein had offered to deal with the wavelike behavior of particle-like photons. ("Once more an idea of Einstein's gave the lead.") Einstein had suggested that the electromagnetic wave field associated with the propagation of light and other radiation is actually a sort of "phantom field" which guides the photons to regions of high and low probability. To connect this interpretation with the mathematical theory of electromagnetic waves (as displayed, for example, in the optical wave equation on page 94), Einstein had postulated that the optical wave amplitude ρ is large in magnitude where photons are likely to be found and small where photons are not likely to be found. The wave amplitude therefore has some resemblance to a probability function which expresses the likelihood of finding a photon in a particular region of the accessible space. The wave amplitude ρ cannot, however, serve directly as a probability function because it is likely to be negative and even complex: legitimate probability functions are always positive (or zero) and real. This difficulty is easily avoided by assuming that the desired probability function is the *square* (always positive) of the *magnitude* (always real) of the amplitude function.† Therefore, the ghostly probability field P that guides the photons to their destinations is simply

$$P = |\rho|^2 = \rho^*\rho = \rho\rho^*$$

where ρ^* is the complex conjugate of ρ.‡

† That the squared magnitude is always positive and real can be seen by writing ρ as a complex number: $\rho = a + ib$, in which a and b are real numbers. Then $\rho^* = a - ib$ and $|\rho|^2 = \rho^*\rho = a^2 + b^2$. Since a and b are real, $a^2 + b^2$ is real and positive.

‡ As it turns out, however, modern quantum theory does not admit the existence of such functions as ρ for the case of photons. No simple physical meaning can be found for the probability of finding a photon at a certain location. But such functions certainly do exist for electrons, and, as will be seen throughout the remainder of the book, they are exceedingly useful. Wrong ideas sometimes lead to right ideas in science.

Born carried this idea over into wave mechanics, with some important modifications. The Schrödinger "wave function" ψ replaces the optical wave amplitude ρ and the appropriate probability function becomes

$$P = |\psi|^2 = \psi^*\psi = \psi\psi^*.$$

The function $|\psi|^2$ is proportional to the probability that an observation will find a particle in the region near the point at which ψ has been evaluated. For simplicity, consider ψ to depend on one space variable, x. To adapt to the methods of integral calculus, the probability function $P(x) = \psi^*(x)\psi(x)$ is then given the special meaning,

$P(x)dx$ = probability that a position measurement will find a particle between x and $x + dx$.

If this differential quantity is integrated over all of the space accessible to the particle the result must be unity:

$$\int_{-\infty}^{+\infty} P(x)dx = \int_{-\infty}^{+\infty} \psi^*(x)\psi(x)dx = 1. \tag{1}$$

The particle must be somewhere in all of the accessible space. This integral states a fundamental restriction on the wave function ψ, which is known to mathematicians as the "normalization" condition.

The wave function ψ is not always independent of time as shown thus far. Especially for systems in transit between stationary states, the wave function, and the probability function as well, become time-dependent. The wave equation that treats these and other problems involving time is introduced in the next chapter. It need only be said here that the probability interpretation for a wave function $\Psi(x,t)$ which changes with time is a simple extension of the interpretation for the problem without time:

$P(x,t)dx = \Psi^*(x,t)\Psi(x,t)dx$

= probability that a position measurement made at time t will find a particle between x and $x + dx$.

Naturally the time-dependent wave function Ψ must also satisfy a normalization condition:

$$\int_{-\infty}^{+\infty} P(x,t)dx = \int_{-\infty}^{+\infty} \Psi^*(x,t)\Psi(x,t)dx = 1. \tag{2}$$

With this mathematical sense the probability Pdx evaluated at a point in space tells what fraction of all the position measurements will find the particle located in the region around x. If $P(x_1,t)dx$ is relatively large, the position x_1 is a relatively likely one; if $P(x_2,t)dx$ is relatively small, the position x_2 is relatively unimportant. These data on the particle's position can be averaged with the procedure used with other normalized statistical data: the contribution of the position x to the average is taken to be $xP(x,t)dx$ and this is large or small according to whether $P(x,t)dx$ is large or small. The complete average $\bar{x}$ is the sum of all these contributions:

$$\bar{x} = \int_{-\infty}^{+\infty} xP(x,t)dx. \tag{3}$$

The principle for calculating other averages such as the momentum and the energy is also established, but the task of completing these calculations presents several problems which are better postponed for the more formal and systematic discussion of the next chapter.

This, in brief, is the statistical interpretation placed by Born on the Schrödinger wave function Ψ (or ψ). It asserts that the wave field generated by the Schrödinger equation is simply a probability field which shows where a particle is likely or unlikely to be found: the waves of wave mechanics are "probability waves." The electron and other atomic entities retain their status as particles, at least as far as detecting devices are concerned, but their distribution in space follows a peculiar wavelike pattern. In this strange way (a "makeshift," according to Schrödinger) wave and particle aspects are effectively brought into the same picture.

Born applied this concept with outstanding success to various kinds of collision experiments, for example, the collision of electrons with heavy atoms in the manner of the Franck-Hertz experiment. He describes the probability waves in such an experiment with a simple water-wave analogy:

> A shower of electrons coming from an infinite distance, represented by an incident wave of known intensity (that is, $|\psi|^2$), impinges on an obstacle, say a heavy atom. In the same way that the water wave caused by a steamer excites secondary circular waves in striking a pile, the incident electron wave is partly transformed by the atom into a secondary spherical wave, whose amplitude of oscillation ψ is different in different directions. The square of the amplitude of this wave at a great distance from the scattering center then determines the relative probability of scattering in its dependence on direction.

The Slit Experiment Revisited

The analogy between probability waves and ordinary waves such as those seen on water is surprisingly complete. In particular, and crucial to the theory, is the fact that two fields of probability waves can mix and produce an interference pattern. To show this, and also give a final account of the perplexing problem which started the discussions of the last chapter, return to the experiment in which electrons pass through a double-slit arrangement.† As the Born statistical interpretation sees it, each electron arrives at the double slit with an associated field of probability waves spread out over the width of the beam supplying the electrons:

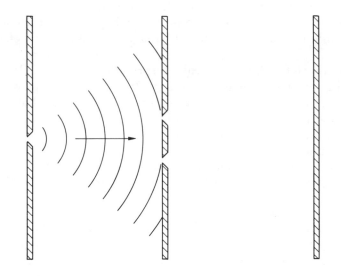

This means simply that the electron may be found anywhere in the beam, and that regions of high and low probability move toward the slit like the crests and troughs of a wave train. After this system of waves passes through the two slits it appears on the other side as two diffracted wave trains which can mix with each other around the center:

---

† Because our concern is primarily with electrons the experiment is to be imagined now with electrons as the particles passing through the apparatus. As mentioned before, the diffculties of the description are resolved in an essentially different way when photons are the diffracted particles. The photon problem is more difficult (at least less familiar) than the electron problem and is not an important part of the story told here.

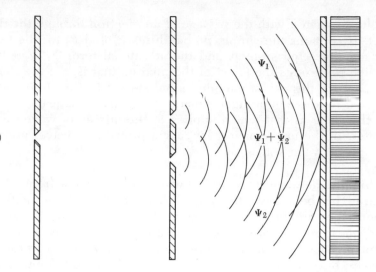

Just as in the mixing of diffracted systems of water waves, regions of cancellation and reinforcement are developed and the familiar interference pattern results. In this way the Born theory pictures the probability field which "guides" an electron through the double slit to the detecting screen, preferentially to the regions of high probability. After many electrons have passed by under the same circumstances the peaks and troughs of the interference pattern become visible on the screen.

In one of the diffracted wave systems the wave amplitudes may be represented by Ψ_1 and the corresponding probability function by $P_1 = \Psi_1{}^*\Psi_1$; in the other diffracted system the amplitudes may be represented by Ψ_2 and the corresponding probability function by $P_2 = \Psi_2{}^*\Psi_2$. Where the two systems mix the wave amplitudes are

$$\Psi_{12} = \Psi_1 + \Psi_2$$

and the probability function is

$$P_{12} = (\Psi_1 + \Psi_2)^*(\Psi_1 + \Psi_2)$$
$$= \Psi_1{}^*\Psi_1 + \Psi_2{}^*\Psi_2 + \Psi_1{}^*\Psi_2 + \Psi_1\Psi_2{}^*$$
$$= P_1 + P_2 + (\Psi_1{}^*\Psi_2 + \Psi_1\Psi_2{}^*).$$

This is a mathematical representation † of the entire probability

---

† Except for the normalization property. The function Ψ_{12} does not satisfy the normalization requirement (2). Normalizing the wave function does not add anything new to the physical argument presented here. That part of the procedure for forming a wave function is therefore temporarily omitted.

field associated with the passage of an electron through the double slit. It contains the simple probabilities P_1 and P_2 for the two unmixed diffracted systems and the additional term $\Psi_1^*\Psi_2 + \Psi_1\Psi_2^*$, which represents the effect of the mixing, that is, the interference. Except for the use of complex numbers (which are frequently required by the Schrödinger equation) this mathematical description is the same as that which applies to the mixing of wave trains on water. In the mathematical language, probability waves are just as simple as water waves.

Simple the waves may be, but where do they come from? Our procedure has been to say that probability waves are there and then use them. *Why* are they there? What mechanism generates them? These are questions which cannot at present be clearly answered. Quantum physics as it now stands asserts the *presence* of probability waves, but finds no way to probe deeper. Richard Feynman, one of the principal contributors to contemporary quantum theory, has this to say about the "law" of the probability waves: "One might still ask: 'How does it work? What is the machinery behind the law?' No one has found any machinery behind the law. No one can 'explain' any more than we have just 'explained.' No one will give you any deeper representation of the situation. We have no ideas about a more basic mechanism from which these results can be deduced." †

The Logic of Complementarity

The story has been told of Heisenberg's thoughts following Schrödinger's visit to Copenhagen in 1926, ideas which led finally to the uncertainty relations. During this same time Bohr was also hard at work on the conceptual problems of quantum physics. For a while Bohr and Heisenberg worked together. "At the time," Heisenberg writes, "I lived in the attic of the institute on Blegdamsvej, and Bohr often came up to my room late at night to talk with me of the difficulties in quantum theory which tortured both of us. On the one hand, we felt that the solution was just around the corner, in so far as we

† These statements are slightly more sweeping than they should be. There is no *well-accepted* mechanism that accounts for the existence and behavior of probability waves. Several conceivable explanations for the waves have, however, been proposed. Since they have not had wide acceptance they are not well known, at least not in the pages of textbooks. Brief sketches of two of these theories are given later in the chapter.

possessed a mathematical description which was obviously free of contradictions, while on the other hand we did not know how this mathematics should be used to describe even the most simple experimental situations." Heisenberg's approach, as we have seen, was to sort out significant patterns from the mathematical formalism and then to imagine experimental situations which fit these patterns.

Bohr found himself confronted with what appeared to be a different question. He could not completely accept the formalism in the first place because it seemed to be built on logical contradictions. Bohr and Heisenberg continued to work on their problems (and on each other), but for once the Copenhagen method of reasoning by strenuous debate was more frustrating than successful: "Our evening discussions quite often lasted till after midnight, and we occasionally parted somewhat discontented, for the difference in the directions in which we sought the solution seemed often to make the problem more difficult." Finally Bohr felt the need for a skiing vacation in Norway. To Bohr in Norway and to Heisenberg in Copenhagen, each left with his own thoughts, the pieces of the great puzzle (not two puzzles, after all) suddenly began to fall in place.

The logical difficulties that disturbed Bohr are most obvious in the basic equations of Einstein and de Broglie, $E = h\nu$ and $p = h\bar{\nu}$. The two quantities on the left, the energy E and the momentum p, are clearly particle properties, whereas the quantities on the right, the frequency ν and the wave number $\bar{\nu}$, are wave properties. Both equations speak of particles and waves at the same time. But how can they? Under no circumstances can a particle be the same thing as a wave. Can any reasonable physical entity be two decidedly different and contradictory things at the same time?

Bohr's answer is that, in spite of the equations and their somewhat misleading form, no *observer* ever finds a physical entity appearing as a particle and a wave at the same time. The energy and momentum of the electrons in a beam, say, can be established by passing the beam through a certain accelerating potential, and the wavelength can be measured by diffracting the beam with a nickel crystal. But it is essential to recognize that these are two *separate* experiments. The "contradictory" wave and particle aspects of an electron actually appear at different times and in distinctly different kinds of experiments: electron waves and particles never appear in the same experiment. From the viewpoint of physical observations, the only viewpoint allowable in quantum physics, there is no contradiction. Waves and particles are mutually exclusive, as they must be.

On the other hand, wave and particle properties, as we have seen repeatedly, are both essential to a complete physical description. They are, in Bohr's terminology, "complementary" aspects of a single entity such as an electron. There emerges here a strange kind of picture which is not complete until account is taken of two sets of properties that are, in the experimental sense, mutually exclusive. This is a pattern which is found in many different forms throughout quantum physics. For each important observable physical property, a complementary one can be found, which, strangely enough, cannot be measured or observed at the same time as the other with certainty. These pairs of properties are *complementary but also exclusive*. Bohr attached the term "complementarity" to the general principle that quantum physics has this dual logical pattern.

When Bohr returned to Copenhagen from Norway he apparently had formed in his mind the rudiments of the complementarity principle, and Heisenberg was able to show him a first draft of the paper which presented the uncertainty relations. Bohr made several corrections of a relatively minor nature, but more important, as Heisenberg writes, "he took objection to the fact that I had not started from the dualism between particles and waves." The Heisenberg mechanics shows more of a preference for the particle viewpoint than Bohr felt was justified by the complementarity viewpoint. But the two physicists resumed their work with discussions "which were not devoid of stress," and soon it was evident "that the uncertainty relations were just a special case of the more general complementarity principle."

That complementarity is a part of Heisenberg's arguments is easy to see when it is remembered that the uncertainty relations always involve pairs of quantities such as momentum and position or energy and time, which are complementary in the physical description, and each quantity of a pair always, to some extent, excludes the other. Unlike the wave-particle complementarity, however, this exclusion need not be entirely rigorous. If, for example, the coordinate x of an electron is measured with the uncertainty Δx, then knowledge of the momentum is not entirely excluded, but it is restricted to what is allowed by the uncertainty $\Delta p_x = \sim h/\Delta x$; only if the coordinate is measured with complete certainty are the momentum and position completely exclusive. Complementarity applied to these quantities seems to require that they have "domains of validity" as specified by the uncertainty relations.

The logic of complementarity can be used to organize a large part of quantum physics. Its use in rationalizing the wave-particle dualism and the various uncertainty relations has been mentioned. Bohr also pointed to a complementarity which spans almost the entire system of quantum physics: "The very nature of the quantum theory forces us to regard the space-time coordination and the claim of causality, the union of which characterizes the classical theories, as complementary but exclusive features of the description . . . ." By "the claim of causality" Bohr meant the energy-momentum mode of description, which in classical physics merges precisely with the "space-time coordination." In quantum physics the uncertainty relations

$$\Delta p_x \Delta x = \sim h \qquad \text{and} \qquad \Delta E \Delta t = \sim h$$

make it clear that this is no longer possible; the two kinds of description, certainly complementary in any physical theory, become completely or largely exclusive.

The major consequence of this viewpoint has already been discussed: that if any degree of certainty is necessary in the specification of the energy and momentum (much of the theory of quantum physics is developed by speaking of states in which the momentum and energy are *entirely* certain), then some degree of uncertainty (perhaps total uncertainty) must be allowed in the specification of the space-time position. This being the case, there is no choice but to organize a statistical procedure for locating the positions of such things as electrons. To serve the purposes of this statistical analysis the wave function Ψ is brought forth. There is, then, a complementarity between the familiar energy-momentum description and the strange Ψ-description. As the probability field generated by Ψ becomes broader and more diffuse the information on energy and momentum usually becomes sharper. If the Ψ-field becomes narrowed to a small region, as it does when an electron's position is measured, the energy-momentum specification becomes almost completely blurred.

Complementarity is a system of logic that builds on a broad dualism. It solves its dilemmas (such as the wave-particle question) by simply accepting both of the dilemma's horns. To some critics this procedure is decidedly questionable. James R. Newman writes: "In this century the professional philosophers have let the physicists get away with murder. It is a safe bet that no other group of scientists could have passed off and gained acceptance for such an extraordinary principle as complementarity . . . ." A number of attempts have been made to invent an interpretation of quantum physics whose methods are more in keeping with the established ways of logic. Some have suggested amputating one of the horns of the dilemma (keeping the Ψ-description but discarding the classically inspired, energy-momentum description). Others have made serious and partially successful attempts to define a more refined world beneath the blurred images of the uncertainty principle. A lively controversy between the "Copenhagen" and "Anti-Copenhagen" advocates has gone on for many years, beginning with the ingenious criticisms of Albert Einstein. At present most physicists prefer the Copenhagen side of the debate, but the other side (or sides) also deserves serious attention.

Einstein's Paradoxes

> The great initial success of the quantum theory cannot convert me to believe in that fundamental game of dice.[†]

Thus far a solution of the quantum riddle has been shown which is based entirely on statistical methods of analysis. This is, certainly, a method which works well, and it clearly accomplishes the first goal of the physicist, prediction of experimental results. But how permanently and inescapably are we committed to statistical methods? To the Copenhagen school, and to many others, some kind of statistical version of the quantum theory is absolutely necessary.

Albert Einstein took strong exception to this judgment. The theory is statistical, he felt, because it is incomplete: "I am, in fact, firmly convinced that the essentially statistical character of contemporary quantum theory is solely to be ascribed to the fact that this theory operates with an incomplete description of physical systems." When the theory is finally made complete it must look beyond the statistical data: "I still believe in the possibility of a model of reality—that is to say, of a theory which represents things themselves and not merely the probability of their occurrence." This underlying reality may be a scene of total confusion: "I can, if the worst comes to worst, still realize that God may have created a world in which there are no natural laws. In short, a chaos." But a universe ultimately controlled by tables of betting odds is intolerable: ". . . that there should be statistical laws with definite solutions, i.e., laws which compel God to throw the dice in each individual case, I find highly disagreeable."

[†] Remark made by Albert Einstein in a letter to Max Born, 1944.

This dice-throwing aspect can be seen in the simple passage of an electron through a double slit. As we have seen, the electron emerges from the slits in a diffraction pattern,

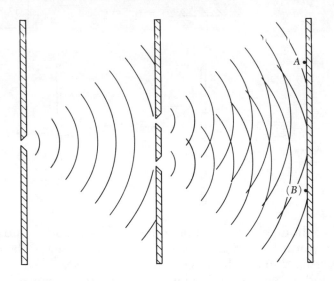

but when the electron arrives at the screen it appears at a particular point A. What in the laws of wave motion, which are apparently applicable here, causes the arrival at A to exclude all other points, such as (B)? The pattern of arrival of many electrons is predicted by a wave model, but individual arrivals are only slightly more predictable than dice throws.

At first Einstein attempted to show the incompleteness of the quantum description by carrying the analysis to a point which was more detailed than the scale of the uncertainty relations. Prodded by Bohr and the other Copenhagen proponents he invented ingenious "thought experiments" in which observations seemed to reveal more than what is allowed by the uncertainty relations. According to Bohr, "the discussions . . . centered on the question of whether the quantum-mechanical description exhausted the possibilities of accounting for observable phenomena or, as Einstein maintained, the analysis could be carried further and, especially, of whether a fuller description could be obtained by bringing into consideration the detailed balance of energy and momentum in individual processes."

One of Einstein's suggestions was to predict the direction of a diffracted photon, or electron as the description will be given here, by calculating its momentum exchange with a slit. An imaginary construction that shows the usefulness of this idea is the following:

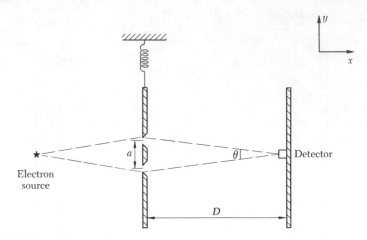

A double-slit diaphragm is hung on a very weak spring and an electron detector is located as shown. If an electron reaches the detector after passing through the lower slit it must be scattered upward by the slit and the entire diaphragm recoils slightly downward, an effect which could be seen with a microscope. If a detected electron passes through the upper slit the diaphragm recoils slightly upward. This is a simple way of deciding which slit an electron chooses without disturbing its passage through the slits.

If this device works as expected it leads to a paradox. As long as two slits are present the usual interference pattern apparently develops and this will, of course, affect the frequency of electron arrivals at the detector. In other words, the likelihood that an electron that passes through one of the slits will reach the detector (especially if it is positioned in one of the dark bands) depends on the presence of a slit *through which the electron never passes.* How can the behavior of a particle be determined by an object with which it has no apparent physical connection?

Bohr answered this paradox by showing that the double-slit-on-the-spring apparatus does not do what it seems to do. If the electrons arrive at the diaphragm with a momentum p, then the y-component of the momentum before the scattering at the slit is $p \sin (\theta/2)$ and $-p \sin (\theta/2)$ after, the momentum change being

$$\Delta p = 2p \sin (\theta/2), \quad \text{or} \quad \Delta p = \sim p\theta = \sim h\bar{\nu}\theta,$$

using the de Broglie relation and assuming θ to be small. Obviously the apparatus must be capable of measuring a momentum change this small: its momentum uncertainty must be $h\tilde{\nu}\theta$ or less. But the recoil motion of the diaphragm must be watched with a position-measuring device such as a microscope. This measurement, according to Heisenberg's argument, must have a minimum uncertainty Δy related to the momentum uncertainty as follows:

$$\Delta y = \sim h/\Delta p = \sim 1/\tilde{\nu}\theta = \sim \lambda/\theta.$$

The small angle θ can also be written $\theta = \sim a/D$, where a is the distance separating the slits and D is the slit-detector distance. This simple argument establishes that the position of a slit system sensitive enough to observe the recoiling diaphragm cannot be measured any better than with the uncertainty

$$\Delta y = \sim \lambda D/a.$$

Each time an electron is scattered the slits may be located in a different position within this range. As it happens, $\lambda D/a$ is approximately the distance between adjacent intense bands in the interference pattern. Thus there is no way by which the position of the device can be controlled well enough to prevent the light and dark bands from merging. *The interference pattern is destroyed.*

We are left with two distinct choices that fit Bohr's complementarity logic: *either* the slit diaphragm is suspended on a spring, each electron's path is followed through a particular one of the slits, and electrons are unambiguously regarded as particles; *or* the slits are made rigid, no electron paths are followed, and each electron passes through the slits as if it were a system of waves. These are two experimental-conceptual situations, complementary but entirely exclusive. Incidentally, we come back here to the conclusion established earlier (see page 74) from a more intuitive viewpoint—that particle paths and interference patterns are incompatible.

The Einstein-Bohr debate went on for many years, becoming more intricate and sophisticated with each discussion. The matter of recoiling diaphragms was argued in 1927 at the Fifth Solvay Conference. In 1930, at the next Solvay Conference, Einstein was ready with an attempt to outwit the

$$\Delta E \Delta t = \sim h$$

uncertainty relation. This time Einstein's imaginary apparatus, as pictured by Bohr, looked like this:

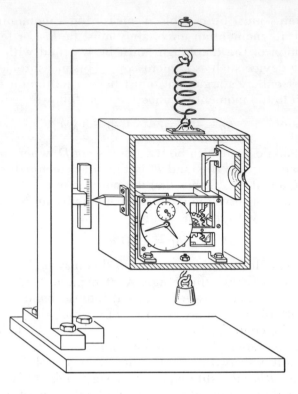

A mirror-lined box (seen in cross section in the illustration) containing a certain amount of radiation and a clock-operated shutter is suspended on a sensitive spring attached to a rigid frame. A pointer reads the box's vertical position on a scale attached to the frame. The entire apparatus is to function as a very sensitive spring balance. If the box changes its mass the extent of the change can be read on the scale, apparently with no uncertainty limitations. Einstein's idea was to measure the energy of a photon by measuring the decrease in the box's mass when the shutter allows a photon to escape at a time determined by the clock mechanism. The energy decrease ΔE (the photon energy) and the mass decrease Δm are related by Einstein's equation

$$\Delta E = (\Delta m)c^2.$$

The weighing can be done with unlimited accuracy and so, it appears, can the shutter be timed with any accuracy desired. There seem to be no restrictions either on the energy measurement or on the setting of the clock (the time of the energy measurement).

Once again Bohr used the simple uncertainty relation

$$\Delta p \Delta x = \sim h$$

to show that things are not what they seem. When the photon passes through the hole opened by the shutter a small force $g\Delta m$ (g = gravitational acceleration) is exerted on the box by the spring. This force continues to be applied for the interval t while the box finds its new position and receives a total impulse $gt\Delta m$. If this effect is to be detectable the spring balance must respond with a momentum uncertainty $gt\Delta m$ or less:

$$\Delta p < gt\Delta m.$$

The Heisenberg argument shows that there is also a position uncertainty:

$$\Delta x = \sim h/\Delta p > h/gt\Delta m,$$

or, since $\Delta m = \Delta E/c^2$,

$$\Delta x > hc^2/gt\Delta E.$$

According to the general theory of relativity,† if a clock changes its position Δx in the direction of a gravitational field the timing of an interval t is changed by the small amount

$$\Delta t = gt\Delta x/c^2.$$

Substitute into this equation the inequality for Δx:

$$\Delta t > (gt/c^2)(hc^2/gt\Delta E).$$

This reduces to $\Delta E \Delta t > h$.

Einstein's contrivance is, after all, limited by the energy-time uncertainty relation. The sensitivity requirements of the balance impose a lower limit on the momentum uncertainty and this necessarily introduces a position uncertainty. Since the latter is in a gravitational field there is an unavoidable uncertainty in the clock-operated timing device that opens the shutter and releases the photon. As the balance is made more sensitive to reduce the weighing uncertainty Δm, and also the energy uncertainty ΔE, the clock and the timing of the shutter become less accurate.

These arguments, and several others in the same vein, eventually convinced Einstein that human ingenuity cannot compete with the

---

† Invented, of course, by Einstein. Bohr used Einstein's own principle in the argument against him.

uncertainty relations. But he remained convinced that the statistical viewpoint which the uncertainty principle seems to imply is essentially incomplete. In a paper published in 1935 with two other authors (Podolsky and Rosen) he presented a rather abstract and subtle argument which put this incompleteness in a particularly acute form. The reasoning used in this paper cannot be followed here, but a roughly equivalent, more pictorial argument due to Epstein † will be outlined.

Imagine a light beam beginning at the very weak source S and falling on a half-silvered mirror N:

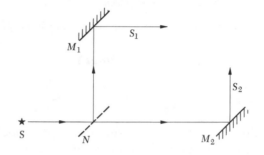

The source is weak enough, so that only one photon passes through the apparatus at a time. Two beams, S_1 and S_2, are formed at the half-silvered mirror, and they fall on the full mirrors M_1 and M_2. The distances and mirror locations in this arrangement can be fixed so that when the two beams combine they exhibit interference: the beams are said to be "coherent." The apparatus in this form provides no means for deciding in which beam a photon travels. To locate the photon make the mirrors movable in a very sensitive way so that they recoil measurably when struck by a single photon. When M_1 recoils we know that the photon is in beam S_1, and when M_2 recoils the photon is in beam S_2. In either case the photon is definitely in only one beam and, consequently, can no longer interfere with itself: the two beams are "incoherent." One can imagine that the movement of the mirrors destroys the coherency of the wave patterns in the two beams.

In the language of the statistical interpretation, the probability field describing the photon when it is in beam S_1 is represented by a certain state function, say Ψ_1, and the photon in beam S_2 is described by another state function, Ψ_2. The fixed-mirror situation

† Paul S. Epstein, "The Reality Problem in Quantum Mechanics," *American Journal of Physics 13*, 127 (1945).

with the photon equally likely to be in either beam is represented by

$$\Psi = \Psi_1 + \Psi_2.$$

When both mirrors are movable the same situation prevails until the photon reaches one of the mirrors. If M_1 is seen to recoil, then the state function suddenly changes from $\Psi_1 + \Psi_2$ to Ψ_1, and if M_2 recoils, it changes to Ψ_2.

Now imagine that only *one* of the mirrors, say M_2, is movable, while the other (M_1) is fixed. As before, if M_2 recoils, the state function becomes $\Psi = \Psi_2$, the photon is known to be in beam S_2, and the two beams are incoherent. But what can be concluded if the movable mirror does *not* recoil? In this situation the photon obviously cannot be in beam S_2 (it would move mirror M_2 if it were), and therefore it *must* be in S_1; the state function is $\Psi = \Psi_1$ and again the two beams are incoherent.

The last case presents a serious paradox. It clearly describes an arrangement in which a photon changes from one state (represented by $\Psi_1 + \Psi_2$) to another (Ψ_1) and the two coherent beams are made incoherent. Yet the system seems to undergo no change whatsoever in its observable physical conditions. According to the Einstein-Podolsky-Rosen evaluation (as interpreted by Epstein), any change of state in an *undisturbed* system (as this one appears to be with no moving mirrors or other observable changes) must be implied in the initial state of the system. Since the latter in the quantum-mechanical description is $\Psi_1 + \Psi_2$, which allows for the photon in *either* beam, and gives no hint of the subsequent transition to a single beam, the argument presented by Einstein and his colleagues (although not applied to this system) concludes that the description as presented by quantum physics is incomplete.

The Einstein-Podolsky-Rosen paper caused a considerable stir in Copenhagen. Leon Rosenfeld, who was Bohr's assistant at the time, writes: "This onslaught came down upon us as a bolt from the blue. Its effect on Bohr was remarkable. We were then in the midst of groping attempts at exploring the implications of charge and current distributions, which presented us with riddles of a kind we had not met in electrodynamics. A new worry could not come at a less propitious time. Yet, as soon as Bohr had heard . . . of Einstein's argument, everything else was abandoned: we had to clear up such a misunderstanding at once." That the argument (especially in its original form) was very subtle soon became apparent. Bohr kept asking: "What *can* they mean? Do *you* understand it?" Then he saw a direction and "the real work now began in earnest: day after day, week after week, the whole argument was patiently scrutinized with the help of simpler and more transparent examples." In about six months an answer to the Einstein "onslaught" was framed and published.

Bohr took issue particularly with Einstein's idea that an undisturbed system is one which shows no observable change in physical conditions, that is, no "mechanical disturbance." In the last mirror system described above, with no recoil in the movable mirror, there is of course no such disturbance. Nevertheless, there is a definite change in conditions when the movable mirror fails to recoil, "an influence on the very conditions which define the possible types of predictions regarding the future behavior of the system." Quantum physics concerns itself with possibilities. When the possibilities change for any reason whatsoever, induced by an observable change or not, a real disturbance is involved. Before the photon reaches the mirrors it can, possibly, be in either beam; but after it passes the mirrors, whether or not a mirror moves, the photon definitely belongs to a single beam. The critical point is that a mirror is *able* to move even though it may not actually do so. With this arrangement of the system its inherent possibilities, and therefore its state, according to Bohr, must change as the photon approaches the vicinity of the mirrors. Reference has been made earlier to the Bohr-Heisenberg argument that measurements (e.g. the gamma-ray microscope experiment) can directly influence a physical system. Bohr's position here is that even a measurement *not made,* as long as it is possible, can cause a system to change its state.

There can be no quarrel with the essential logic of Bohr's discussion. Einstein did not hesitate to say that he accepted the logical force of the argument and its possible validity; yet he still had reservations. Effects equivalent to what has appeared in the example analyzed—a coherent wave system suddenly converted to an incoherent one with precisely no change in the geometrical arrangement of the apparatus and no hint from the initial conditions—left him with a profound scepticism. Descriptions of this kind, he said, were entirely "contrary to my scientific instinct" and left him with no choice but to "search for a more complete description." He was never successful, but his belief that more complete descriptions exist never wavered. He wrote to Max Born: "I cannot provide logical argument for my conviction, but can only call on my little finger as a witness, which cannot claim any authority to be respected outside my own skin." And, in another letter to Born: "I can quite well understand why you take me for an obstinate old sinner, but I feel clearly that you do not understand how I came to travel my lonely way. It would certainly amuse you, although it would be impossible for you to appreciate my attitude. I would also have great pleasure in tearing to pieces your positivistic-philosophical viewpoint."

Various Other Discontents

Einstein was not alone in his opposition to the statistical and the Copenhagen interpretations of quantum physics. Planck, de Broglie and Schrödinger, among others, also expressed various kinds and degrees of criticism.† Nor are these interpretations unopposed today. To state all of the numerous sides the argument has developed, some attacking the duality doctrine, and others attempting to eliminate the necessity for statistical methods, would take much more than the space available, but brief accounts will be given of three alternative interpretations that can be found in the current literature.

Perhaps the most outspoken recent critic of prevailing quantum physics interpretations is Alfred Landé. He attacks particularly the "magic" of the duality doctrine. He finds that the "supernatural" transformations of particles to waves and back again is entirely unnecessary. Like Born, he begins with a statistical analysis of particle behavior that involves probability waves. He goes considerably further than Born, however, toward *explaining* the probability waves, especially their interference properties. The explanation rests on several rather abstract (but plausible) assumptions concerning the transition probabilities which predict statistically the effects of measurements. On the basis of two such assumptions he justifies the identification of the probability P with a function of the type $|\Psi|^2$, where Ψ is a (possibly complex) quantity with certain transformation properties. The $P = |\Psi|^2$ relation provides a mathematical mechanism for the all-important effect of probability interference if Ψ has a periodic nature. Landé uses a third, physical but non-quantal, postulate to establish that Ψ must be periodic and complex. Among other things, Landé's arguments amount to a derivation of the Schrödinger equation.

The "new foundations" of quantum mechanics provided by Landé are impressive. More than anyone else Landé seems to have found a way to remove the mysteries built into the Copenhagen interpretation. His derivations will probably receive more attention, especially as they are shaped into a clearer physical context.

---

† Born suspects that this potent opposition may have had something to do with the twenty-eight-year delay in the award of his Nobel prize.

The quest for the more detailed and complete "sub-quantum" description originally sought by Einstein still goes on in the work of Louis de Broglie, David Bohm, and Jean-Pierre Vigier. There has always been some doubt whether such a description can in fact be made. A famous theorem proved by John von Neumann seems to establish that it is useless to probe for "hidden variables" lying beneath the commonly used observable variables such as momentum and position. Bohm makes the point, however, that von Neumann's proof depends on the assumption that observable variables *must* be used and that the hidden variables serve merely to refine the picture. Bohm suggests that this assumption may be too limiting, for it omits the possibility that on the sub-quantum level the familiar observable variables may be inappropriate, and a description of that level may require an entirely different scheme of variables.

Bohm presents a schematic picture of the detailed motion of a particle, such as an electron, which accounts for the peculiarities of the double-slit experiment in an attractively simple way. With each particle there are associated two real physical entities: a "body existing in a small region of space" and a wave assumed to be "an oscillation in a new kind of field." The small "body" is the aspect of the electron that triggers detecting devices, and the wave field, represented mathematically by Schrödinger's Ψ-function, can undergo diffraction and interference effects in the manner of all wave systems. The body and the Ψ-field are interconnected in the sense that the Ψ-field exerts a certain new kind of "quantum-mechanical" force on the body: the force has a tendency "to pull the body into regions where $|\Psi|$ is largest." The body also has a random motion similar to Brownian movement, this effect perhaps originating in random fluctuations of the Ψ-field.

Bohm illustrates the progress of an electron body through a double slit as follows:

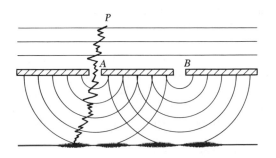

The erratic nature of the electron paths accounts for the random arrivals of electrons at the detecting screen and also for the possible passage through either slit. Since the Ψ-wave-system spreads out over a broad region it is diffracted by both slits and interference patterns are generated. Due to the attractive force associated with the Ψ-field the arrivals of electrons at the screen on the average follow the design of the interference pattern. When one slit is closed the interference effect is destroyed and the arrivals of electrons no longer occur in light and dark bands:

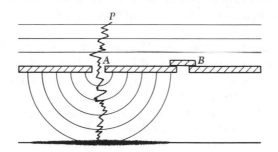

Bohm recognizes that this picture probably oversimplifies "what is basically a very complex process." He notes that the model is not as plausible as it might be since it regards "wave and particle . . . as basically different entities" interacting "in a way that is not essential to their modes of being." Nevertheless, the theory has internal consistency and it points to some promising possibilities.

Complementarity, as a method of logic, has annoyed and disturbed professional philosophers for some time. A legitimate logic, they feel, should not attack the duality dilemma by "paying its respects to both horns." Henry Margenau has expressed this criticism and presented an interpretation which is cleared of the offending dualism. He asks us to take a radical step: we are to discard the notion that electrons and other particles have a permanent property that can be regarded as position. Just as an electron has no color, neither does it usually have a discernible position. Position is a *latent* aspect of an electron which is not real unless a position measurement is made. "If this notion seems grotesque, let it be remembered that other sciences, indeed common sense, employ it widely." Happiness, for example, is a latent quality of human beings, frequently not present at all, though it "can spring into being or be destroyed by an act of inquiry, a psychological measurement." How can this peculiarity of latency be explained? Margenau is inclined to think that there is an "irreducible haziness in . . . perceived phenomena," the extent of which is measured by Planck's constant h. When a measurement is made the electron acquires a definite position; when it is not measured it may be "nowhere." An electron may even change its identity and its intrinsic observable properties between measurements. Having discarded position as a meaningful concept, Margenau feels that both the particle concept and the wave concept also lack significance. The particle-wave question has no proper physical meaning, and therefore should not even be asked. Only one mode of description remains valid, that which is based on the Schrödinger Ψ-function.

These are drastic statements. We are left with a purely statistical description. The familiar observable laboratory variables are all but wiped out. Margenau feels that this step is helpful and perhaps inevitable. He recalls that taste was once considered an intrinsic property of materials and that all objects large and small were once thought to have definite shape and color. These "commonsense" attitudes have been abandoned for very small objects. Perhaps we are about to forfeit one more commonsense conclusion, that electrons and other particles have a physically meaningful and useful position property.

The argument goes on. Most physicists defend the Copenhagen doctrine, but a significant number, some with imposing credentials, oppose it. Three rival interpretations have been described above. Several others of equal importance can be found in the recent literature. There is, evidently, no resolution to the problem in sight. This is no ordinary puzzle, and as Margenau observes, "nature is not generous in providing hints." Solutions to the puzzle can be found, but they cannot be tested well enough to prove one better than another. For all the efforts of dozens of first-rate physicists, philosophers, and physicist-philosophers, the meaning of quantum physics is not much clearer than it was forty years ago. Margenau's remark is appropriate: "The sphinx is noncommittal."

5

The Formal Basis

The story of the quantum now emerges from the "erratic ways and byways of history," and, as a textbook argument must, takes a straighter and more relentless course. The statistical interpretation of quantum physics, by far the most prevalent version, is presented formally and mathematically, and without much respect for historical order and diversity. The central theme at first is Schrödinger's wave equation, discussed briefly in Chapter 3. Schrödinger's derivation of the equation using an extension of Hamilton's analogy has been mentioned. The equation is introduced and "derived" here in a different way to show more fully its basis in the empirical facts of quantum physics. This broader derivation will lead us to an equation that contains time as an independent variable, as well as the position coordinates.† The equation (7) introduced in Chapter 3 is applicable only to stationary or time-independent problems.

The Schrödinger Equation

The statistical theory of quantum physics builds on the premise that a function P can be calculated which determines the probability that

† One time-dependent equation, involving a second-order derivative with respect to time, has already been mentioned (see page 95). This equation leads to Schrödinger's wave equation (7) of Chapter 3 if it is assumed that the potential energy V is time independent. Thus the equation applies only to "conservative" systems, those for which the total energy E is constant, and must be used within this restriction. The time-dependent wave equation which this chapter presents contains a first-order time derivative and is applicable to a wider variety of problems.

a position measurement will find a particle such as an electron in a certain differential region of space. Formally, the assumption (for a one-dimensional problem) is that

$Pdx =$ Probability that a position measurement made at time t will find a particle located between x and $x + dx$.

If the function P is to be an acceptable probability function it must be both real and positive (or zero). These conditions are assured if a second, mathematically simpler, function Ψ is introduced. This, the so-called "wave function," has a magnitude which is large where the particle is likely to be found and small where it is unlikely to be found. The wave function Ψ need not be real and positive, but when it is multiplied by its complex conjugate, forming either $\Psi^*\Psi$ or $\Psi\Psi^*$, it produces a positive, real function,† which is large in regions frequently inhabited by the particle. The required probability function is identified with this product:

$$P = \Psi^*\Psi = \Psi\Psi^*.$$

To continue with the development of a wave-function physics an equation must be provided from which the wave function, and hence the probability function, can be calculated. What *kind* of an equation is likely to serve the intended purpose? Experience with other fundamental equations of physics — Newton's laws, Maxwell's equations, and the laws of thermodynamics — strongly suggests that a *differential* equation of some kind is needed. For this differential equation to do what is required the dependent variable, that is, the wave function Ψ, must evidently be what is to be calculated. And to permit the calculation of Ψ in the regions of space and time where physical events of interest take place the independent variables must be the time t and the coordinate variables of the collection of particles involved. The mathematical problem will be simplified at first by limiting the discussion to one particle moving in one dimension, so that only a single coordinate variable x is needed. Systems in three-dimensional space, which consist of more than one particle, with the accompanying profusion of coordinate variables, will be introduced in Chapter 6.

The variable Ψ must occur in the equation in a "linear" fashion: if Ψ_1 and Ψ_2 are solutions to the equation then $\Psi_1 + \Psi_2$ must also be a solution. The solutions Ψ_1 and Ψ_2 might, for example, represent an electron propagated from one or the other of the slits in the two-slit

† See the footnote on page 115 for a proof of this statement.

experiment (mentioned in Chapters 3 and 4), so that $\Psi_1 + \Psi_2$ is the state representing the situation when both slits are open. The linearity requirement becomes a valuable criterion for sorting out the various candidates for the fundamental Ψ equation. It tells us, for example, that the equation

$$A(d\Psi/dx) + B\Psi = 0$$

is acceptable: the equations

$$A(d\Psi_1/dx) + B\Psi_1 = 0 \qquad \text{and} \qquad A(d\Psi_2/dx) + B\Psi_2 = 0$$

add to give

$$Ad(\Psi_1 + \Psi_2)/dx + B(\Psi_1 + \Psi_2) = 0,$$

showing that Ψ_1, Ψ_2 and $\Psi_1 + \Psi_2$ are all solutions, as required. On the other hand,

$$A(d\Psi/dx) + B = 0$$

is not acceptable: the equations

$$A(d\Psi_1/dx) + B = 0 \qquad \text{and} \qquad A(d\Psi_2/dx) + B = 0$$

add to give

$$Ad(\Psi_1 + \Psi_2)/dx + 2B = 0,$$

but not

$$Ad(\Psi_1 + \Psi_2)/dx + B = 0;$$

$\Psi_1 + \Psi_2$ is not a solution.

On the physical side, the equation we seek must be consistent with the Einstein equation for energy, $E = h\nu$, and with the de Broglie equation for momentum, $p = h\bar{\nu}$. To these add the equation that connects the energy and the momentum; this can have the familiar "particle version,"

$$p^2/2m + V = E, \tag{1}$$

where V is a potential energy function expressing any force field present ($V = 0$ if no forces are present), or the Einstein and de Broglie equations can be used to convert it to a "wave version,"

$$h^2\bar{\nu}^2/2m + V = h\nu. \tag{2}$$

A differential equation linear in the wave function Ψ must be found which is consistent with (1) and (2).

When this equation is solved explicit information on the wave function is obtained. Not much can be said in advance concerning the form expected for the wave function Ψ except that it should display wave properties (so as to generate probability waves) and be confined to the general region inhabited by the particle. Outside the particle's habitat the wave function must vanish since a nonzero Ψ-value there would imply an appreciable probability for finding the particle where it cannot be. If the particle is confined to a finite region, as will always be the case in the problems of interest here, the wave function must decrease toward zero for increasing values of the coordinate variables. This is easily shown for the one-dimensional case: a wave function with the behavior

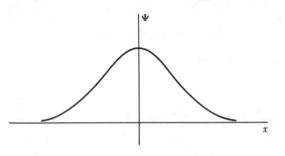

is allowed, but wave functions such as

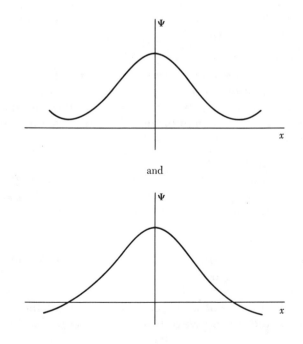

and

are not allowed because they imply an appreciable probability for finding the particle at $+\infty$ and $-\infty$. When circumstances lead to a wave function of the kind allowed, we can always find a region where the wave function vanishes at the limits.

In its role as a generator of probability functions, the wave function has another general mathematical restriction. The probability that a particle will be found in the infinitesimal region between x and $x + dx$ is, according to the basic assumption of the statistical method, taken to be

$$P dx = \Psi^*\Psi dx = \Psi\Psi^* dx.$$

The probability that a particle will be found between $x = 0$ and $x = a$ is

$$\int_0^a \Psi^*\Psi dx,$$

and the probability that a particle will be found in the entire region accessible to it (this must certainly lie in the range from $x = +\infty$ to $x = -\infty$) is

$$\int_{-\infty}^{+\infty} \Psi^*\Psi dx.$$

Since the particle must always be *somewhere*, the last probability mentioned must in fact be unity, that is, a certainty:

$$\int_{-\infty}^{+\infty} \Psi^*\Psi dx = 1.$$

This is the "normalization" condition introduced earlier (page 116).

To simplify, consider an electron or other particle in a force field which supplies a constant potential V_0 (as, for example, in the Davisson-Germer experiment). This is a "free" particle with a constant energy and momentum. It is equally likely to be found anywhere in the apparatus confining it, allowing a range of the position coordinate (as before, in a one-dimensional problem) from $x = +L/2$ to $x = -L/2$ in an apparatus of length L. If the apparatus is large compared to the electron size, as is usually the case, then the position coordinate effectively ranges from $x = +\infty$ to $x = -\infty$. The corresponding free-particle wave function must have a constant amplitude over this same range. Perhaps a traveling wave expressed by the simple trigonometric function

$$\Psi = \cos 2\pi(\bar{\nu}x - \nu t)$$

will suffice to describe this situation (ν and $\tilde{\nu}$ are the wave's frequency and wave number).†

But still there is no differential equation in sight. Derivatives can be introduced in a rather contrived but plausible way by differentiating the above tentative wave function with respect to x and t. A term proportional to $\tilde{\nu}^2$ is formed by differentiating twice with respect to x:

$$\partial^2\Psi/\partial x^2 = -4\pi^2\tilde{\nu}^2 \cos 2\pi(\tilde{\nu}x - \nu t)$$

$$= -4\pi\tilde{\nu}^2\Psi$$

or
$$\tilde{\nu}^2 = -(1/4\pi^2\Psi)(\partial^2\Psi/\partial x^2).$$

It appears from this that it might be legitimate to replace $\tilde{\nu}^2$ in (2) with the expression

$$-(1/4\pi^2\Psi)(\partial^2\Psi/\partial x^2).$$

The last term in (2) contains ν, suggesting differentiation once with respect to t:

$$\partial\Psi/\partial t = 2\pi\nu \sin 2\pi(\tilde{\nu}x - \nu t)$$

$$= 2\pi\nu \sqrt{1 - \Psi^2}$$

or
$$\nu = (1/2\pi \sqrt{1 - \Psi^2})(\partial\Psi/\partial t).$$

These maneuvers produce the differential equation

$$-(h^2/8\pi^2 m\Psi)(\partial^2\Psi/\partial x^2) + V_0 = (h/2\pi \sqrt{1 - \Psi^2})(\partial\Psi/\partial t),$$

or

$$-(h^2/8\pi^2 m)(\partial^2\Psi/\partial x^2) + V_0\Psi = (h/2\pi)(\Psi/\sqrt{1 - \Psi^2})(\partial\Psi/\partial t),$$

but this equation can never be satisfactory because it contains the factor $\Psi/\sqrt{1 - \Psi^2}$, which is decidedly nonlinear in Ψ.

Next try a slightly more complicated wave function of the type

$$\Psi = \cos 2\pi(\tilde{\nu}x - \nu t) + A \sin 2\pi(\tilde{\nu}x - \nu t), \tag{3}$$

where A is a constant. Differentiate this twice with respect to x and once with respect to t:

† This wave function extends from $+\infty$ to $-\infty$ and is therefore not strictly acceptable, since it should vanish at the walls of the apparatus. For the present, this condition need not be considered explicitly, however.

$$\partial^2\Psi/\partial x^2 = -4\pi^2\tilde{\nu}^2[\cos 2\pi(\tilde{\nu}x - \nu t) + A \sin 2\pi(\tilde{\nu}x - \nu t)]$$

$$= -4\pi^2\tilde{\nu}^2\Psi$$

$$\partial\Psi/\partial t = 2\pi\nu[\sin 2\pi(\tilde{\nu}x - \nu t) - A \cos 2\pi(\tilde{\nu}x - \nu t)].$$

To save effort the last quantity enclosed in brackets will be written [ ], so that the last equation is simply

$$\partial\Psi/\partial t = 2\pi\nu[\ \ ].$$

The substitution used for ν in (2) is now

$$\nu = (1/2\pi[\ \ ])(\partial\Psi/\partial t)$$

and, as before,

$$\tilde{\nu}^2 = -(1/4\pi^2\Psi)(\partial^2\Psi/\partial x^2).$$

The differential equation becomes

$$-(h^2/8\pi^2 m\Psi)(\partial^2\Psi/\partial x^2) + V_0 = (h/2\pi[\ \ ])(\partial\Psi/\partial t)$$

or $\qquad -(h^2/8\pi^2 m)(\partial^2\Psi/\partial x^2) + V_0\Psi = (h\Psi/2\pi[\ \ ])(\partial\Psi/\partial t).$

The first two terms in this equation are suitably linear, and so is the third term if [ ] can be made proportional to the wave function Ψ, that is, if [ ] $= \alpha\Psi$, where α is a constant. Written in full, this last condition is

$$[\sin 2\pi(\tilde{\nu}x - \nu t) - A \cos 2\pi(\tilde{\nu}x - \nu t)] = \alpha\Psi. \qquad (4)$$

The differential equation now becomes entirely linear in the variable Ψ:

$$-(h^2/8\pi^2 m)(\partial^2\Psi/\partial x^2) + V_0\Psi = (h/2\pi\alpha)(\partial\Psi/\partial t). \qquad (5)$$

It remains now to calculate the two constants A and α. Combine (3) and (4) and rearrange to the form

$$(A + \alpha) \cos 2\pi(\tilde{\nu}x - \nu t) + (\alpha A - 1) \sin 2\pi(\tilde{\nu}x - \nu t) = 0.$$

This equation must hold for all values of x and t; therefore the two factors in the parentheses must vanish:

$$\alpha A - 1 = 0 \quad \text{or} \quad \alpha A = 1, \qquad \text{and} \qquad A + \alpha = 0 \quad \text{or} \quad A = -\alpha.$$

We conclude that $A^2 = -1$, or $A = \pm i$, and $\alpha = \mp i$ supply the necessary conditions. Either sign choice can be made. Customarily $A = i$ and $\alpha = -i$ are used, so that

$$\Psi = \cos 2\pi(\tilde{\nu}x - \nu t) + i \sin 2\pi(\tilde{\nu}x - \nu t)$$

$$= e^{2\pi i(\tilde{\nu}x - \nu t)} \qquad\qquad (\dagger)$$

The form of the Schrödinger equation stated in (5) applies to a free particle moving in a field of constant potential V_0, and

$$\Psi = e^{2\pi i(\tilde{\nu}x - \nu t)}$$

is the free-particle wave function. When more complicated force fields are considered, such as the electrostatic field which confines the electron in the atom, the choices for the wave function are not as simple and no longer predictable. The argument which led to (5) cannot, therefore, be made entirely general. There is no choice but to require that the general form of the Schrödinger equation be *postulated.* A suitable modification of (5) must be found which contains a general potential function $V(x,t)$ instead of the constant one, V_0. Evidently the simplest possibility is to replace V_0 directly with the general potential $V(x,t)$:

$$-(h^2/8\pi^2 m)(\partial^2\Psi/\partial x^2) + V(x,t)\Psi = (ih/2\pi)(\partial\Psi/\partial t).$$

or $\qquad\qquad -(\hbar^2/2m)(\partial^2\Psi/\partial x^2) + V(x,t)\Psi = i\hbar\partial\Psi/\partial t, \qquad (6)$

where $\hbar$ ("cut-h") represents $h/2\pi$. This is, in fact, the form of the

---

† The Euler relation $e^{ix} = \cos x + i \sin x$ is used. This strange statement is easily proved by writing infinite series for the two trigonometric functions:

$$\cos x = 1 - x^2/2! + x^4/4! - x^6/6! + \cdots$$

$$\sin x = x - x^3/3! + x^5/5! - x^7/7! + \cdots.$$

Multiply the second series by i, rearrange, and add to it the first series with i-factors introduced:

$$i \sin x = ix - ix^3/3! + ix^5/5! - ix^7/7! + \cdots$$

$$= (ix) + (ix)^3/3! + (ix)^5/5! + (ix)^7/7! + \cdots$$

$$\cos x = 1 + (ix)^2/2! + (ix)^4/4! + (ix)^6/6! + \cdots$$

$$\cos + i \sin x = 1 + (ix) + (ix)^2/2! + (ix)^3/3! + (ix)^4/4! + \cdots.$$

The last series is identical to the series expansion for e^{ix}:

$$e^{ix} = 1 + (ix) + (ix)^2/2! + (ix)^3/3! + (ix)^4/4! + \cdots.$$

Q.E.D.

Notice that the complex conjugate of e^{ix} is formed, as usual, by reversing the signs preceding all i's: if $\Psi = e^{ix}$ then $\Psi^\circ = e^{-ix}$. When $x = \pi$, an amazing equation emerges: it relates e, i, π, and 1, the four fundamental numbers of mathematics: $e^{i\pi} = -1$.

Schrödinger equation which has been found to have very broad validity.

But how can this equation have any useful physical meaning when it contains the *imaginary* term $i\hbar\partial\Psi/\partial t$? This raises the question of how much "reality" an equation in the variable Ψ can be expected to convey. Remember that Ψ *need* not be (and frequently is not) real. The only mathematical requirement on Ψ we have met thus far is that the probability function formed by the prescription $P = \Psi^*\Psi$ or $P = \Psi\Psi^*$ be real (and also positive). As long as the equation produces wave functions which are suitable for calculation of probabilities (and averages in the theory developed later) and these probabilities (and averages) are themselves real and possessed of the appropriate physical qualifications, no more can be expected.

Average Momentum

The probability function $P(x,t)$ tells of the relative importance of each point in space at each moment in time. In regions where P is large a particle is likely to be found; where it is small a particle is not likely to be found. Such a function can be applied to the calculation of an average value for a particle's position, as shown in the argument on page 117. The contribution to the average made by positions in the infinitesimal range between x and $x + dx$ is

$$xPdx = x\Psi\Psi^*dx$$

and the complete average for the position is

$$\bar{x} = \int x\Psi\Psi^*dx,$$

the integral being carried out over the entire accessible space.

An analogous momentum calculation, also with x as the independent variable, appears to be

$$\bar{p} = \int pPdx = \int p\Psi\Psi^*dx,$$

where p is the momentum and $\bar{p}$ is its average value. There is, however, a basic mathematical difficulty with this equation. The variable of integration is x and therefore $p\Psi\Psi^*$ must be expressed as a function of x. Presumably the dependence of $P = \Psi\Psi^*$ on x and t can be calculated using the Schrödinger equation, but how is $p\Psi\Psi^*$ calculated? So far this question has not been answered.

The problem is better approached by taking another tack. Write the average momentum in a form that resembles the classical momentum definition:

$$\bar{p} = m(d\bar{x}/dt),$$

where m is the mass of the particle and $d\bar{x}/dt$ represents its average velocity.†

The velocity derivative is evaluated as follows:

$$d\bar{x}/dt = (d/dt)\int x\Psi^*\Psi dx$$

$$= \int [(x\partial\Psi^*/\partial t)\Psi + x\Psi^*(\partial\Psi/\partial t)]dx. \qquad (\ddagger)$$

Notice that the only functions of time under the integral are Ψ and Ψ^*. The necessary time derivatives are supplied by the Schrödinger equation:

$$\partial\Psi/\partial t = (i\hbar/2m)(\partial^2\Psi/\partial x^2) - (i/\hbar)V\Psi$$

$$\partial\Psi^*/\partial t = (-i\hbar/2m)(\partial^2\Psi^*/\partial x^2) + (i/\hbar)V\Psi^*,$$

so that $\quad d\bar{x}/dt = (i\hbar/2m)\int [x\Psi^*\partial^2\Psi/\partial x^2 - x\Psi\partial^2\Psi^*/\partial x^2]dx.$

The second term in the integrand is reduced with two integrations by parts and the assumption that the wave function vanishes for the limits of the integral. The first integration is

$$-\int (x\Psi\partial^2\Psi^*/\partial x^2)dx = -\int x\Psi d(\partial\Psi^*/\partial x)$$

$$= -x\Psi\partial\Psi^*/\partial x| + \int (\partial\Psi^*/\partial x)d(x\Psi) \qquad (\S)$$

$$= \quad 0 \quad\quad + \int (\partial\Psi^*/\partial x)d(x\Psi)$$

$$= \int (\partial\Psi^*/\partial x)[\partial(x\Psi)/\partial x]dx$$

$$= \int [\partial(x\Psi)/\partial x]d\Psi^*,$$

† This is still another use of the Bohr correspondence principle. The quantum law is formulated so that it has a form which is parallel to the classical law. Each element in the quantum law has a corresponding element in the classical law. If the quantum law is to merge into and become the classical law as the size scale increases, this requirement, among others, must be fulfilled.

‡ A comment on the status of the independent variables is needed here. The variable x is not used in quantum mechanics in the same sense that it is used in classical mechanics. In the quantum realm it serves mainly to describe the spatial framework in which a particle can be found. It has no dependency on time. Changes in a particle's location are reflected in Ψ, which can, of course, depend on time as well as on the spatial variable. Therefore, when the time derivatives of $x\Psi^*\Psi$ are taken, partial derivatives of Ψ and Ψ^* are called for but no time derivative of x appears.

§ The vertical line to the right of the first term means that this term is to be evaluated for the limits of the integral. These limits are chosen where Ψ vanishes, as is always possible for a particle confined to a finite region. Return to the remarks on pages 140–41.

and the second integration is

$$\int [\partial(x\Psi)/\partial x]d\Psi^* = \Psi^*\partial(x\Psi)/\partial x| - \int \Psi^*[\partial^2(x\Psi)/\partial x^2]dx$$

$$= \qquad 0 \qquad - \int \Psi^*[\partial^2(x\Psi)/\partial x^2]dx$$

$$= -\int \Psi^*[\partial^2(x\Psi)/\partial x^2]dx.$$

The integral for $d\bar{x}/dt$ now reads

$$d\bar{x}/dt = (i\hbar/2m)\int \Psi^*[x\partial^2\Psi/\partial x^2 - \partial^2(x\Psi)/\partial x^2]dx,$$

and this reduces further when the second term in the brackets is expanded:

$$d\bar{x}/dt = (i\hbar/2m)\int \Psi^*[x\partial^2\Psi/\partial x^2 - x\partial^2\Psi/\partial x^2 - 2\partial\Psi/\partial x]dx$$

$$= -(i\hbar/m)\int \Psi^*(\partial\Psi/\partial x)dx.$$

Therefore the average momentum is

$$\bar{p} = (-i\hbar)\int \Psi^*(\partial\Psi/\partial x)dx$$

$$= \int (-i\hbar\partial\Psi/\partial x)\Psi^*dx. \qquad (7a)$$

The last writing of the equation is in a form which resembles closely the original tentative expression for the momentum average:

$$\bar{p} = \int pPdx$$

$$= \int p\Psi\Psi^*dx.$$

It appears that the integrand $p\Psi\Psi^*$ expressed as a function of x is $(-i\hbar\partial\Psi/\partial x)\Psi^*$, that

$$p\Psi = -i\hbar\partial\Psi/\partial x$$

$$= (-i\hbar\partial/\partial x)\Psi,$$

and that

$$p = -i\hbar\partial/\partial x.$$

We seem to have arrived at the curious conclusion that, at least in the average value calculation, the momentum is associated with the fragment of a derivative $-i\hbar\partial/\partial x$.

It is customary to write the average momentum integral in an equivalent form,

$$\bar{p} = \int \Psi^*(-i\hbar\partial\Psi/\partial x)dx$$

$$= \int \Psi^*(-i\hbar\partial/\partial x)\Psi dx, \qquad (7b)$$

with the momentum association $-i\hbar\partial/\partial x$ sandwiched between Ψ^* and Ψ, making it definite that $-i\hbar\partial/\partial x$ applies to Ψ, not to $\Psi\Psi^*$, a point that might not always be clear if $\bar{p} = \int(-i\hbar\partial/\partial x)\Psi\Psi^* dx$ is written instead. The average value for the position variable x can also be rearranged in this way:

$$\bar{x} = \int xP dx$$

$$= \int (x\Psi)\Psi^* dx$$

$$= \int \Psi^* x\Psi dx.$$

We have found that if $\bar{x} = \int \Psi^* x\Psi dx$ is used to evaluate the average position of a particle, where the wave function Ψ and its complex conjugate form Ψ^* are calculated using Schrödinger's equation, then the average momentum has the peculiar form

$$\bar{p} = \int \Psi^*(-i\hbar\partial/\partial x)\Psi dx$$

and the imaginary symbol $-i\hbar\partial/\partial x$ seems to be a stand-in for the momentum. Unlikely as this conclusion may appear, there can be no objection to it as long as the *average* calculated in this way is real and has the expected physical characteristics. That $\bar{p}$ has all the legitimate properties of momentum can be seen by returning to the original statement

$$\bar{p} = m(d\bar{x}/dt).$$

It is clear from this that $\bar{p}$ depends on a mass and a velocity factor, as it should, and also that it is real, since m, $\bar{x}$, and t are real.

The momentum symbol $-i\hbar\partial/\partial x$, with all its strangeness, sheds a great deal of light on the inner workings of the quantum theory. Notice first that it cannot stand in an equation by itself. It tells us to differentiate with respect to x, an order that cannot be carried out unless a function of x, such as the wave function Ψ, follows; thus it is used in terms such as

$$(-i\hbar\partial/\partial x)\Psi = -i\hbar\partial\Psi/\partial x.$$

This is a mathematical entity known as an "operator": it gives instructions to "operate" in some way on a function called an "operand." What we have arrived at in this section is an *operator representation for the momentum.*

The next step in the argument is to put together a suitable operator representation for the energy from which average energies can be calculated. This operator can, in fact, be read directly from the

Schrödinger equation, since both sides of the equation stand for energy. It will be better, though, not to plunge immediately into the *use* of operators. A section is inserted here on the formal properties of operators. This will present something of the "grammar" of the operator language.

Rules of Operator Algebra

Operators play a central role in the Schrödinger formulation of quantum physics. They are used as symbolic representations for all the fundamental observable quantities, especially the momentum and the energy. The algebra involved in the manipulation of operators is similar to the algebra of ordinary numbers, but is also freed of certain of the restrictions of ordinary algebra. The various rules of operator algebra are listed here to prepare for their application in the problems of quantum physics that follow.

Definition. An operator is a symbol which supplies instructions for a calculation to be carried out on a function called an operand. The calculation generally converts the operand into another function. Examples of operators are $x(\ )$, $d(\ )/dx$, and $\int(\ )dx$. The operand in each case is placed in the parentheses. If x is the operand the operators listed lead to the following equations:

$$x(x) = x^2$$

$$d(x)/dx = 1$$

$$\int(x)dx = x^2/2.$$

Addition. The sum of two operators applied to an operand leads to the sum of the effects of the two individual operators. If $\hat{A}$ and $\hat{B}$ are operators † and u is the operand, then the sum $\hat{A} + \hat{B}$ is defined by

$$(\hat{A} + \hat{B})u = \hat{A}u + \hat{B}u.$$

Multiplication. The product of two operators is formed by applying them in order, one after the other. The product $\hat{A}\hat{B}$ applied to the operand u implies that $\hat{B}$ is applied first and then $\hat{A}$ operates on this result:

$$\hat{A}\hat{B}u = \hat{A}(\hat{B}u).$$

† To designate a symbol as an operator, the overhead caret, or hat notation, as in $\hat{A}$ (read this "A hat"), will always be used.

Linearity. All operators of interest in quantum physics are linear. When a linear operator $\hat{A}$ is applied to the sum of two operands u and v the sum of $\hat{A}$ applied separately to u and v is obtained:

$$\hat{A}(u + v) = \hat{A}u + \hat{A}v.$$

A linear operator $\hat{A}$ also has the property

$$\hat{A}(cu) = c\hat{A}u,$$

if c is a constant (real or complex).

Commutation. When operator products are formed the order of the product may be important. If $\hat{A}$ is d/dx, $\hat{B}$ is x (taken to be a multiplying operator), and the operand is x^2, then

$$\hat{A}\hat{B}x^2 = 3x^2$$

$$\hat{B}\hat{A}x^2 = 2x^2,$$

and
$$\hat{A}\hat{B} \neq \hat{B}\hat{A}.$$

This product is said to be "noncommutative." On the other hand, if $\hat{A}$ is y, another multiplying operator, then

$$\hat{A}\hat{B}x^2 = yx^3$$

$$\hat{B}\hat{A}x^2 = yx^3,$$

and
$$\hat{A}\hat{B} = \hat{B}\hat{A}.$$

This product is "commutative."

Of all the many possible kinds of operators two types are of particular importance in quantum physics: those that are multiplying, and those that are differential. Thus far only one differential operator has been introduced, that for the momentum:

$$\hat{p} = -i\hbar\partial/\partial x.$$

Its symbol can be used to good advantage to shorten the writing of (7b):

$$\bar{p} = \int \Psi^* \hat{p} \Psi dx. \tag{7c}$$

In the following sections differential operators will also be developed for p^2, the momentum squared, and

$$E = (p^2/2m) + V,$$

the total energy. When the operator formalism is extended to the position variable x, an operator of a simple multiplying type appears. In the operator parlance, following the form of the average momentum calculation (7c), the average position calculation is written

$$\bar{x} = \int \Psi^* \hat{x} \Psi \, dx,$$

where $\hat{x}$ is a suitable position operator. This operator is easily identified, with much less difficulty than in the case of the momentum operator, by comparing with the previous calculation of the average position,

$$\bar{x} = \int \Psi^* x \Psi \, dx.$$

The integrands in the last two equations are equivalent:

$$\Psi^* \hat{x} \Psi = \Psi^* x \Psi.$$

Therefore $\hat{x}\Psi = x\Psi$, and $\hat{x} = x$. The position operator is simply the position variable itself, and the operation it performs in a factor such as $\hat{x}\Psi$ is ordinary multiplication.

Any quantity which is constant, that is, independent of the position variable x, also has a simple multiplying operator representation. To establish this, return once again to average value calculations. If α is a constant having the same value for all points in space, it forms its own average value: $\bar{\alpha} = \alpha$. Write this in the alternative form

$$\bar{\alpha} = \alpha \int \Psi^* \Psi \, dx \qquad (\dagger)$$

$$= \int \Psi^* \alpha \Psi \, dx.$$

In operator language,

$$\bar{\alpha} = \int \Psi^* \hat{\alpha} \Psi \, dx.$$

Equate the two integrands:

$$\Psi^* \hat{\alpha} \Psi = \Psi^* \alpha \Psi,$$

$$\hat{\alpha} = \alpha.$$

Constants, like position coordinates, form their own operators.

More Operator Associations

An entire system of operator associations can now be put together, based on the differential operator $\hat{p} = -i\hbar \partial/\partial x$ for the momentum

---

† Remember that the normalization property, required of all wave functions, supplies a value of unity for the integral $\int \Psi^* \Psi \, dx$ evaluated over the space accessible to the particle.

and the multiplying operator $\hat{x} = x$ for the position variable.† More complicated operators can be assembled by combining these basic ones according to the rules of operator addition and multiplication. For example, if $\hat{A}$ and $\hat{B}$ are operators representing two physical quantities A and B, then the operator $\hat{A} + \hat{B}$ represents the physical quantity $A + B$. $\hat{A}^2$ and $\hat{B}^2$ are the operators associated with the physical quantities A^2 and B^2, and frequently, though not always, $\hat{A}\hat{B}$ is the operator associated with AB. The operator $\alpha\hat{A}$, where α is a constant, is associated with the quantity αA.

In this way the operator $\hat{p}^2$ for p^2 is put together by multiplying $-i\hbar\partial/\partial x$ by $-i\hbar\partial/\partial x$ to form $-\hbar^2\partial^2/\partial x^2$. This operator may be familiar; it was used, in effect, as a symbol for p^2 in formulating the Schrödinger equation. Remember that the Schrödinger equation is a differential version of the energy relation

$$h\nu = h^2\bar{\nu}^2/2m + V,$$

which is arrived at by making the following replacements:

$$-(1/4\pi^2\Psi)(\partial^2\Psi/\partial x^2) \quad \text{for} \quad \bar{\nu}^2,$$

or $$-(1/4\pi^2)(\partial^2\Psi/\partial x^2) \quad \text{for} \quad \bar{\nu}^2\Psi,$$

or $$-(h^2/4\pi^2)(\partial^2\Psi/\partial x^2) \quad \text{for} \quad p^2\Psi,$$

or $$(-\hbar^2\partial^2/\partial x^2)\Psi \quad \text{for} \quad p^2\Psi.$$

The operator association $-\hbar^2\partial^2/\partial x^2$ for p^2 is thus a part of the makeup of the Schrödinger equation.

Operators for various powers of x are easily formed. Since $\hat{x} = x$ it follows that $\hat{x}^2 = x^2$, $\hat{x}^3 = x^3$, $\hat{x}^{-1} = x^{-1}$, $\hat{x}^{-2} = x^{-2}$, etc. All of the potential energy functions of interest to us can be formed from functions of x as simple as these. For example, the potential function which describes the spring-like force connecting the two nuclei of a diatomic molecule is $V = kx^2/2$, where k is a constant, and the electrostatic potential energy between an electron of charge $-e$ and a nucleus of charge Ze is $-Ze^2/x$, where x is the distance separating the two charges. The operators associated with such potential energy functions are therefore the potential functions themselves: $\hat{V}(x) = V(x)$.

---

† The operator method of interpreting quantum physics seems to have been first conceived by Max Born and Norbert Wiener (better known for his work in cybernetics). The procedure used here, based on the association of $-i\hbar\partial/\partial x$ with the momentum, was introduced by Schrödinger to show the identity of his method with the Heisenberg-Born-Jordan matrix method.

The operator for the total energy expression $(p^2/2m) + V$ can now be stated. For p^2 use $-\hbar^2 \partial^2/\partial x^2$ and for $p^2/2m$ use $(-\hbar^2/2m)(\partial^2/\partial x^2)$. For the potential energy function V the operator is V itself. The complete operator is

$$(-\hbar^2/2m)(\partial^2/\partial x^2) + V.$$

This is usually labeled $\hat{H}$,

$$\hat{H} = (-\hbar^2/2m)(\partial^2/\partial x^2) + V,$$

and is called the "Hamiltonian" † operator.

The Hamiltonian operator applied to a wave function operand forms one side of the Schrödinger equation,

$$(-\hbar^2/2m)(\partial^2\Psi/\partial x^2) + V\Psi = [(-\hbar^2/2m)(\partial^2/\partial x^2) + V]\Psi$$
$$= \hat{H}\Psi,$$

making it possible to write the equation in a much shortened notation,

$$\hat{H}\Psi = i\hbar \partial\Psi/\partial t.$$

Since the operator on the left in this equation represents energy, so must the operator $i\hbar \partial/\partial t$ on the right. This operator was, in fact, used in the formulation of the Schrödinger equation. Remember the substitutions,

$$(-1/2\pi i\Psi)(\partial\Psi/\partial t) \quad \text{for} \quad \nu,$$

or
$$(i/2\pi)(\partial\Psi/\partial t) \quad \text{for} \quad \nu\Psi,$$

or
$$(ih/2\pi)(\partial\Psi/\partial t) \quad \text{for} \quad h\nu\Psi,$$

or
$$(i\hbar\partial/\partial t)\Psi \quad \text{for} \quad E\Psi,$$

which were used to transcribe the energy variable into differential language. Notice that the two basic physical entities, energy and momentum, are represented by operators which are similar in form:

$$\hat{E} = i\hbar\partial/\partial t \quad \text{and} \quad \hat{p} = -i\hbar\partial/\partial x.$$

When all of the operator symbols are put into the Schrödinger equation the result is remarkably simple, in fact nothing more than an algebraic equation:

† In the system of mechanics invented by Hamilton the symbol H usually represents total energy. The name and symbol are used in quantum physics to remind us of Hamilton and his prophetic accomplishments.

$$\hat{p}^2\Psi/2m + \hat{V}\Psi = \hat{E}\Psi \qquad\qquad (8)$$

or $\qquad\qquad (\hat{p}^2/2m + \hat{V})\Psi = \hat{E}\Psi.$

This, obviously, is the energy equation (1), transformed entirely into its quantum physics disguise.

Average Values

The operators of quantum physics serve two vital purposes. They are the symbols or "sign-language" used to represent energy, momentum, and position in the Schrödinger equation. These same operators also serve to calculate average values. This has already been seen with the position and momentum operators: the probability interpretation for the wave function makes it reasonable that

$$\bar{x} = \int\Psi^*x\Psi dx = \int\Psi^*\hat{x}\Psi dx$$

measures average position and the Schrödinger equation establishes that

$$\bar{p} = \int\Psi^*(-i\hbar\partial/\partial x)\Psi dx = \int\Psi^*\hat{p}\Psi dx$$

is an average momentum. Physically these averages are understood to be mean values obtained in many measurements all made on a particle initially (before the measurement) in a condition represented by the wave function Ψ.

Both of the averages mentioned are calculated in the same way: the appropriate operator, $\hat{p}$ or $\hat{x}$, is placed between Ψ^* and Ψ written for the system of interest, and this is integrated over the space accessible to the particle. There seems to be a general rule implied here, that the average value for an observable quantity can be calculated by placing the corresponding operator between Ψ^* and Ψ and integrating this over the space accessible to the particle. For example, the average value for p^2 appears to be

$$\overline{p^2} = \int\Psi^*(-\hbar^2\partial^2/\partial x^2)\Psi dx.$$

As it turns out, proof of this equation and others like it requires an unhandy amount of mathematical apparatus. The rule for forming average value integrals is more satisfactorily stated as a postulate.

If $\hat{A}$ is a suitable operator for the observable physical quantity A, then the average value $\bar{A}$ obtained in many identical measurements of A is *assumed* to be given by

$$\bar{A} = \int \Psi^* \hat{A} \Psi dx. \tag{†}$$

Using this rule an average can be calculated with each of the operator associations mentioned earlier. For the potential energy the operator is simply the potential energy function V; the average is therefore

$$\bar{V} = \int \Psi^* V \Psi dx.$$

The differential operator $-\hbar^2 \partial^2 / \partial x^2$ for p^2 leads to

$$\overline{p^2} = \int \Psi^* (-\hbar^2 \partial^2 / \partial x^2) \Psi dx,$$

and therefore the average energy is

$$\bar{E} = \int \Psi^* [(-\hbar^2 / 2m)(\partial^2 / \partial x^2) + V] \Psi dx.$$

The alternative energy operator $i\hbar \partial / \partial t$ can also be used:

$$\bar{E} = \int \Psi^* (i\hbar \partial / \partial t) \Psi dx.$$

Since the averages calculated in this way are taken to represent the results of actual measurements, it follows that they must be real. The condition that assures the reality of an average value $\bar{A}$ is

$$\bar{A} = \bar{A}^*. \tag{‡}$$

$\bar{A}$ must be equal to its complex conjugate $\bar{A}^*$. This condition is fulfilled if it is true for the corresponding operator $\hat{A}$ that

$$\int \Psi^* \hat{A} \Psi dx = \int \Psi \hat{A}^* \Psi^* dx. \tag{9}$$

That the momentum operator $\hat{p} = -i\hbar \partial / \partial x$ has this property can be seen with an integration by parts:

---

† Remember that, for simplicity, all problems are considered initially in one dimension. Extension to more dimensions will be given later, in Chapter 6.
‡ Write the imaginary and real parts of the quantity separately: $\bar{A} = F + iG$. The condition $\bar{A} = \bar{A}^*$ implies then that

$$F + iG = F - iG$$

$$2iG = 0$$

$$G = 0;$$

that is, $\bar{A} = F$, and must therefore be real.

$$\int \Psi^*(-i\hbar\partial/\partial x)\Psi dx = -i\hbar \int \Psi^*(\partial\Psi/\partial x)dx$$

$$= -i\hbar \int \Psi^* d\Psi$$

$$= -i\hbar[\Psi^*\Psi| - \int \Psi d\Psi^*]$$

$$= -i\hbar[0 - \int \Psi(\partial\Psi^*/\partial x)dx]$$

$$= \int \Psi(i\hbar\partial/\partial x)\Psi^* dx$$

$$= \int \Psi(-i\hbar\partial/\partial x)^*\Psi^* dx. \qquad (\dagger)$$

In the same manner, another, stronger statement can be proved for the momentum operator. The operator is placed between two *different* wave functions Ψ_1 and Ψ_2, and an integration by parts establishes that

$$\int \Psi_1^*(-i\hbar\partial/\partial x)\Psi_2 dx = \int \Psi_2(i\hbar\partial/\partial x)\Psi_1^* dx$$

$$= \int \Psi_2(-i\hbar\partial/\partial x)^*\Psi_1^* dx. \qquad (\dagger)$$

The momentum operator therefore belongs to a class of operators any one of which $\hat{A}$ satisfies

$$\int \Psi_1^*\hat{A}\Psi_2 dx = \int \Psi_2\hat{A}^*\Psi_1^* dx. \qquad (10)$$

The momentum-squared operator $\hat{p}^2$ and the Hamiltonian operator $\hat{H}$ can also be shown (for exercise) to satisfy this condition. An operator for which this is true is said to be "Hermitian." ‡ *All operators which stand for observable physical quantities will be assumed to have the Hermitian property.*

If an operator $\hat{A}$ is Hermitian it is assured that the average value calculated from it,

$$\bar{A} = \int \Psi^*\hat{A}\Psi dx,$$

is real. This, of course, also follows from (9), without the more rigorous requirement (10). The general Hermitian property will, nevertheless, be required, since it has additional uses which will be essential in later sections.§

† A complex conjugate is formed by reversing signs on all i-factors. Thus $(i\hbar\partial/\partial x) = (-i\hbar\partial/\partial x)^*$.

‡ For Charles Hermite, a major nineteenth-century French mathematician who seems to have been an even worse student than Einstein. He was barely able to pass his bachelor of science examinations and held minor teaching positions until he was forty-seven years old.

§ It is also true that with the mathematical theory more extensively developed (10) can be proved as a consequence of (9).

By now it is apparent that the principal source of almost all quantitative information in quantum physics is the wave function Ψ. Because it generates a probability function, it can be used to show the average distribution of a particle in space. Combined with various operators, it is used to calculate average values for a useful assortment of observable physical quantities. Everything that can be known about a particle is derived in one way or another from the wave function. It is appropriately called a "state function," since it determines everything that is important about the state of a system.

Correspondence Formulation of Operators

Quantum physics presents us with many disturbing departures from the familiar classical principles. But it is a source of comfort that many of these departures are carefully framed to have forms parallel to basic classical equations. Quantum physics is organized wherever possible in the image of classical physics. For guidance in this process of matching the quantum laws to classical laws we turn to the correspondence principle, formulated here to the effect that each element in a quantum equation has a corresponding element in a classical equation.

This "correspondence formulation" has, in fact, been a fundamental aim of the discussions of this chapter. The starting point was the classical energy equation (1):

$$p^2/2m + V = E.$$

Working with each term of the energy equation a suitable differential version of it, the Schrödinger equation (6), was devised. At this point the correspondence was difficult to see; the differential equation (6) does not look much like an energy equation. The form of the classical equation (1) was restored, however, by introducing and making clever use of the device of operator representations: the operator equation (8),

$$(\hat{p}^2/2m + \hat{V})\Psi = \hat{E}\Psi,$$

was formed with a more obvious resemblance to the classical energy equation.

But the correspondence argument is not complete without one more step. The two equations (1) and (8) have formal similarities, but they are obviously far from identical and they are applicable in separate domains. Full correspondence requires that the classical and quantum equations be brought together in a common domain where they must be equivalent, at least to a very good approximation. A device for completing the correspondence in this way has already been supplied in the average-value postulate introduced in the last section. Multiply (8) by Ψ^* and integrate over the accessible space; the result is

$$\overline{p^2}/2m + \bar{V} = \bar{E}.$$

This equation becomes identical with the original classical energy equation, $p^2/2m + V = E$, if the classical quantities p^2, V, and E are simply interpreted as the averages $\overline{p^2}$, $\bar{V}$, and $\bar{E}$.

To what extent are we justified in making this move? In the quantum domain, average values are not at all like the corresponding classical quantities: $\overline{p^2}$, for example, resembles p^2 no more than $\hat{p}^2$ does. But there is a trend in the physical qualifications of average values that brings them closer to the classical quantities as the object to which they apply becomes larger. It proves to be mathematically and physically valid to assume that averages calculated according to the prescriptions of quantum physics approach and finally become equivalent to the corresponding classical quantities as the size scale increases. The energy equation applied to increasingly larger objects is therefore transformed as follows:

$$\overline{p^2}/2m + \bar{V} = \bar{E} \rightarrow p^2/2m + V = E.$$

Energy equations are not the only equations of classical form to be brought into the theory. We have also used as a fundamental part of the argument the momentum equation $p = mdx/dt$. The average-value version of this, $\bar{p} = md\bar{x}/dt$, was used to justify the average-value calculation of the momentum, and even the basic momentum operator $\hat{p} = -i\hbar\partial/\partial x$.

The formulation of more complicated operator representations is nearly always guided by correspondence rules. We have seen this with the Hamiltonian operator. The classical Hamiltonian quantity for a single particle influenced by a potential energy function V is

$$H = \frac{p^2}{2m} + V$$

and the Hamiltonian operator is

$$\hat{H} = \frac{\hat{p}^2}{2m} + \hat{V}.$$

Other Hamiltonians also follow a correspondence formulation. If two particles have kinetic energies $p_1{}^2/2m_1$ and $p_2{}^2/2m_2$, and if the total potential energy of the system is V, the classical Hamiltonian for the system is

$$H = \frac{p_1{}^2}{2m_1} + \frac{p_2{}^2}{2m_2} + V$$

and the Hamiltonian operator is

$$\hat{H} = \frac{\hat{p}_1{}^2}{2m_1} + \frac{\hat{p}_2{}^2}{2m_2} + \hat{V}. \tag{†}$$

The correspondence formulation applies with the same simplicity to the invention of operators for other physical quantities. For example, the classical expression for the z-component of a particle's angular momentum is

$$l_z = xp_y - yp_x,$$

where x,y locate the particle with respect to an axis and p_x, p_y are corresponding linear momentum components. The position and momentum operators already introduced convert this to

$$\hat{l}_z = -i\hbar \left(x \frac{\partial}{\partial y} - y \frac{\partial}{\partial x} \right). \tag{‡}$$

This operator and two more for the x and y components form the basis for a quantum theory of electron orbital rotational motion.

Uncertainty

The operator and average-value concepts will first be applied to the calculation of uncertainty. It is necessary to determine the extent of fluctuation between an observable quantity A and its average value $\bar{A}$: the difference $A - \bar{A}$ must be calculated. If this, on the average, is large, the corresponding uncertainty in A is large.

   To proceed with the calculation an operator must be written for $A - \bar{A}$. Since $\bar{A}$ is independent of the position variable x (having been formed by an integration over x), it forms its own operator. Then if $\hat{A}$ is the operator for A, the operator for $A - \bar{A}$ is $\hat{A} - \bar{A}$. To avoid can-

† In a single dimension $p_1 = -i\hbar\partial/\partial x_1$ and $p_2 = -i\hbar\partial/\partial x_2$, where x_1 and x_2 are co-ordinates locating the two particles.
‡ When three dimensions are involved the three momentum component operators are $p_x = -i\hbar\partial/\partial x$, $p_y = -i\hbar\partial/\partial y$, $p_z = -i\hbar\partial/\partial z$.

cellation of positive fluctuations $(A - \bar{A} > 0)$ by negative fluctuations $(A - \bar{A} < 0)$ in the averaging procedure, an effect which would result in an erroneously small uncertainty, it is advisable to calculate $(A - \bar{A})^2$, which is always positive, instead of $A - \bar{A}$. The operator for the squared quantity is $(\hat{A} - \bar{A})^2$, and it is the average calculated from this that is desired. This average will be called the "mean-square" uncertainty and will be labeled $\overline{(\Delta A)^2}$:

$$\overline{(\Delta A)^2} = \int \Psi^*(\hat{A} - \bar{A})^2 \Psi dx.$$

To simplify, expand the operator:

$$\overline{(\Delta A)^2} = \int \Psi^*[\hat{A}^2 - 2\bar{A}\hat{A} + (\bar{A})^2]\Psi dx$$

$$= \int \Psi^* \hat{A}^2 \Psi dx - 2\bar{A} \int \Psi^* \hat{A} \Psi dx + (\bar{A})^2 \int \Psi^* \Psi dx$$

$$= \overline{A^2} - 2(\bar{A})(\bar{A}) + (\bar{A})^2 \qquad\qquad (\dagger)$$

$$= \overline{A^2} - (\bar{A})^2.$$

In other words,

$$\overline{(\Delta A)^2} = \text{mean of the square} - \text{square of the mean}.$$

This formula will be set aside for the present and brought out for several applications later.

Separation of the Schrödinger Equation

Nothing has been said for some time about quantization and the quantum. It seems that we have mixed every aspect of the quantum theory into the Schrödinger equation except the quantization concept itself. In fact, quantization was deliberately left out of the treatment. The Schrödinger formulation, unlike the Bohr quantum theory, does not *impose* the quantum conditions. ‡ Aspects of the wave-particle duality, uncertainty, and probability-wave concepts were introduced in the equation, but nothing was said explicitly concerning quantization. Nevertheless, when the Schrödinger equation is solved for such problems as an electron in an atom, the energy and other dynamical quantities appear in a form which is quantized in exactly the right way. Quantization is therefore inherent in the other concepts of the quantum theory and in the mathematical statements

† The normalization property provides $\int \Psi^* \Psi dx = 1$ in the last term.
‡ This was an aspect of Schrödinger's equation that particularly interested him. See page 96.

they generate. A world built from probability waves and the uncertainty principle is *naturally* quantized.

These hidden quantization aspects will now be brought out. The Schrödinger equation is discussed for the simplified, yet practical, case in which the potential energy function is dependent only on the space variables, and not on time — a so-called "conservative" system. We will also assume that the potential function is one which confines the particle to a more or less definite region (as in an atom), and that the wave function can be partitioned into a space-dependent factor, $\psi(x)$, and a time-dependent factor, $\phi(t)$:

$$\Psi(x,t) = \psi(x)\phi(t).$$

With these conditions, which happen to fit most problems of interest, the solutions to the Schrödinger equation automatically come in quantized sets of wave functions, Ψ_1, Ψ_2, . . . , and energy values, E_1, E_2, ...

The first simplification, that the potential energy function is time-independent, leads to a Hamiltonian operator which is also independent of time:

$$\hat{H} = (-\hbar^2/2m)(\partial^2/\partial x^2) + V(x).$$

This is always the case for a particle (or system of particles) that is isolated from outside disturbances. An isolated system has a constant or "conserved" energy: the energy (strictly, the average energy) does not change with time. (Hamiltonian operators that are time-independent will be used throughout this chapter and the next.)

With the further simplification that the wave function can be partitioned into a space-dependent and a time-dependent part, $\Psi = \psi(x)\phi(t)$, the Schrödinger equation becomes

$$-(\hbar^2/2m)d^2\psi/dx^2)\phi + V(x)\psi\phi = i\hbar\psi(d\phi/dt).$$

Divide both sides of this equation by $\Psi = \psi\phi$:

$$-(\hbar^2/2m)(d^2\psi/dx^2)(1/\psi) + V(x) = (i\hbar/\phi)(d\phi/dt).$$

This has the useful effect of separating the equation into one side (on the left) that contains x only and another side (on the right) that contains t only.† The former equals the latter and this raises the question: What can they both equal? First write a function F for the left side of the equation

† This maneuver was mentioned earlier (page 95) in connection with Schrödinger's handling of the classical wave equation.

$$-(\hbar^2/2m)(d^2\psi/dx^2)(1/\psi) + V(x) = F.$$

According to this, F cannot contain t. The same function must also be equal to the right side:

$$(i\hbar/\phi)(d\phi/dt) = F,$$

which shows that F cannot contain x. The only possible conclusion is that F contains *neither x nor t*, and is therefore a constant.

The equation for ϕ has the simple solution

$$\phi = e^{Ft/i\hbar}, \quad \text{or} \quad \phi = e^{-iFt/\hbar}.$$

Expanded in trigonometric functions, using Euler's relation, this is

$$\phi = \cos(Ft/\hbar) - i\sin(Ft/\hbar),$$

a function which oscillates in time with a frequency ν given by $2\pi\nu = F/\hbar$ or $F = h\nu$. It is clear from this what physical interpretation can be attached to the constant F: it is evidently the energy E, which is also equal to $h\nu$. The time-dependent function $\phi(t)$ is therefore $\phi(t) = e^{-iEt/\hbar}$, the full wave function is

$$\Psi(x,t) = \psi(x)e^{-iEt/\hbar}, \tag{11}$$

and the differential equation for ϕ is

$$i\hbar d\phi/dt = E\phi. \tag{12}$$

The spatial (x-dependent) part of the Schrödinger equation is now

$$(-\hbar^2/2m)(d^2\psi/dx^2) + V(x)\psi = E\psi, \tag{13a}$$

or, using the Hamiltonian notation

$$\hat{H} = (-\hbar^2/2m)(\partial^2/\partial x^2) + V(x),$$

the equation simplifies to

$$\hat{H}\psi = E\psi. \tag{13b}$$

This is frequently called the time-independent Schrödinger equation. Notice that the solutions $\psi(x)$ need not be imaginary, although imaginary solutions are possible.

From (12) it follows that

$$i\hbar\partial\Psi/\partial t = E\Psi,$$

and from (11) and (13a) that

$$\hat{H}\Psi = E\Psi. \tag{14}$$

When either energy operator, $i\hbar\partial/\partial t$ or $\hat{H}$, is applied to a valid wave function Ψ, the wave function is returned multiplied by a possible value of the energy E.

The three equations $\hat{H}\psi = E\psi$, $\hat{H}\Psi = E\Psi$, and $i\hbar\partial\Psi/\partial t = E\Psi$ all have a special form which can be expressed, in general, as $\hat{A}f = af$. $\hat{A}$ is an operator; a and f are a constant and a function, respectively, which satisfy the equation. Usually a large number of constants and functions are valid for such an equation. In mathematical parlance, the constants a are "eigenvalues," the functions f "eigenfunctions," and equations of this general type are called "eigenvalue equations." In the energy problem the eigenvalues are the various possible energy values E and the eigenfunctions are the wave functions Ψ or ψ which prescribe the states in which the energy values E are measured. As the formalism becomes more elegant it will be seen that *all* physical quantities, not just the energy, have eigenvalue-eigenfunction modes of expression.

In the next two sections we will discuss in detail the eigenfunctions ψ and eigenvalues E produced by the time-independent Schrödinger equation (13a). These eigenfunctions and eigenvalues are the ingredients from which the full time-dependent solutions of the Schrödinger equation, $\Psi(x,t) = \psi(x)e^{-iEt/\hbar}$, are constructed.

Electrons in Boxes

The Schrödinger equation, like many other mathematical equations applied to physical situations, has certain solutions which are mathematically valid but not acceptable from the physical viewpoint. These physical restrictions will now be explored for the spatial wave functions $\psi(x)$, and we will see that they lead naturally to the occurrence of discrete eigenfunctions and energy eigenvalues in the mathematical problem—that is, to an explanation of the quantization phenomenon.

First sort out the appropriate quantized eigenfunction-eigenvalue solutions to the Schrödinger equation for a particularly simple case. Consider a particle—an electron, say—confined to a peculiar "one-dimensional box" † of length L. While the electron is in the space

---

† This is not as impossible a concept as it sounds. Certain highly conjugated dye molecules can be treated with surprising accuracy by simply assuming that π-electrons travel back and forth along the conjugated chain as if they are moving freely in a linear box.

lying between $x = 0$ and $x = L$ it is entirely free, that is, $V(x) = 0$, but there is the restriction that it cannot go beyond the "walls" of the box located at $x = 0$ and L. To express the latter condition mathematically, take the spatial wave function $\psi(x)$ (and therefore the probability for finding the particle) to be zero at the walls and beyond:

$$\psi(x) = 0 \quad \text{for } x \leq 0 \quad \text{and } x \geq L.$$

The electron located in the box (where $V = 0$) is described by the Hamiltonian

$$\hat{H} = -(\hbar^2/2m)(d^2/dx^2),$$

and the time-independent Schrödinger equation is simply

$$-(\hbar^2/2m)(d^2\psi/dx^2) = E\psi, \quad \text{or} \quad d^2\psi/dx^2 = -\alpha^2\psi.$$

where $\alpha^2 = 2mE/\hbar^2$ collects all of the constants together. The solutions

$$\psi = \psi_0 \sin \alpha x$$

fit this equation, with ψ_0 being a constant amplitude factor.

The constant α has a further restriction, caused by the requirement that the wave function must vanish at the box's walls. The $\sin \alpha x$ wave function always vanishes at the wall located at $x = 0$, but the other wall, at $x = L$, does not produce a vanishing wave function unless $\alpha x = \pi, 2\pi, 3\pi, \ldots$, or, since $x = L$, the necessary condition on α is $\alpha = n\pi/L$, n being any positive integer. This is also a restriction on the energy, because α and the energy E are related:

$$E = \alpha^2\hbar^2/2m$$

$$E_n = n^2\pi^2\hbar^2/2mL^2 \qquad\qquad (\dagger)$$

$$= n^2h^2/8mL^2.$$

These are the various possible energy eigenvalues. The corresponding eigenfunctions are

$$\psi = \psi_0 \sin \alpha x$$

$$\psi_n = \psi_0 \sin (n\pi x/L). \qquad\qquad (\dagger)$$

The probability functions which these eigenfunctions generate are

† The discrete nature of eigenfunctions and eigenvalues is frequently indicated by numbering them with subscripts (ns in this case). This subscript will often be used later and will be considered (but not stated explicitly) to have positive integer values.

$$P_n = \psi_n^2$$
$$= \psi_0^2 \sin^2 (n\pi x/L).$$

It is helpful to look at some of these functions graphically:

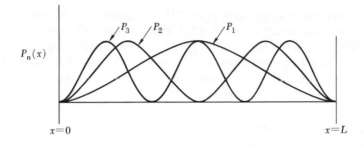

We conclude in the physical sense that an electron confined in a box can have only certain energies E_n, no energy values between these being possible. The state of an electron with energy E_n is defined by the wave function ψ_n, the various possible electron locations and their relative probabilities being indicated by the probability function $P_n = \psi_n^2$.

Beneath this seemingly straightforward solution to the electron-in-the-box problem there lurks a remarkable paradox. Suppose, for example, an electron-in-a-box has the energy

$$E_2 = 4h^2/8mL^2.$$

Then its state is expressed by

$$\psi_2 = \psi_0 \sin (2\pi x/L)$$

and its spatial distribution in the box has the appearance:

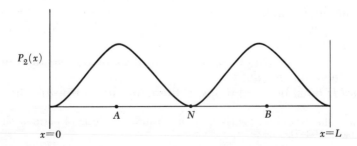

The electron can, presumably, be located at two points, such as A or B. But how can it conceivably get from A to B when it must go through a point N where it is *never* located?

If this question can be asked, if it has physical meaning, it must make sense to speak of the electron traveling the path A through N to B. But for any statement to make sense in quantum physics it must imply observable processes. If an electron is in the state ψ_2, can its progress along the path ANB, particularly the passage through the dubious point N, be observed? The answer, obviously, is no. An electron cannot be observed at a point—A, N, B, or any other—without severely disturbing its state.† After such a measurement ψ_2 no longer describes the electron's state, and the probability distribution pictured above is no longer applicable. If an electron is in a precise energy state, as assumed, then statements concerning motion between points and through points have no physical meaning.

Electrons in Wells

Electrons, of course, are not very often found in linear boxes. A much more general analysis, one which puts electrons into wells rather than boxes, can also be developed to demonstrate the quantization of energy values and energy states.

As before, we begin with a careful definition of the necessary physical restrictions. The following general requirements can be enumerated for any wave function ψ and its derivatives $d\psi/dx$:

1. ψ must vanish at least at the most extreme limits $x = \pm\infty$ of the space accessible to the particle. This condition has been used several times previously.

2. ψ must be finite. This is obviously required in order for the spatial part $\psi^*\psi$ of the probability function to have physical sense.

3. $d\psi/dx$ must be finite. This derivative appears in several places. For example, it can be seen in the partial integrations used to evaluate the average momentum (see page 147). Infinite values cannot be allowed.

4. ψ must be continuous. Discontinuities in the ψ-function lead to infinite values for $d\psi/dx$.

5. $d\psi/dx$ must be continuous. If there are discontinuities in $d\psi/dx$,

† Return to the Heisenberg analysis of the disturbing effects of position measurements (pages 103–7).

the second-order derivative $d^2\psi/dx^2$ becomes infinite and the Schrödinger equation loses physical sense.

With these requirements noted, the acceptable wave functions can be separated from the unacceptable ones. As mentioned before, a wave function with the behavior

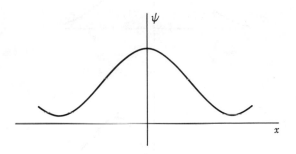

is unacceptable because it tends toward infinity for $x = \pm\infty$. The wave functions

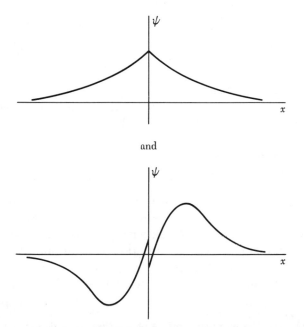

and

are also unacceptable; the first one has a $d\psi/dx$-discontinuity and the second one a ψ-discontinuity. On the other hand, the wave functions

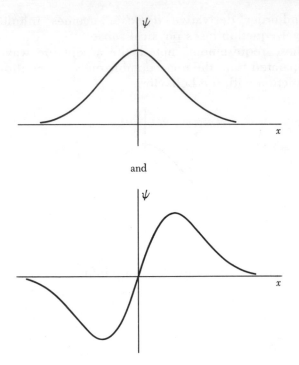

and

are acceptable on all counts.

These various features of the wave-function curves can be sketched mathematically by constructing a general type of potential energy function and applying the time-independent Schrödinger equation written in the form

$$(1/\psi)(d^2\psi/dx^2) = (2m/\hbar^2)(V - E). \qquad (15)$$

The potential function is taken to be one that has a constant value except in a region where it dips down to form a "potential well" † as shown at the top of the following page. Customarily such potential functions are taken to be zero outside the well and negative inside.

In the realm of classical physics the total energy E of a particle cannot be exceeded by the potential energy V. ‡ When a classi-

---

† The analysis is simplified here by assuming that the potential well is symmetrical around the V-axis. The major conclusions of this discussion do not, however, depend on this symmetry. An asymmetrical well leads to a similar energy quantization.

‡ Among other things, this would require that the momentum of the particle, $p = \sqrt{2m(E - V)}$, be imaginary, or that the particle's mass be negative.

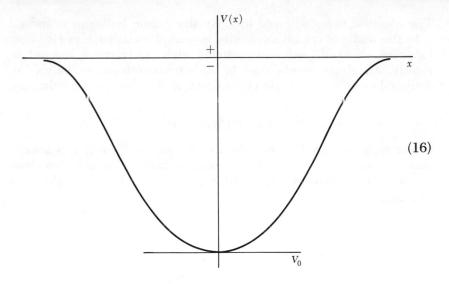

(16)

cal particle—say an electron—with total energy in the range
$V_0 < E < 0$, is put into a well such as the one shown above, there is
a definite region in which the electron can move without violating
the $V \leq E$ condition. The limits of this region are marked out by
superimposing the total energy E (a constant) on the potential
well V:

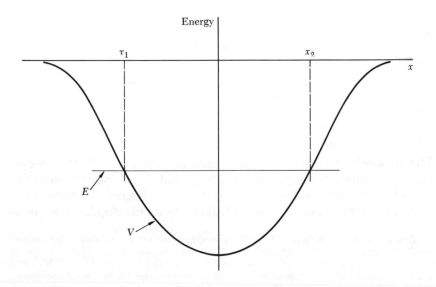

The electron is not allowed to leave the region between x_1 and x_2.

In the realm of quantum physics potential wells such as (16) also have the effect of confining particles such as electrons, but not as rigidly. An electron subjected to the situation diagramed above is confined *mostly* to the region between x_1 and x_2, but not entirely. According to (15),

$$(1/\psi)(d^2\psi/dx^2) > 0$$

in any region where $V > E$. A ψ-curve for which this is true is always convex toward the x-axis.† A convex wave function which also satisfies the requirement that it vanish for $x = +\infty$ has the qualitative appearance

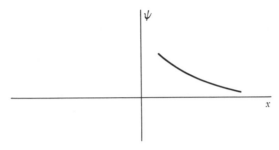

in the first quadrant. In the second, third, and fourth quadrants it must look like

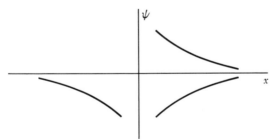

The general conclusion is that in regions where $V > E$ the magnitude of ψ must decrease, and that the probability $\psi^*\psi$ for finding the particle in these regions must also decrease. Regions outside a potential well are therefore not prohibited to an electron in the quan-

---

† A function $\psi(x)$ for which $d^2\psi/dx^2 > 0$ is shaped so that its convex side points downward. A function for which $d^2\psi/dx^2 < 0$ is "convex upward." In the first and second quadrants, where $\psi > 0$, the former are convex toward the x-axis, and in the third and fourth quadrants ($\psi < 0$) the latter are convex toward the x-axis. In all quadrants, therefore, the condition $(1/\psi)(d^2\psi/dx^2) > 0$ assures that the function is convex toward the x-axis.

tum domain, but the probability of finding the electron decreases rapidly with increasing distance beyond the well.

The electron outside the well has a negative kinetic energy T: $E = T + V$ and $V > E$, so that $T = E - V$ must be negative. This is another situation unheard of in classical physics. Classical kinetic energies are invariably positive: a negative kinetic energy equivalent to the classical formula $mv^2/2$ implies either a negative mass or an imaginary velocity. That any sensible physics could propose peculiarities such as negative mass and negative kinetic energy is inconceivable in the classical framework. Nevertheless, we have here an acceptable theory that contains the concept of negative kinetic energy.

If there is no potential well, or if the electron energy E always lies below the level of the bottom of the well (V_0), there is no way the two branches of the wave-function curve from the left and right can be joined at $x = 0$ with continuity in both ψ and $d\psi/dx$. If ψ-values are made equal at $x = 0$,

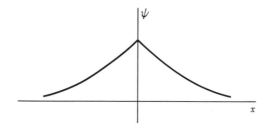

there is a discontinuity in $d\psi/dx$. If the $d\psi/dx$-values are made equal at $x = 0$,

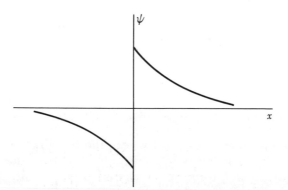

there is a discontinuity in the ψ-value.

To have full continuity where the two branches of the ψ-curve join it is apparent that the curve must bend toward the x-axis and not away from it. The Schrödinger equation specifies the physical condition for this: the electron must enter the region of the potential well with an energy greater than V_0 (but still negative), so that $E > V$ and

$$(1/\psi)(d^2\psi/dx^2) < 0.$$

This is mathematically equivalent to the requirement that the ψ-curve be *concave* toward the x-axis.

The points at which the convex curve becomes concave, where $E = V$, are labeled "turning points." They are located by superimposing the energy E on the potential energy curve (choose a relatively low energy at first):

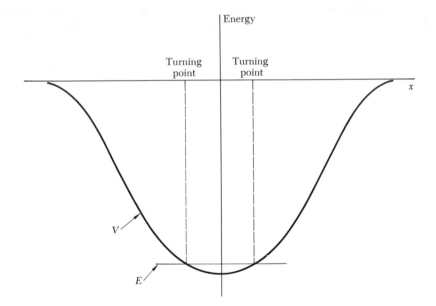

The location of the turning points, and the magnitude of the difference $E - V$, determine how sharply the ψ-curve becomes concave as it approaches the center where the two branches must join. Evidently if the turning points are close to each other, and if the energy is quite low, the concavity may not be sufficiently great where the branches join to give the necessary continuity:

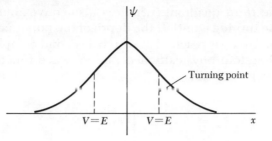

As the energy level is raised the turning points move out, and finally a definite energy E_1 is reached for which the wave-function curve can be developed with complete continuity:

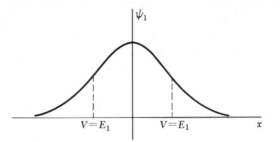

This is a physically acceptable wave function or eigenfunction ψ_1, and the energy E_1 from which it is obtained is a physically possible energy eigenvalue.

Raising the energy level further (but still holding it negative) develops the concavity of the ψ-curve more, so that the two branches from the first and second quadrants meet in a way which is again discontinuous:

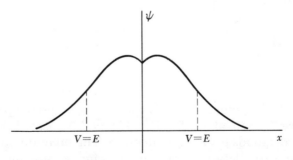

For energies in this range, continuity can be achieved only by joining the branch of the wave-function curve in the first quadrant with

that from the *third* quadrant (which is also convex before and concave after the turning point). If the depth of the potential well allows,
a second energy E_2 is reached at which a second completely continuous, and therefore physically acceptable, wave function or eigenfunction ψ_2 is generated:

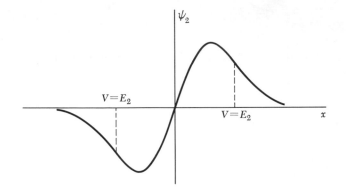

Above E_2 a third energy eigenvalue E_3 may be found, which locates the turning points so that an acceptable wave function or eigenfunction ψ_3 of the type

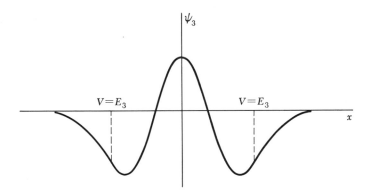

is formed. If the potential well is wide enough and deep enough, further energy eigenvalues E_4, E_5, . . . can be located, each one of
which corresponds to an eigenfunction. The eigenfunctions become
increasingly oscillatory as the energy eigenvalues increase. It can
be seen from the first three eigenfunctions that each has one more
point, or "node," where it crosses the x-axis than the preceding one.

Discrete solutions to the Schrödinger equation are obtained only so long as the electron is "confined" by a potential well something like (16). When the electron is found in the well its energy exceeds the potential energy and the ψ-curve is concave and oscillatory. Outside the well the ψ-curve becomes convex, bends toward the x-axis, and eventually becomes very small. It is the piecing together of these convex and concave sections of the ψ-curve which limits the number of acceptable solutions and leads to the quantization effect.

If the energy of the electron exceeds the height of the potential well, if E becomes positive, there is no region in which $E < V$ and no condition

$$(1/\psi)(d^2\psi/dx^2) > 0.$$

At no point is the ψ-curve convex toward the x-axis. Thus there are no turning points and no need to join convex sections with concave sections. A *continuous* range of energy eigenvalues gives acceptable wave functions.

The occurrence of quantized and continuous energy levels is conveniently represented by superimposing them on top of the potential energy curve:

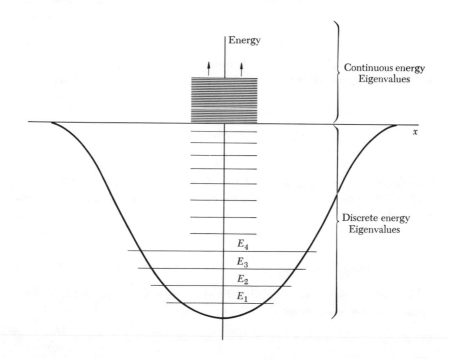

The eigenvalue-eigenfunction characteristics of the time-independent Schrödinger equation are usually summarized by writing the equation as follows:

$$\hat{H}\psi_n = E_n\psi_n,$$

where

$$\hat{H} = (-\hbar^2/2m)(\partial^2/\partial x^2) + V \qquad \text{and} \qquad n = 1, 2, 3, \ldots \qquad (17)$$

If there are regions inside which $V < E$, but outside which $V > E$, the energy eigenvalues E_n have discrete values. If $E > V$ at all points throughout space then the E_n are produced with continuous values.

If ψ_n is an eigenfunction and E_n is an eigenvalue of the time-independent Schrödinger equation (17), then time-dependent wave functions,

$$\Psi_n(x,t) = \psi_n(x)e^{-iE_nt/\hbar},$$

can be formed, which are, as shown before, solutions to the general Schrödinger equation,

$$\hat{H}\Psi = i\hbar\partial\Psi/\partial t,$$

provided that $\hat{H}$ is independent of time. It is also clear from (14) that such a wave function is an eigenfunction whose eigenvalue is E_n:

$$\hat{H}\Psi_n = E_n\Psi_n.$$

Two energy eigenfunctions therefore come into use: the time-dependent ones $\Psi_n(x,t)$ and the time-independent ones $\psi_n(x)$. The two are related by the simple oscillatory time factor $e^{-iE_nt/\hbar}$. Formation of a probability function from the Ψ_n-eigenfunctions gives the same result as the probability function formed from the ψ_n-eigenfunctions:

$$\Psi_n{}^*\Psi_n = e^{iE_nt/\hbar}e^{-iE_nt/\hbar}\psi_n{}^*\psi_n$$

$$= \psi_n{}^*\psi_n.$$

Electrons in a state described by Ψ_n therefore have a "stationary" probability function. The probability for locating the electron at the accessible points in space does not change with time.†

Energy Eigenstates

When many electrons initially in the state Ψ_n have their energy measured the average of these measurements is

† In the language of the Bohr theory, this is a "stationary state."

$$\bar{E} = \int \Psi_n{}^* \hat{H} \Psi_n dx$$
$$= \int \Psi_n{}^* E_n \Psi_n dx$$
$$= E_n \int \Psi_n{}^* \Psi_n dx$$
$$= F_{\iota m \iota}$$

The last step follows from the normalization property of wave functions. The *average* energy measured is therefore the eigenvalue E_n. This is also the *only* value measured, since there is no uncertainty in the energy measurement:

$$\overline{(\Delta E)^2} = \overline{E^2} - (\bar{E})^2$$
$$= \int \Psi_n{}^* \hat{H}^2 \Psi_n dx - (\int \Psi_n{}^* \hat{H} \Psi_n dx)^2$$
$$= E_n \int \Psi_n{}^* \hat{H} \Psi_n dx - (E_n \int \Psi_n{}^* \Psi_n dx)^2$$
$$= E_n{}^2 \int \Psi_n{}^* \Psi_n dx - E_n{}^2 (\int \Psi_n{}^* \Psi_n dx)^2$$
$$= E_n{}^2 - E_n{}^2$$
$$= 0.$$

A definite energy E_n is always measured for an electron in the state Ψ_n. We will refer to a state such as that determined by Ψ_n, which assures a definite result when an energy measurement is made, as an "energy eigenstate." The wave functions Ψ_n could be called "energy eigenstate wave functions," but this term seems too cumbersome for frequent use. The Ψ_n-functions (also the ψ_n-functions, as explained below) will continue to be called "energy eigenfunctions."

As long as the discussion concerns systems whose energy is conserved, as it will throughout this book, an energy eigenstate can just as well be described by the spatial eigenfunction ψ_n and the energy eigenvalue E_n as by the full eigenfunction Ψ_n. The first two quantities determine the third:

$$\Psi_n = \psi_n e^{-iE_n t/\hbar}.$$

The spatial eigenfunctions can also be regarded as determining the energy eigenvalues E_n by virtue of the spatial eigenvalue equation

$$\hat{H} \psi_n = E_n \psi_n.$$

For most purposes, therefore, it is appropriate and simpler to consider that ψ_n rather than Ψ_n determines an eigenstate.

When the Schrödinger equation (usually the time-independent version (13a)) is formulated for any situation, and then solved, it generates a list of the possible energy eigenfunctions ψ_n (all of the physically acceptable solutions to the equation) together with the corresponding energy eigenvalues E_n. It will be assumed that this is a *complete* list of all the energies that can possibly be measured when an electron is in the physical situation expressed by the Schrödinger equation. When an energy measurement is made it must be *one* of these energy eigenvalues. And it follows that if an eigenvalue E_n is measured, the state of the electron, even if it is uncertain before the measurement, must be the definite eigenstate determined by ψ_n and E_n *after* the measurement. A second measurement made immediately after the first one definitely gives E_n again.

The measurement process seems to have the effect of forcing an electron or other particle into a definite energy eigenstate and establishing certainty in the energy value. The eigenstate-eigenvalue description therefore makes sense *after* a measurement has been made. But *before* the measurement, when there may be *uncertainty* in the energy, the status of an electron cannot be expressed by a single eigenstate. The theory must now be extended to show how the wave function is formulated when the energy is uncertain. In effect, this situation calls for a wave function which is a linear combination or superposition of all the eigenfunctions whose energy eigenvalues have any probability of occurring in a measurement. This will be a "superposition state." Before a measurement is made the electron must be considered to be in all the accessible energy eigenstates *at once;* then a measurement puts it into a particular eigenstate.

This part of the story is better told with the elegance of the mathematical language, and for that we need another chapter.

6

Beautiful Equations

It seems that if one is working from the point of view
of getting beauty in one's equations, and if one has a
really sound insight, one is on a sure line of progress.†

The scientist builds his theories as much with a kind of inspired artistry as with the strict procedures of logic. A great theory can no more be put together entirely with straightforward reasoning processes than a great symphony can be written with textbook principles of composition. The composer must have a finely tuned ear; the scientist must have a finely tuned insight. Just as the composer "hears" his incomplete symphony as if it were being played by a full orchestra, the scientist must "see" his theory extending far beyond its early, primitive limitations. In the beginning the work has a strange, complex sound; its beauty is subtle and few are able to understand and appreciate it. But gradually, with patience and faith and mastery of technique, the artist-scientist manages to bring the essential elements of his art together and to weave them into a powerful and moving whole (in music this is the creation of a single artist, but in science it finally requires the efforts of many). Eventually, sometimes much later, the work plays to larger audiences and is accepted into the standard repertoire.

We have before us a finished theory of unsurpassed beauty. Excerpts from it were presented in the last chapter. It is time now to hear the complete theory, beginning with a statement (partly a restatement) of its themes.

† Paul A. M. Dirac in an article, "The Evolution of the Physicist's Picture of Nature," *Scientific American,* May 1963.

Summary of the Postulates

The style of a theory must be as general as possible. Obviously, not many problems can be treated with the one-dimensional, one-particle picture developed thus far. When a single, isolated particle is described in three dimensions the one space variable x must be converted to the three space variables, x, y, and z. The probability function becomes $P(x,y,z,t)$, the wave functions $\Psi(x,y,z,t)$ and $\psi(x,y,z)$ and the potential energy function $V(x,y,z)$. In all of the integrals written previously the differential dx is replaced with the differential volume element $dv = dxdydz$; the integral $\int \Psi^* \Psi dx$, for example, becomes $\int \Psi^* \Psi dv$ and the integration extends throughout the accessible parts of three-dimensional space. When the Schrödinger equation is extended to three dimensions it contains three space variables instead of one: the Hamiltonian operator is

$$\hat{H} = (-\hbar^2/2m)(\partial^2/\partial x^2 + \partial^2/\partial y^2 + \partial^2/\partial z^2) + V(x,y,z), \qquad (\dagger)$$

$$= (-\hbar^2/2m)\nabla^2 + V,$$

where ∇^2 stands for the three-dimensional differential operator

$$\nabla^2 = \partial^2/\partial x^2 + \partial^2/\partial y^2 + \partial^2/\partial z^2$$

(the ∇-symbol is called "del"; read ∇^2 as "del squared"). The Hamiltonian operator forms the time-dependent and time-independent versions of the Schrödinger equation in the same manner as before:

$$\hat{H}\Psi = i\hbar \partial \Psi/\partial t$$

$$\hat{H}\psi = E\psi.$$

Operator associations must be stated for the three spatial components of vectorial quantities such as the momentum:

$$\hat{p}_x = -i\hbar\partial/\partial x, \qquad \hat{p}_y = -i\hbar\partial/\partial y, \qquad \text{and} \qquad \hat{p}_z = -i\hbar\partial/\partial z.$$

And the total momentum-squared operator in three dimensions is

$$\hat{p}^2 = \hat{p}_x{}^2 + \hat{p}_y{}^2 + \hat{p}_z{}^2 = -\hbar^2 \nabla^2.$$

The component operators lead to corresponding averages for the components:

$$\bar{p}_x = \int \Psi^*(-i\hbar\partial/\partial x)\Psi dv, \qquad \bar{p}_y = \int \Psi^*(-i\hbar\partial/\partial y)\Psi dv, \qquad \text{etc.}$$

† Remember that V, for the constant-energy systems under discussion, is assumed to be independent of time: $V(x,y,z)$, not $V(x,y,z,t)$.

Going beyond the single particle to a description of N particles increases the number of variables of the coordinate type to $3N$. These may all be rectangular coordinates, but when the particles are the nuclei of a molecule it is more practical to have all but three of these (the coordinates of the center of mass) express rotational and vibrational degrees of freedom. However the coordinates are disposed, the probability function and the wave function must depend on all of the coordinates required to account for all the degrees of freedom. If there are f of these the wave function becomes $\Psi(q_1, \ldots, q_f, t)$ where $q_1, \ldots, q_f$ are the various coordinates, rectangular and otherwise, and the probability function is

$$P(q_1, \ldots, q_f, t) = \Psi^*(q_1, \ldots, q_f, t)\Psi(q_1, \ldots, q_f, t).$$

Then $P(q_1, \ldots, q_f, t)dq_1 \ldots dq_f$ is the probability that the entire collection of particles will be found arranged with the coordinates in the infinitesimal intervals between q_1 and $q_1 + dq_1$, q_2 and $q_2 + dq_2, \ldots, q_f$ and $q_f + dq_f$. All of the integrals are generalized accordingly. The normalization integral, for example, becomes

$$\int\Psi^*(q_1, \ldots, q_f, t)\Psi(q_1, \ldots, q_f, t)dq_1 \ldots dq_f = 1,$$

and an average value integral for the quantity A has the appearance

$$\bar{A} = \int\Psi^*(q_1, \ldots, q_f, t)\hat{A}\Psi(q_1, \ldots, q_f, t)dq_1 \ldots dq_f.$$

These integrals extend over the f-dimensional "phase space" with $q_1, \ldots, q_f$ as its dimensions. This is not a real space, but a mathematical contrivance designed to satisfy the needs of multiple integrals such as those containing the wave function. It is a fictitious space represented by f perpendicular axes with a separate coordinate plotted on each axis. To write the Schrödinger equation for more than one particle, start with the general statement

$$\hat{H}\Psi = i\hbar\partial\Psi/\partial t,$$

where $\hat{H}$ is the Hamiltonian operator translated into appropriate operator language for the collection of particles. We must omit the task of writing such Hamiltonians explicitly, though, to avoid a rather lengthy digression from the main purpose of the book. Just note that we are mostly concerned with isolated collections of particles whose energy is constant.

Some kind of code is needed to condense the rather cumbersome notation and terminology which accompanies these generalized descriptions. From now on the term "system" will be used for the object described, whether it is a single electron or a complex molecule. Volume elements in integrals are written dq to condense the complete expression $dq_1 \ldots dq_f$. Coordinate dependence in the wave function and the probability function are written $\Psi(q,t)$ and $P(q,t)$. The Hamiltonian operator is simply $\hat{H}(q)$ (for isolated systems).

After this lengthy preamble we can proceed to the main business of this section, a statement of the essential postulates of the theory.

I. *The probability function.* There exists a function $P(q,t)$ which gives the probability that, under the circumstances of the physical situation, a measurement at time t will find the particles of a system in a small region around the point in phase space defined by the set of coordinates q. To have the required physical significance the probability function must be positive (or zero), real, continuous, single-valued, and finite. When it is integrated over all the accessible regions of space it must give a value of unity:

$$\int P\,dq = 1. \tag{1}$$

II. *Probability waves.* In most situations the probability function shows a curious wavelike behavior: there are regions of alternately high and low probability. It has not been found possible to explain these probability waves with more fundamental concepts.† They are simply a basic and ubiquitous part of the physical description.

III. *The wave function.* There exists a function $\Psi(q,t)$, known as the wave function, which guarantees that the probability function is both real and positive:

$$P(q,t) = \Psi^*(q,t)\Psi(q,t). \tag{2}$$

This function is less restricted than the probability function: it can be real or complex, positive or negative. Otherwise the wave function is restricted in the same way as the probability function: it must be finite, continuous, and single-valued. In addition, first derivatives such as $\partial\Psi/\partial x$ must be continuous and single-valued. The wave function must be normalizable:

† That is, no *consensus* has been reached concerning the basis for the probability waves. Various interpretations for the waves have been proposed (see the work of Bohm and Landé described in Chapter 4), but none of these has yet been widely accepted.

$$\int \Psi^* \Psi \, dq = 1, \qquad (3)$$

as is implied by combining (1) and (2). The wave function has the highly important property of being able to generate interference effects.

IV. *The Schrödinger equation.* The wave function changes with time according to the Schrödinger equation,

$$\hat{H}\Psi = i\hbar \partial \Psi / \partial t, \qquad (4)$$

where $\hat{H}$ is an operator formulated in accordance with the physical situation. For a single particle in one dimension

$$\hat{H} = -(\hbar^2/2m)(\partial^2/\partial x^2) + V(x),$$

in which $V(x)$ is a suitable potential energy function. For a single particle moving in three dimensions

$$\hat{H} = -(\hbar^2/2m)\nabla^2 + V(x,y,z).$$

V. *Operator associations.* Corresponding to every observable physical quantity there is a linear operator. These linear operators, written to apply to the operand Ψ, serve to translate basic physical statements into the terms of quantum physics. The operator for the spatial variable x is the variable itself, $\hat{x} = x$, and the operator for the corresponding momentum component is $\hat{p}_x = -i\hbar \partial/\partial x$. Operators for the other two spatial dimensions and momentum components are formed in the same way: $\hat{y} = y$, $\hat{p}_y = -i\hbar \partial/\partial y$, $\hat{z} = z$, $\hat{p}_z = -i\hbar \partial/\partial z$. The operator for the total energy is written $\hat{H}$ and is called the Hamiltonian operator; its prescription follows a "correspondence formulation," in which operators replace classical variables: the classical Hamiltonian $H = p^2/2m + V$ becomes

$$\hat{H} = \hat{p}^2/2m + \hat{V},$$

where $\hat{V} = V(q)$, $V(q)$ being a suitable potential energy function, and $\hat{p}^2$ is an operator for the total momentum squared. For the motion of a single particle in three spatial dimensions, $\hat{p}^2 = -\hbar^2\nabla^2$. The Hamiltonian operator $\hat{H}$ is identical to the $\hat{H}$ operator used to write the Schrödinger equation. In operator language, therefore, the Schrödinger equation is a simple energy equation.

VI. *Average values.* If an observable quantity A is measured many times for a system of a given type and in a state
specified by the wave function Ψ, the average value obtained in these measurements is

$$\bar{A} = \int \Psi^* \hat{A} \Psi dq, \tag{5}$$

where $\hat{A}$ is the operator associated with A and the integral
extends over the accessible regions of phase space.

VII. *The Hermitian property.* All operators associated
with physically observable quantities have the Hermitian
property. For any Hermitian operator $\hat{A}$,

$$\int \Psi_1^* \hat{A} \Psi_2 dq = \int \Psi_2 \hat{A}^* \Psi_1^* dq, \tag{6}$$

where Ψ_1 and Ψ_2 are two different functions that can
qualify as wave functions. This assures that the average
values calculated according to the last postulate are real
and not complex. It also establishes a valuable property of
eigenfunctions known as "orthogonality," which we will
discuss presently.

Eigenstates

The discussion in Chapter 5 has established that when a particle is
in an eigenstate expressed by the energy eigenfunction

$$\Psi_n = \psi_n e^{-iE_n t/\hbar},$$

where ψ_n and E_n come from the eigenvalue equation $\hat{H}\psi_n = E_n\psi_n$,
there is only one possible value that the energy may have: measurements always give the value E_n. Attempt now to find a more general
version of this. Search for an eigenstate wave function $\Psi(q,t_0)$ which
specifies that at time t_0 a state of the system exists in which only the
precise value a_n is measured for the observable quantity A whose
associated operator is $\hat{A}$. Designate these wave functions as
$u_n(q)$: $u_n(q) = \Psi(q,t_0)$. The appropriate equation for the calculation of
the functions u_n is derived in a

Theorem: The functions u_n must be eigenfunctions which satisfy the
following eigenvalue equation:

$$\hat{A}u_n = a_n u_n. \tag{7}$$

Proof:

$$\bar{A} = \int \Psi^* \hat{A} \Psi dq$$
$$= \int u_n^* \hat{A} u_n dq$$
$$= \int u_n^* a_n u_n dq$$
$$= a_n \int u_n^* u_n dq$$
$$= a_n.$$

The last step is the result of the requirement that the wave functions Ψ_n and u_n be normalized:

$$\int \Psi_n^* \Psi_n dq = 1 \quad \text{and} \quad \int u_n^* u_n dq = 1.$$

This establishes that when the system is in the state u_n the average value measured for A is a_n. It is also true that a_n is the only value measured, because there is no uncertainty in what is measured:

$$\overline{(\Delta A)^2} = \overline{A^2} - (\bar{A})^2$$
$$= \int u_n^* \hat{A}^2 u_n dq - (\int u_n^* \hat{A} u_n dq)^2$$
$$= a_n \int u_n^* \hat{A} u_n dq - (a_n \int u_n^* u_n dq)^2$$
$$= a_n^2 \int u_n^* u_n dq - a_n^2 (\int u_n^* u_n dq)^2$$
$$= a_n^2 - a_n^2$$
$$= 0.$$

$\therefore$ Measurement of A gives the precise value a_n.   Q.E.D.

The functions u_n are generalized eigenfunctions and the constants a_n are the corresponding eigenvalues.[†] These eigenfunctions and eigenvalues serve a purpose parallel to that of the energy eigenfunctions ψ_n and eigenvalues E_n; they are, in other words, "A-eigenfunctions" and "A-eigenvalues." When the behavior of a system is described by a single A-eigenfunction u_n, the system is in an "A-eigenstate," and a measurement of the quantity A must, as the theorem shows, lead to the definite value a_n. So that the eigenfunctions u_n can be used to develop physically significant probability functions, they must, like other wave functions, be finite, continuous, and single-valued, and, as already noted, they must be normalized.

[†] The discussion will proceed on the assumption that all eigenvalues and eigenfunctions are discrete and not continuous. This simplifies the mathematical problems considerably, without (for our purposes) seriously limiting the physical aspects of the argument.

These eigenfunctions will be used to describe the behavior of a system at a certain time. (The question of how the theory should be developed when time becomes a variable remains to be discussed in a later section.)

In general, and most often, the state of a system is not represented by a single eigenfunction, but rather by some combination of the eigenfunctions obtained from (7). What happens when a measurement of A is made in this situation is important and fundamental enough to be stated as a postulate:

> VIII. *Eigenstates.* When a measurement of the quantity A is made it disturbs the system, so that it is forced into *one* of the A-eigenstates u_n given by
>
> $$\hat{A}u_n = a_n u_n,$$
>
> where $\hat{A}$ is the operator associated with A, and the eigenvalue a_n is measured. The full list of physically valid solutions to this equation gives *all* the eigenstates u_n and eigenvalues a_n that can possibly result when A is measured.

Two different A-eigenfunctions, u_n and u_m, may or may not belong to different eigenvalues. As in classical physics, it is not necessary that all arrangements of a system develop different values for physical quantities, such as the energy. When two different eigenfunctions have the same eigenvalues ($u_n \neq u_m$ but $a_n = a_m$), they are said to be "degenerate."

Since the eigenvalues a_n are understood as possible results of actual measurements, they clearly must be real and not complex. This is guaranteed by the Hermitian property required of all physical operators in postulate VII:

Theorem: The eigenvalues a_n produced by the Hermitian operator $\hat{A}$ in the eigenvalue equation $\hat{A}u_n = a_n u_n$ are real.

Proof:

$$\int u_n{}^* \hat{A} u_n dq = \int u_n{}^* a_n u_n dq$$
$$= a_n \int u_n{}^* u_n dq$$
$$= a_n$$

$$\int u_n{}^*\hat{A}u_n dq = \int u_n \hat{A}^* u_n{}^* dq \qquad (\dagger)$$

$$= \int u_n a_n{}^* u_n{}^* dq$$

$$= a_n{}^* \int u_n u_n{}^* dq$$

$$= a_n{}^*$$

$$a_n = a_n{}^*.$$

$\therefore$ The eigenvalues a_n must be real.   Q.E.D.

Eigenfunctions obtained from (7) have a general property known to mathematicians as "orthogonality," which turns out to be very useful for developing the general theory further. This, like the real nature of the eigenvalues, is a direct result of the Hermitian property of the operators used.

Theorem: If u_1 and u_2 are two different eigenfunctions satisfying $\hat{A}u_n = a_n u_n$, where $\hat{A}$ is an Hermitian operator, and if $a_1 \neq a_2$, then $\int u_1{}^* u_2 dq = 0$. Two eigenfunctions for which this is true are said to be "orthogonal."

Proof:

$$\int u_1{}^*\hat{A}u_2 dq = \int u_1{}^* a_2 u_2 dq$$

$$= a_2 \int u_1{}^* u_2 dq$$

$$\int u_1{}^*\hat{A}u_2 dq = \int u_2 \hat{A}^* u_1{}^* dq \qquad (\dagger)$$

$$= a_1{}^* \int u_2 u_1{}^* dq$$

$$- a_1 \int u_1{}^* u_2 dq \qquad (\ddagger)$$

From the second equation and the last one,

$$a_2 \int u_1{}^* u_2 dq = a_1 \int u_1{}^* u_2 dq$$

$$(a_1 - a_2) \int u_1{}^* u_2 dq = 0.$$

$\therefore$ Since $a_1 \neq a_2$ by hypothesis, it follows that $\int u_1{}^* u_2 dq = 0$: u_1 and u_2 are orthogonal.   Q.E.D.

The orthogonality property for nondegenerate wave functions can be combined with the normalization requirement into a single statement:

† The Hermitian property.
‡ Eigenvalues of an Hermitian operator are real.

$$\int u_n{}^* u_m dq = \delta_{nm}. \tag{8}$$

The symbol δ_{nm} stands for the "Kronecker delta," a mathematical invention which behaves in this way:

$$\delta_{nm} = 0 \quad \text{when} \quad n \neq m$$

$$\delta_{nm} = 1 \quad \text{when} \quad n = m.$$

A set of functions whose integral $\int u_n{}^* u_m dq$ is evaluated as in (8) is said to be "orthonormal."

Properly constituted *nondegenerate* eigenfunctions are therefore orthonormal. Functions with the orthonormal property can also be formed from *degenerate* eigenfunctions, but with somewhat greater difficulty.

Theorem: If two eigenfunctions u_1 and u_2 are degenerate, it is not necessarily true that they are orthogonal. However, if the new eigenfunction

$$u_2{}' = u_2 - u_1 \int u_1{}^* u_2 dq$$

is formed from u_1 and u_2, it is orthogonal to u_1:

$$\int u_1{}^* u_2{}' dq = 0.$$

Proof:

$$\int u_1{}^* u_2{}' dq = \int u_1{}^* u_2 dq - \int u_1{}^* u_1 dq \int u_1{}^* u_2 dq$$

$$= \int u_1{}^* u_2 dq - \int u_1{}^* u_2 dq \tag{$\dagger$}$$

$$= 0.$$

$\therefore u_1$ and the revised eigenfunction $u_2{}'$ are orthogonal.   Q.E.D.

The same' procedure (known to mathematicians as the "Schmidt orthogonalization procedure") can be applied to any number of degenerate eigenfunctions. The new eigenfunctions have the same eigenvalues as the original ones (they are still degenerate). If, for example, a is the eigenvalue belonging to u_1 and u_2, derived from the eigenvalue equations $\hat{A} u_1 = a u_1$ and $\hat{A} u_2 = a u_2$, then $u_2{}'$ also has this eigenvalue:

$$\hat{A} u_2{}' = \hat{A} u_2 - \hat{A} u_1 (\int u_1{}^* u_2 dq)$$

$$= a u_2 - a u_1 (\int u_1{}^* u_2 dq)$$

$$= a(u_2 - u_1 \int u_1{}^* u_2 dq)$$

$$= a u_2{}'.$$

† Assume that u_1 is normalized.

The functions formed in this way are orthogonal, but not necessarily normalized. It is always possible, however, to normalize them by attaching the right numerical factor to each function. If u_2' is not normalized, but produces the integral $\int u_2'^* u_2' dq = C$ instead, we can revise it to form another function u_2'': $u_2'' = N u_2'$, where N is a numerical factor such that $N^* N = |N|^2 = 1/C$. The normalization property now applies to the eigenfunction u_2'':

$$\int u_2''^* u_2'' dq = N^* N \int u_2'^* u_2' dq$$
$$= (1/C)(C)$$
$$= 1.$$

The general conclusion is that any set of eigenfunctions derived from an Hermitian operator, and, therefore, the eigenfunctions derived from any operator of physical significance, can be made into an orthonormal set of functions. This is true for both degenerate and nondegenerate eigenfunctions. In the subsequent discussion the sets of eigenfunctions used will always be assumed to be orthonormal, that is, (8) will be assumed to be applicable to any two eigenfunctions from the set.

In this discussion of eigenfunctions, eigenvalues, and eigenstates we are proceeding with due mathematical deliberation toward a general theory of the "superposition states" introduced in Chapter 5. The intention is to consider a system in an arbitrary situation—not necessarily an eigenstate of any kind—and to express this general state in a reasonable extension of the eigenstate language. It is clear in the first place that, no matter how arbitrary and uncertain the state, a measurement of the quantity A must force the system into one of the A-eigenstates u_n generated by (7). All of the *possible* eigenstates, and eigenvalues as well, are contained in the list of eigenfunctions u_n and eigenvalues a_n that we obtained from (7). Is it possible, then, to construct the desired arbitrary state by combining all of the possible eigenfunctions u_n? In order to go on we need another postulate.

The Expansion Postulate

A combination of the general eigenfunctions $u_n(q)$ must be made mathematically equivalent to a wave function $\psi(q)$, which describes a system at a particular time but otherwise in an arbitrary state. What kind of a combination? The statistical interpretation of quantum physics demands that all wave-function combinations must be *linear:* if u_1 and u_2 are possible eigenstates, then $u_1 + u_2$ expresses a state in which u_1 and u_2 are both possible. The physical basis for the method of linear combinations has been discussed in Chapter 4 (pages 118–20).

In mathematical parlance, the problem is to form an expansion for the arbitrary wave function $\psi(q)$, using A-eigenfunctions $u_n(q)$ in the terms of the expansion:

$$\psi = \sum_n c_n u_n, \tag{9}$$

where the coefficients c_n are constants. We hope that eigenfunctions of any type, the complete collection of eigenfunctions belonging to any observable quantity A, can be used for this purpose. This expansion, if it is possible, expresses a superposition state comprised of all the eigenstates that can be produced when a measurement of A is made. The measurement must force the system into one of these eigenstates u_n, and the value of A measured must be the corresponding single eigenvalue a_n. This is an attempt to extend the concepts and methods of quantum physics to form a general physical theory that will predict in a statistical sense what the outcome will be when any kind of an observable quantity is measured.

The expansion problem will be partly solved if a method can be devised for calculating the coefficients c_n in (9). First multiply both sides of (9) by the complex conjugate of the eigenfunction whose coefficient is wanted, say the mth one:

$$u_m{}^{*}\psi = \sum_n c_n u_m{}^{*} u_n.$$

Then integrate both sides of this equation over the accessible space:

$$\int u_m{}^{*}\psi dq = \sum_n c_n \int u_m{}^{*} u_n dq$$

$$= \sum_n c_n \delta_{mn} \tag{†}$$

$$= c_m. \tag{10}$$

This is a formula which can be used to evaluate each coefficient, starting with information on the general wave function (frequently

† The functions u_n are all orthonormal.

this information is quite rough) and on the set of eigenfunctions u_n. If all the necessary integrals $\int u_m{}^*\psi dq$ can be evaluated, the fundamental expansion (9) is feasible.

A theorem now appears possible to the effect that a general expansion such as (9) can be formed using an orthonormal set of eigenfunctions u_n obtained from any Hermitian operator $\hat{A}$. In mathematical terminology, the u_n's comprise a "complete set" if they can be used to expand an arbitrary wave function. A general proof that the eigenfunctions derived from an Hermitian operator comprise a complete set is lengthy and difficult, but one simple fact can be stated: that expansions developed from all the Hermitian operators known to quantum physics have been used widely and with impressive success. It is appropriate, therefore, to state the necessary conclusion in a final postulate:

> IX. *Eigenfunction expansions.* The eigenfunctions $u_n(q)$ obtained in the eigenvalue equation $\hat{A}u_n = a_n u_n$ from an operator $\hat{A}$ corresponding to an observable quantity A can be used in a linear expansion to express any physically valid wave function $\psi(q)$:
>
> $$\psi = \sum_n c_n u_n.$$
>
> The assumption that the expansion is possible implies that all of the necessary coefficients c_n are obtainable by using (10): $c_n = \int u_n{}^*\psi dq$.

Measurements

This rather prolonged discussion comes now to one of its major conclusions:

Theorem: Consider an observable quantity A with the associated operator $\hat{A}$, and eigenfunctions u_n and eigenvalues a_n determined by $\hat{A}u_n = a_n u_n$. If a system at a particular time is in a state determined by the expansion

$$\psi(q) = \sum_n c_n u_n(q),$$

then the average value obtained in many measurements of A is

$$\bar{A} = \sum_n (c_n{}^* c_n) a_n$$

$$= \sum_n |c_n|^2 a_n. \tag{11}$$

Each eigenvalue a_n contributes to the over-all average $\bar{A}$, and the extent of each contribution is determined by the magnitude of $|c_n|^2$.

Proof:

$$\bar{A} = \int \psi^* \hat{A} \psi \, dq$$

$$= \int \left(\sum_n c_n{}^* u_n{}^* \right) \hat{A} \left(\sum_m c_m u_m \right) dq \tag{†}$$

$$= \int \left(\sum_n c_n{}^* u_n{}^* \right) \left(\sum_m c_m \hat{A} u_m \right) dq$$

$$= \int \left(\sum_n c_n{}^* u_n{}^* \right) \left(\sum_m c_m a_m u_m \right) dq$$

$$= \sum_n c_n{}^* \left(\sum_m c_m a_m \int u_n{}^* u_m \, dq \right)$$

$$= \sum_n c_n{}^* \left(\sum_m c_m a_m \delta_{nm} \right)$$

$$\therefore \quad \bar{A} = \sum_n c_n{}^* c_n a_n$$

$$= \sum_n |c_n|^2 a_n. \qquad \text{Q.E.D.}$$

This theorem presents another aspect of the theory of measurements. From the previous discussion we found that a single measurement of A must lead to one of the precise values from the list of eigenvalues a_n. It is evident that the various eigenvalues obtained in the measurement do not all have the same probability. Equation (11) derived in this theorem now attaches to each eigenvalue a_n a probability term $|c_n|^2$, which we construct from the coefficients c_n used in the fundamental eigenfunction expansion

† Different indices n and m are used in the two summations in the integrand as a reminder that they are, in general, different numbers.

$$\psi = \sum_n c_n u_n.$$

The relative probability that the eigenvalue a_n will be obtained in the measurement of A is $|c_n|^2$.

If there are degeneracies, some of the eigenvalues will occur more than once in the summation (11). The probability of the occurrence of one of these degenerate eigenvalues therefore contains more than one of the $|c_n|^2$ terms. For instance, if $a_1 = a_2 = a_3$ (u_1, u_2, and u_3 are degenerate), then the probability that this eigenvalue will be obtained in a measurement is $|c_1|^2 + |c_2|^2 + |c_3|^2$.

Like the probability functions used before, the quantities $|c_n|^2$ introduced here must be real and positive (or zero). And when all the possible $|c_n|^2$ terms are summed they must, as expressions of probability, total unity:

$$\sum_n |c_n|^2 = 1. \tag{12}$$

This last statement has a proof similar to that of the theorem just proved. Begin with the normalization property required of the arbitrary wave function ψ:

$$\int \psi^* \psi \, dq = 1.$$

Use of the expansion for ψ leads to

$$\int \left(\sum_n c_n^* u_n^* \right) \left(\sum_m c_m u_m \right) dq = 1$$

$$\sum_n c_n^* \left(\sum_m c_m \int u_n^* u_m dq \right) = 1$$

$$\sum_n c_n^* \left(\sum_m c_m \delta_{nm} \right) = 1$$

$$\sum_n c_n^* c_n = 1$$

$$\sum_n |c_n|^2 = 1.$$

Thus far time has not been a variable factor. The wave function ψ, provided to describe arbitrary behavior of a system, was assumed to apply at a particular time. The eigenfunctions u_n and the coefficients c_n in the expansion

$$\sum_n c_n u_n$$

made equivalent to this wave function must of course be appropriate to the same particular time.

Now, if the same kind of analysis is developed·at a different time, the wave function ψ is, in general, different, and so also is the expansion

$$\sum_n c_n u_n.$$

It may prove possible to place all of the time dependence in the coefficients of the expansion. Write these now as $\alpha_n(t)$, and write the expansion for a time-dependent wave function as

$$\Psi(q,t) = \sum_n \alpha_n(t) u_n(q). \tag{13}$$

The coefficients $\alpha_n(t)$ are calculated in much the same way as the c_n-coefficients. Multiply both sides of (13) by the complex conjugate of the eigenfunction, say the mth one, whose coefficient is to be calculated, and integrate the result over the accessible space:

$$\int u_m{}^*(q)\Psi(q,t)dq = \sum_n \alpha_n(t) \int u_m{}^*(q)u_n(q)dq$$

$$= \sum_n \alpha_n(t)\delta_{mn}$$

$$= \alpha_m(t).$$

The further theory is developed in a way parallel to the analysis we used when time was not a factor. The quantity $|\alpha_n|^2$ is found to have a probability interpretation: it is the probability that, at time t, a measurement of A will produce the eigenvalue a_n, this being the eigenvalue belonging to the eigenfunction u_n whose coefficient in the expansion at time t is $\alpha_n(t)$.

Another, and more useful, approach to problems in which time is a variable is to consider that all of the time dependence in the Hamiltonian $\hat{H}$ is contained in a small term $\hat{v}(t)$ added to a time-independent part $\hat{H}_0$:

$$\hat{H} = \hat{H}_0 + \hat{v}(t).$$

In physical jargon the v-term is called a "perturbation." The "unperturbed" system is expressed by $\hat{H}_0$; the Schrödinger equation, written and solved with this Hamiltonian alone,

$$i\hbar\partial\Psi_n^{(0)}/\partial t = \hat{H}_0\Psi_n^{(0)},$$

defines the unperturbed states $\Psi_n^{(0)}$. The "perturbed" states Ψ are solutions of the Schrödinger equation written with the full (and now time-dependent) Hamiltonian:

$$i\hbar\partial\Psi/\partial t = \hat{H}\Psi$$
$$= [\hat{H}_0 + \hat{v}(t)]\Psi.$$

To solve this equation write an expansion in the previously determined unperturbed wave functions $\Psi_n^{(0)}$:

$$\Psi = \sum_n \alpha_n(t)\Psi_n^{(0)}.$$

The expansion coefficients α_n, and the unperturbed wave functions as well, are dependent on time.

Changes are pictured as transitions from one of the unperturbed states $\Psi_n^{(0)}$ to another. An electron might, for example, be induced by the perturbation to move from the first state $\Psi_1^{(0)}$ to one of the other states, $\Psi_2^{(0)}$, $\Psi_3^{(0)}$, etc. Before the effect of the perturbation is felt, $\Psi = \Psi_1^{(0)}$, $\alpha_1 = 1$, and all of the other coefficients vanish. After the perturbation appears there is an appreciable probability (but still a small one if the perturbation itself is small, as it should be) that the electron can be found in a different state (not $\Psi_1^{(0)}$, but $\Psi_2^{(0)}$, $\Psi_3^{(0)}$, . . .) and this is clearly reflected in the magnitudes of the α_n's for the different states. If α_2 (rather, $\alpha_2^*\alpha_2 = |\alpha_2|^2$, which forms the true probability function) is relatively large, the transition $\Psi_1^{(0)} \rightarrow \Psi_2^{(0)}$ is an important one. From this simple scheme a large part of the theory of atomic spectra can be developed. Further discussion on this matter becomes rather involved, however, and lies beyond the scope of this book. The reader should consult another text or the sequel volume in this series.

Simultaneous Measurements

So far, the theory presented gives a statistical account of what to expect in a measurement insofar as a *single* quantity such as the energy is concerned. But the uncertainty principle dictates that many measurements inescapably have an effect on more than one physical quantity. These are measurements of "incompatible" quantities: one quantity cannot be measured without interfering with one or more others. An energy measurement affects not only the energy but also the position in time. A momentum measurement has an effect on the position in space as well as the momentum. How does uncertainty, and the incompatibility it implies, fit into the mathematical scheme? If uncertainty is, as it seems, the soul of quantum physics, we have not done it justice, at least in the mathematical discussion.

There are two questions to be answered: first, which observable quantities are, and which are not, of the incompatible variety, and then, for those that are incompatible, what are the domains of uncertainty in measurements of varying degrees of exactness? An answer to the first question appears in this section, and this answer contains a valuable criterion for recognizing those (compatible) quantities that can be measured simultaneously with exactness. Until now the emphasis has been on quantities which could not be measured simultaneously; but we need a theory to deal with the equally important quantities that *are* susceptible to simultaneous measurement. The answer to the second question, the subject of the section following this one, presents a more exact and general formulation of the uncertainty principle presented earlier in a largely qualitative fashion.

First we search for functions that serve as eigenfunctions at the same time for two different operators associated with two different observable quantities. Suppose a quantity A is measured whose associated operator is $\hat{A}$. As a result of the measurement the system is forced into an eigenstate expressed by an eigenfunction u_n, and an eigenvalue a_n is measured. The operator, the eigenfunctions, and the eigenvalues are all related by the familiar equation $\hat{A}u_n = a_n u_n$. Now consider the further possibility: can these *same* eigenfunctions serve to describe *another* observable quantity, measured simultaneously with the first one? Designate the second quantity as B, its operator as $\hat{B}$, and its eigenvalues as b_n. When a measurement of B is made can it lead to the same eigenstate u_n and also to one of the eigenvalues b_n? The answer is yes, if we can find eigenfunctions u_n that are simultaneously solutions of

$$\hat{A}u_n = a_n u_n \qquad \text{and} \qquad \hat{B}u_n = b_n u_n. \qquad (14)$$

Theorem: If two operators $\hat{A}$ and $\hat{B}$ associated with the observable quantities A and B commute, that is, if for any suitable operand u

$$\hat{A}\hat{B}u = \hat{B}\hat{A}u, \tag{15}$$

then eigenfunctions that belong to $\hat{A}$ are also eigenfunctions of $\hat{B}$; a set of eigenfunctions can be found the members of which satisfy both of the equations (14).

Proof: The proof is quite simple if either of the operators, say $\hat{A}$, has nondegenerate eigenvalues. Then $\hat{A}u_n = a_n u_n$ can be written with a single eigenfunction u_n attached to each eigenvalue a_n. Apply the second operator to this equation and then use the commutation relation:

$$\hat{B}(\hat{A}u_n) = \hat{B}(a_n u_n)$$

$$\hat{A}(\hat{B}u_n) = a_n(\hat{B}u_n).$$

Make a comparison now of $\hat{A}u_n = a_n u_n$ with the last equation derived, $\hat{A}(\hat{B}_{un}) = a_n(\hat{B}u_n)$. Since the eigenvalue a_n belongs only to the eigenfunction u_n, these two equations must be the same, except possibly for a multiplied constant. We conclude that

$$\hat{B}u_n = b_n u_n,$$

where b_n is the constant mentioned: there are simultaneous eigenfunctions as required.

If neither operator has nondegenerate eigenvalues, the proof becomes lengthier. Suppose now that an eigenvalue a belongs to m eigenfunctions $v_1, v_2, \ldots, v_m$:

$$\hat{A}v_j = av_j \qquad (j = 1, 2, \ldots, m).$$

The subscript j implies that there are m such equations; the eigenvalue a is "m-fold" degenerate. Apply the second operator $\hat{B}$ to $\hat{A}v_j$ for any value of j, say i, and make use of the commutation relation:

$$\hat{B}\hat{A}v_i = \hat{B}av_i$$

$$\hat{A}(\hat{B}v_i) = a(\hat{B}v_i),$$

showing that $\hat{B}v_i$ is an eigenfunction of $\hat{A}$. Comparison of the two equations $\hat{A}v_j = av_j$ and $\hat{A}(\hat{B}v_i) = a(\hat{B}v_i)$ is not as straightforward as before, however. The second equation is valid if $\hat{B}v_i$ is any linear combination of the m degenerate eigenfunctions:

$$\hat{B}v_i = \sum_{j=1}^{m} \beta_{ij}v_j, \tag{16}$$

in which the β_{ij} are constant coefficients. Equation (16) is not a simple eigenvalue equation. The original functions v_j are therefore not necessarily simultaneous eigenfunctions of both $\hat{A}$ and $\hat{B}$. But look for a linear combination of the v_j,

$$u = \sum_i^m c_i v_i,$$

which serves the required purpose. The new function must be an eigenfunction of $\hat{B}$, $\hat{B}u = bu$, and also an eigenfunction of $\hat{A}$, $\hat{A}u = au$.

Return to the expression (16) for $\hat{B}v_i$ and multiply by one of the constants c_i,

$$c_i \hat{B} v_i = \sum_j^m c_i \beta_{ij} v_j$$

$$\hat{B}(c_i v_i) = \sum_j^m \beta_{ij} c_i v_j.$$

There are m of these equations. Add them all together, summing over the index i:

$$\sum_i^m \hat{B}(c_i v_i) = \sum_{i,j}^m \beta_{ij} c_i v_j$$

$$\hat{B} \sum_i^m (c_i v_i) = \sum_{i,j}^m \beta_{ij} c_i v_j$$

$$\hat{B}u = \sum_{i,j}^m \beta_{ij} c_i v_j. \qquad (17)$$

If the function u is to serve as an eigenfunction of $\hat{B}$, the left side of the last equation must be equivalent to bu: $\hat{B}u = bu$. And the same can be said for the right side of the equation:

$$\sum_{i,j}^m c_i \beta_{ij} v_j = bu$$

$$= b \sum_j^m c_j v_j, \qquad (\dagger)$$

or

$$\sum_{i,j}^m c_i \beta_{ij} v_j - b \sum_j^m c_j v_j = 0,$$

or

$$\sum_j^m \left(\sum_i^m c_i \beta_{ij} - b c_j \right) v_j = 0.$$

† The index in the summation for u has been changed from i to j. Since this index disappears in the summation process its symbol is arbitrary; anything convenient can be used.

Because in general $v_j \neq 0$, the expression in the parentheses must vanish for each value of j:

$$\sum_i^m c_i \beta_{ij} = b c_j \quad (j = 1, 2, \ldots, m).\qquad (18a)$$

These are m homogeneous, linear equations in the m unknowns $c_1, c_2, \ldots, c_m$, which have the following appearance when written in expanded form:

$$(\beta_{11} - b)c_1 + \beta_{21}c_2 + \beta_{31}c_3 + \cdots + \beta_{m1}c_m = 0$$

$$\beta_{12}c_1 + (\beta_{22}\ \ b)c_2 + \beta_{32}c_3 + \cdots + \beta_{m2}c_m = 0$$

$$\beta_{13}c_1 + \beta_{23}c_2 + (\beta_{33} - b)c_3 + \cdots + \beta_{m3}c_m = 0 \quad (\dagger) \quad (18b)$$

$$\vdots$$

$$\beta_{1m}c_1 + \beta_{2m}c_2 + \beta_{3m}c_3 + \cdots + (\beta_{mm} - b)c_m = 0.$$

Nontrivial solutions to these equations can be found if the following determinantal equation holds:

$$\begin{vmatrix} \beta_{11} - b & \beta_{21} & \beta_{31} & \cdots & \beta_{m1} \\ \beta_{12} & \beta_{22} - b & \beta_{32} & \cdots & \beta_{m2} \\ \beta_{13} & \beta_{23} & \beta_{33} - b & \cdots & \beta_{m3} \\ & & \vdots & & \\ \beta_{1m} & \beta_{2m} & \beta_{3m} & \cdots & \beta_{mm} - b \end{vmatrix} = 0.$$

This is an $m \times m$ determinant which leads to an equation for the eigenvalue b of the mth degree and therefore to m roots $b = b_1$, $b_2, \ldots, b_m$. Each one of these values of b is separately substituted back into the original set of simultaneous equations (18b); m sets of the constants c_i and m eigenfunctions u_i are obtained, one set for each of the m values of b. A second subscript is used to label and distinguish these:

$\dagger\, j = 1$ in the first equation, $j = 2$ in the second equation, etc., down to $j = m$ in the last equation.

$$c_{11}, c_{12}, \ldots, c_{1m} \quad \text{and} \quad u_1 = \sum_j^m c_{1j} v_j \quad \text{from} \quad b_1$$

$$c_{21}, c_{22}, \ldots, c_{2m} \quad \text{and} \quad u_2 = \sum_j^m c_{2j} v_j \quad \text{from} \quad b_2$$

.

.

.

$$c_{m1}, c_{m2}, \ldots, c_{mm} \quad \text{and} \quad u_m = \sum_j^m c_{mj} v_j \quad \text{from} \quad b_m.$$

For one of these m sets, say the kth one, the eigenfunction expansion is

$$u_k = \sum_i^m c_{kj} v_j,$$

and it is found from the original linear simultaneous equations after adding the second subscript in (18a), that

$$\sum_i^m \beta_{ij} c_{ki} = b_k c_{kj} \qquad (j = 1, 2, \ldots, m).$$

The corresponding eigenvalue equation is formed by adding the second subscript to (17):

$$\hat{B} u_k = \sum_{i,j}^m \beta_{ij} c_{ki} v_j$$

$$= \sum_j^m \left(\sum_i^m \beta_{ij} c_{ki} \right) v_j$$

$$= \sum_j^m (b_k c_{kj}) v_j$$

$$= b_k \sum_j^m c_{kj} v_j$$

$$= b_k u_k.$$

This demonstrates explicitly that the m functions u_k ($k = 1, 2, \ldots, m$) are eigenfunctions of the operator $\hat{B}$ and that the m values of b_k obtained from the determinantal equation are the corresponding eigenvalues. These same functions are also eigenfunctions of the operator $\hat{A}$:

$$\hat{A}u_k = \hat{A}\left(\sum_j^m c_{kj}v_j\right)$$

$$= \sum_j^m c_{kj}\hat{A}v_j$$

$$= \sum_j^m c_{kj}av_j$$

$$= a\sum_j^m c_{kj}v_j$$

$$= au_k.$$

The proof of the theorem is therefore accomplished. If two operators $\hat{A}$ and $\hat{B}$ commute, functions can be found which are simultaneous eigenfunctions of both $\hat{A}$ and $\hat{B}$. A measurement that forces a system into an eigenstate characterized by one of these eigenfunctions produces an exact value (an eigenvalue) for both the quantities A and B. Q.E.D.

The converse of this theorem can be proved with much less difficulty.

Theorem: If two operators $\hat{A}$ and $\hat{B}$ have simultaneous eigenfunctions, they commute.

Proof: By hypothesis, $\hat{A}u_n = a_n u_n$ and $\hat{B}u_n = b_n u_n$. Apply operator $\hat{B}$ to the first equation and $\hat{A}$ to the second:

$$\hat{B}(\hat{A}u_n) = \hat{B}(a_n u_n)$$

$$= a_n(\hat{B}u_n)$$

$$= a_n b_n u_n$$

$$\hat{A}(\hat{B}u_n) = \hat{A}(b_n u_n)$$

$$= b_n(\hat{A}u_n)$$

$$= b_n a_n u_n.$$

Since $a_n b_n = b_n a_n$, it follows that $\hat{A}\hat{B}u_n = \hat{B}\hat{A}u_n$. Therefore the operators $\hat{A}$ and $\hat{B}$ commute. Q.E.D.

With the proofs completed, the implications of these theorems can be stated quite simply. If two operators $\hat{A}$ and $\hat{B}$ commute, if $\hat{A}\hat{B} = \hat{B}\hat{A}$, then simultaneous eigenstates can be found in which both of the quantities A and B corresponding to the operators have precise values. The simple commutation property $\hat{A}\hat{B} = \hat{B}\hat{A}$ therefore determines whether or not two observable quantities A and B are compatible, whether or not they can be measured simultaneously and exactly. To shorten the notation, the "commutator" $[\hat{A},\hat{B}]$ of two operators $\hat{A}$ and $\hat{B}$ is defined:

$$[\hat{A},\hat{B}] = \hat{A}\hat{B} - \hat{B}\hat{A}.$$

If the operators $\hat{A}$ and $\hat{B}$ are associated with compatible quantities then $[\hat{A},\hat{B}] = 0$.

A number of examples of commuting operators can be found. Two different components of the momentum, for example, those whose operators are $\hat{p}_x = -i\hbar\partial/\partial x$ and $\hat{p}_y = -i\hbar\partial/\partial y$, are easily shown to be compatible: $[\hat{p}_x,\hat{p}_y] = 0$. Position operators, that is, the variables x, y, and z, commute with the operators for momentum components so long as the pairs are taken for different directions:

$$[\hat{p}_y,\hat{x}] = 0, [\hat{p}_z,\hat{x}] = 0, \text{ etc.}$$

The energy E (whose operator is $\hat{E} = i\hbar\partial/\partial t$) and the momentum components are also compatible:

$$[\hat{E},\hat{p}_x] = [\hat{E},\hat{p}_y] = [\hat{E},\hat{p}_z] = 0.$$

On the other hand, when position and momentum operators corresponding to the *same* direction are paired they are no longer commuting:

$$[\hat{p}_x,\hat{x}] = [\hat{p}_y,\hat{y}] = [\hat{p}_z,\hat{z}] = -i\hbar.$$

The energy operator and the time operator are also noncommuting: $[\hat{E},\hat{t}] = i\hbar$. Energy and time, and parallel position and momentum components, are incompatible. They are, in fact, quantities of the complementary type mentioned earlier. That the commutators do not vanish for the associated operators expresses in a concise mathematical way that these quantities cannot be measured simultaneously with precision.

A General Version of the Uncertainty Principle

More needs to be said about the so-called incompatible observable quantities whose operators are noncommuting. Theorems have been proved which show that these quantities cannot be measured simultaneously with unlimited precision. If there are limits on the precision of such measurements what exactly are these limits? A famous theorem answers this question in an exact and entirely general way. The conditions of the theorem include not only the case of incompatible quantities whose operators do not commute, but also the case of compatible quantities for which the associated operators are commuting.

Theorem: If A and B are two observable quantities whose associated Hermitian operators are $\hat{A}$ and $\hat{B}$, then the mean-square uncertainties,†

$$\overline{(\Delta A)^2} = \int \Psi^* (\hat{A} - \bar{A})^2 \Psi dq$$

$$\overline{(\Delta B)^2} = \int \Psi^* (\hat{B} - \bar{B})^2 \Psi dq,$$

are related by the inequality

$$\overline{(\Delta A)^2} \, \overline{(\Delta B)^2} \geqslant -(\overline{[A,B]})^2/4,$$

where $\overline{[A,B]}$ is the average quantity $\int \Psi^* (\hat{A}\hat{B} - \hat{B}\hat{A}) \Psi dq$.

Proof: If $\hat{G}$ is an Hermitian operator, then

$$\int \Psi_1^* \hat{G} \Psi_2 dq = \int \Psi_2 \hat{G}^* \Psi_1^* dq$$

$$= \int \Psi_2 (\hat{G}\Psi_1)^* dq,$$

but if $\hat{G}$ is *not* Hermitian, then *another* operator $\hat{G}^+$ must be written in the integrand on the right side of the equation:

$$\int \Psi_1^* \hat{G} \Psi_2 dq = \int \Psi_2 (\hat{G}^+ \Psi_1)^* dq.$$

In mathematical parlance, $\hat{G}^+$ is called the "adjoint" of $\hat{G}$. Notice that Hermitian operators are "self-adjoint": $\hat{G} = \hat{G}^+$. An important inequality can be proved for the average of the quantity whose operator is the product $\hat{G}\hat{G}^+$:

$$\overline{(GG^+)} = \int \Psi^* (\hat{G}\hat{G}^+) \Psi dq$$

$$= \int \Psi^* \hat{G} (\hat{G}^+ \Psi) dq$$

$$= \int (\hat{G}^+ \Psi)(\hat{G}^+ \Psi)^* dq \qquad (‡)$$

$$= \int |\hat{G}^+ \Psi|^2 dq.$$

The integrand is simply the square of the magnitude of the complex quantity $\hat{G}^+ \Psi$. Since the square is positive, so are the integrand and the integral positive, and it follows that $\overline{(GG^+)} \geqslant 0$.

† Return to the discussion on page 159 for a justification of the method used to calculate the average uncertainties.
‡ Use the definition of the adjoint.

Now introduce two Hermitian operators $\hat{A}$ and $\hat{B}$, and form the complex operator $\hat{A} + i\lambda\hat{B}$, where λ is a real number. The adjoint of this is

$$(\hat{A} + i\lambda\hat{B})^+ = \hat{A}^+ - i\lambda\hat{B}^+,$$

as is demonstrated below:

$$\int\Psi_1^*(\hat{A} + i\lambda\hat{B})\Psi_2 dq = \int\Psi_1^*\hat{A}\Psi_2 dq + i\lambda\int\Psi_1^*\hat{B}\Psi_2 dq$$

$$= \int\Psi_2(\hat{A}^+\Psi_1)^* dq + i\lambda\int\Psi_2(\hat{B}^+\Psi_1)^* dq \qquad (\dagger)$$

$$= \int\Psi_2(\hat{A}^+\Psi_1)^* dq + \int\Psi_2(-i\lambda\hat{B}^+\Psi_1)^* dq$$

$$= \int\Psi_2[(\hat{A}^+ - i\lambda\hat{B}^+)\Psi_1]^* dq.$$

Since $\hat{A}$ and $\hat{B}$ are Hermitian and therefore self-adjoint, $\hat{A}^+ = \hat{A}$ and $\hat{B}^+ = \hat{B}$ and $(\hat{A} + i\lambda\hat{B})^+ = \hat{A} - i\lambda\hat{B}$. The inequality $\overline{(GG^+)} \geqslant 0$ just proved for any operator $\hat{G}$ and its adjoint $\hat{G}^+$ is now stated for $\hat{A} + i\lambda\hat{B}$ whose adjoint is $\hat{A} - i\lambda\hat{B}$:

$$\overline{[(A + i\lambda B)(A - i\lambda B)]} \geqslant 0,$$

or
$$\overline{A^2} + \lambda^2\overline{B^2} - i\lambda\overline{(AB - BA)} \geqslant 0.$$

Since $\overline{A^2}$ and $\overline{B^2}$ for Hermitian operators must be real and positive, the same must also be true for the last term in the inequality, $-i\lambda\overline{(AB - BA)}$; it follows that $\overline{(AB - BA)}$ is purely imaginary.

The form of the inequality just calculated is now used to calculate the uncertainties by replacing $\hat{A}$ with the new operator $\hat{A} - \bar{A}$, and $\hat{B}$ with the operator $\hat{B} - \bar{B}$. These operators lead to the following replacements for $\overline{A^2}$ and $\overline{B^2}$:

for $\overline{A^2}$, $\overline{(\Delta A)^2} = \overline{(A - \bar{A})^2} = \int\Psi^*(\hat{A} - \bar{A})^2\Psi dq$

for $\overline{B^2}$, $\overline{(\Delta B)^2} = \overline{(B - \bar{B})^2} = \int\Psi^*(\hat{B} - \bar{B})^2\Psi dq,$

which have the form and designations introduced in Chapter 5 to calculate the mean-square uncertainties. The quantity $\overline{(\Delta A\Delta B - \Delta B\Delta A)}$, which replaces $\overline{(AB - BA)}$, simplifies as follows:

$$\overline{(\Delta A\Delta B - \Delta B\Delta A)} = \overline{[(A - \bar{A})(B - \bar{B}) - (B - \bar{B})(A - \bar{A})]}$$

$$= \overline{(AB - BA)}.$$

† The definition of the adjoint is used.

The inequality now becomes

$$\overline{(\Delta A)^2} + \lambda^2\overline{(\Delta B)^2} - i\lambda\overline{(AB - BA)} \geqslant 0.$$

Multiply this by $\overline{(\Delta B)^2}$,

$$\overline{(\Delta A)^2}\ \overline{(\Delta B)^2} + \lambda^2\overline{(\Delta B)^2}\ \overline{(\Delta B)^2} - i\lambda\overline{(AB - BA)}\ \overline{(\Delta B)^2} \geqslant 0,$$

so that

$$\overline{(\Delta A)^2}\ \overline{(\Delta B)^2} \geqslant i\lambda\overline{(AB - BA)}\ \overline{(\Delta B)^2} - \lambda^2\overline{(\Delta B)^2}\ \overline{(\Delta B)^2}.$$

The product $\overline{(\Delta A)^2}\ \overline{(\Delta B)^2}$ is least when the equality holds in the last statement and when, at the same time, λ has a value that makes the expression

$$i\lambda\overline{(AB - BA)}\ \overline{(\Delta B)^2} - \lambda^2\overline{(\Delta B)^2}$$

have its minimum value. This value of λ is found to be

$$\lambda = i\overline{(AB - BA)}/2\overline{(\Delta B)^2}, \qquad (\dagger)$$

and the minimum value of the uncertainty product is

$$\overline{(\Delta A)^2}\ \overline{(\Delta B)^2} = -\overline{(AB - BA)}^2/4.$$

The general statement, including the inequality, is

$$\overline{(\Delta A)^2}\ \overline{(\Delta B)^2} \geqslant -\overline{(AB - BA)}^2/4$$

or

$$\overline{(\Delta A)^2}\ \overline{(\Delta B)^2} \geqslant -\overline{([A,B])}^2/4. \qquad \text{Q.E.D.}$$

This is still a mathematical result, valid for *any* Hermitian operators $\hat{A}$ and $\hat{B}$. It takes the familiar form known in quantum physics when the average commutator $\overline{[A,B]}$ is evaluated for the operators of quantum physics. Consider, for example, the x-component of the momentum and the x-variable of position. The commutator for the associated operators is $[\hat{p}_x,\hat{x}] = -i\hbar$ (see page 202), so that

$$\overline{[p_x,x]} = \int \Psi^*[\hat{p}_x,\hat{x}]\Psi dq = -i\hbar \int \Psi^*\Psi dq = -i\hbar,$$

and

$$\overline{(\Delta p_x)^2}\ \overline{(\Delta x)^2} \geqslant \hbar^2/4.$$

† Differentiate $[i\lambda\overline{(AB - BA)}\ \overline{(\Delta B)^2} - \lambda^2\overline{(\Delta B)^2}\ \overline{(\Delta B)^2}]$ with respect to λ and set the result equal to zero.

If $\overline{(\Delta p_x)}$ and $\overline{(\Delta x)}$ are taken to be "root-mean-square" quantities,

$$\overline{(\Delta p_x)} = \sqrt{\overline{(\Delta p_x)^2}} \quad \text{and} \quad \overline{(\Delta x)} = \sqrt{\overline{(\Delta x)^2}},$$

this inequality takes a more familiar form:

$$\overline{(\Delta p_x)}\,\overline{(\Delta x)} \geqslant \hbar/2.$$

The energy and time variables can be treated similarly. For the energy operator $\hat{E} = i\hbar\partial/\partial t$ and the time operator $\hat{t} = t$ the operator commutator is $[\hat{E},\hat{t}] = i\hbar$ (see page 202), the average of the commutator is $\overline{[E,t]} = i\hbar$, and the uncertainty statement is $\overline{(\Delta E)^2}\,\overline{(\Delta t)^2} \geqslant \hbar^2/4$ or $\overline{(\Delta E)}\,\overline{(\Delta t)} \geqslant \hbar/2$, with $\overline{(\Delta E)}$ and $\overline{(\Delta t)}$ taken to be root-mean-square quantities.

If the operators of two physical quantities A and B are of the commuting type, then $[\hat{A},\hat{B}] = \overline{[A,B]} = 0$; the uncertainty product can vanish: $\overline{(\Delta A)}\,\overline{(\Delta B)} \geqslant 0$. Two such quantities can be measured simultaneously with precision, so that the uncertainty product vanishes $\overline{(\Delta A)}\,\overline{(\Delta B)} = 0$. This was, of course, also established in the previous theorem, together with the existence of simultaneous eigenstates.

A Quantum Equation of Motion

Here is one more contribution to this collection of broad, general theorems. This one has a pleasantly short proof—just two sentences. It frames an equation which is something of a quantum version of an equation of motion. It describes motion in the sense that it shows the time rate of change of a physical quantity. The physical quantity is represented in its real form, as an average value.

Theorem: Consider any physical quantity A whose associated operator $\hat{A}$ is Hermitian and does not depend on time, and whose average value is $\bar{A} = \int \Psi^* \hat{A} \Psi dq$. The time rate of change in this average value is given by

$$d\bar{A}/dt = (i/\hbar)\int \Psi^*[\hat{H},\hat{A}]\Psi dq = (i/\hbar)\overline{[H,A]},$$

where $\hat{H}$, the Hamiltonian operator, is also assumed to be independent of time.

Proof: Since the operator $\hat{A}$ does not depend on time,

$$d\bar{A}/dt = \int[(\partial\Psi^*/\partial t)\hat{A}\Psi + \Psi^*\hat{A}(\partial\Psi/\partial t)]dq.$$

The Schrödinger equation provides

$$\partial\Psi/\partial t = (1/i\hbar)\hat{H}\Psi \qquad \text{and} \qquad \partial\Psi^*/\partial t = (-1/i\hbar)(\hat{H}\Psi)^*$$

for the time derivatives, so that

$$d\bar{A}/dt = \int[(-1/i\hbar)(\hat{H}\Psi)^*\hat{A}\Psi + (1/i\hbar)\Psi^*\hat{A}(\hat{H}\Psi)]dq$$

$$= (-1/i\hbar)\int[(\hat{H}\Psi)^*\hat{A}\Psi - \Psi^*\hat{A}(\hat{H}\Psi)]dq$$

$$= (-1/i\hbar)\int\Psi^*(\hat{H}\hat{A} - \hat{A}\hat{H})\Psi dq \qquad\qquad (\dagger)$$

$$= (-1/i\hbar)\overline{(HA - AH)}$$

$$= (i/\hbar)\overline{[H,A]}. \qquad \text{Q.E.D.}$$

Apply this theorem first to the energy. The operator used for $\hat{A}$ in the theorem is the Hamiltonian, and therefore

$$d\bar{E}/dt = (i/\hbar)\overline{[H,H]}$$

$$= (i/\hbar)\overline{(HH - HH)}$$

$$= 0.$$

Thus the average energy is conserved: it is constant in time. This is the quantum counterpart of the classical theorem of conservation of energy. The result applies, of course, only when the Hamiltonian has no explicit dependence on time, the quantum condition for conservative behavior.

Any other physical operator $\hat{F}$ that is independent of time and commutes with the Hamiltonian, $[\hat{H},\hat{F}] = 0$, has an average value $\bar{F} = \int\Psi^*\hat{F}\Psi dq$ that is also constant in time:

$$d\bar{F}/dt = (i/\hbar)\overline{[H,F]}$$

$$= 0.$$

This is a "constant of motion." If, initially, F has the eigenvalue f_n, then it will continue with this value as long as the system is not disturbed.

There is apparent now a general and strikingly simple method for the description of a great variety of physical systems: physical descriptions are formulated (wherever possible) using *time-inde-*

† The first term in the brackets is transformed from $(\hat{H}\Psi)^*\hat{A}\Psi$ to $\Psi^*\hat{H}\hat{A}\Psi$ as follows:

$$\int(\hat{H}\Psi)^*\hat{A}\Psi dq = \int(\hat{A}\Psi)(\hat{H}\Psi)^* dq \qquad \text{(rearrangement of factors)}$$

$$= \int\Psi^*\hat{H}(\hat{A}\Psi)dq \qquad (\hat{H} \text{ is Hermitian})$$

$$= \int\Psi^*\hat{H}\hat{A}\Psi dq.$$

pendent quantities *whose operators commute with each other and with the Hamiltonian operator.* This assures, as the last three theorems have shown, that states exist which are simultaneous eigenstates of the energy and of all the commuting quantities, that the energy and the commuting quantities can have simultaneous eigenvalues, and that these are invariant in time. A large part of the theory of quantum physics is guided by this simple rule.

The Dirac Equation

The Schrödinger equation and the operator method built around it have a serious flaw: there is no recognition of the principles of special relativity. The energy of a particle is taken to be

$$E = p^2/2m + V \quad \text{or} \quad E - V = p^2/2m.$$

Particles of comparatively low energy, the electrons in an atom, for example, are more or less accurately described in this way. But highly energetic particles, such as the electrons produced by accelerators (with hundreds of thousands or millions of electron volts of energy), no longer conform even approximately to this energy equation. To discuss electrons in the realm of relativistic behavior a complete change in the basic energy equation becomes necessary. The energy equation is no longer $E - V = p^2/2m$; it is, instead,

$$(E - V)^2 = c^2 p^2 + m_0{}^2 c^4, \tag{19}$$

where m_0 is the electron's rest mass.

Schrödinger was well aware of the limitations of the classical $E - V = p^2/2m$ energy equation. In fact, his first attempts at the development of a wave equation were based on the relativistic expression (19). Transformation of this equation to a differential form, with the operators $\hat{E} = i\hbar\partial/\partial t$ and $\hat{p}^2 = -\hbar^2\nabla^2$, leads to

$$(i\hbar\partial/\partial t - V)^2\Psi = -\hbar^2 c^2\nabla^2\Psi + m_0{}^2 c^4\Psi. \tag{20}$$

It seemed to Schrödinger that the implications of this equation, when it was extended to the case of the hydrogen atom, were inconsistent with experimental behavior. He could find no interpretive scheme which made physical sense in all aspects of the equation. He lost faith in the equation's usefulness and even abandoned the entire wave mechanics project for several months. Finally he came upon the nonrelativistic wave equation, which we saw in Chapter 5, and found it to be highly effective where the relativistic equation had apparently failed.

Schrödinger was, in fact, on the right track in his attempt to develop a differential equation from (19), but considerable mathematical skill and physical insight were needed to develop a complete theory around the peculiarities of this equation. Probably the theory of electron behavior available at the time was unequal to the task. It was natural for Schrödinger to turn to the simpler task of forming a theory around the nonrelativistic equation.

A relativistic version of quantum physics, in which equation (19) is correctly interpreted, was invented in 1928 by Paul Dirac. Dirac's ingenious handling of the mathematical problem and his extraordinary faith in the theoretical equations, even though they led him to some practically unbelievable conclusions, make his theory an achievement that ranks with Schrödinger's.

Dirac's method of handling the relativistic energy equation (19) can be seen by first working toward a suitable Hamiltonian operator. Solve equation (19) for the total energy E:

$$E = V \pm c\sqrt{p^2 + m_0^2 c^2}. \tag{21}$$

A crucial peculiarity appears here. When the square root is taken, *two* ways of writing the total energy appear, corresponding to positive and negative versions of $E - V$, the kinetic energy:

$$E - V = \pm c\sqrt{p^2 + m_0^2 c^2}.$$

Classical physics can make no sense of negative kinetic energy, but quantum physics admits negative values for the kinetic energy, as we have seen when electrons are confined by potential energy wells (see page 171). Consequently there is no reason to reject the negative sign in equation (21). We must be willing to accept two kinds of energies: they are conveniently called negative and positive energy states, referring to the negative and positive kinetic parts of the energy.

The relativistic Hamiltonian operator, like all Hamiltonians, must express the total energy in operator language. We begin, therefore, with the total energy expression indicated by (21), written now with the symbol H:

$$H = V \pm c\sqrt{p^2 + m_0^2 c^2}. \tag{22}$$

To proceed from this point, as Dirac did, required a creative mathematical talent of exceptional genius. No useful operator can be fashioned directly from (22) with the familiar momentum operators such as $\hat{p}_x = -i\hbar\partial/\partial x$, because the resulting Hamiltonian used in an energy eigenvalue equation such as $\hat{H}\psi = E\psi$ is decidedly nonlinear in the variable ψ. Some device must be invented to *make* equation (22) linear.

Dirac resorted to a procedure which seems quite simple. Introduce four coefficients, α_x, α_y, α_z, and β, that convert the expression

$$p^2 + m_0^2 c^2 = p_x^2 + p_y^2 + p_z^2 + m_0^2 c^2,$$

whose square root is required in (22), into a perfect square: write

$$p_x^2 + p_y^2 + p_z^2 + m_0^2 c^2 = (\alpha_x p_x + \alpha_y p_y + \alpha_z p_z + \beta m_0 c)^2.$$

If the α and β coefficients can be found, (22) is appropriately linear,

$$H = V \pm (\alpha_x c p_x + \alpha_y c p_y + \alpha_z c p_z + \beta m_0 c^2),$$

and it becomes possible to use the familiar momentum operator to replace p_x, p_y, and p_z. The necessary restrictions on the α's and β appear when the right side of the defining equation is expanded: †

$$p_x^2 + p_y^2 + p_z^2 + m_0^2 c^2 = \alpha_x^2 p_x^2 + \alpha_y^2 p_y^2 + \alpha_z^2 p_z^2 + \beta^2 m_0^2 c^2$$

$$+ (\alpha_x \alpha_y + \alpha_y \alpha_x) p_x p_y + (\alpha_y \alpha_z + \alpha_z \alpha_y) p_y p_z$$

$$+ (\alpha_x \alpha_z + \alpha_z \alpha_x) p_x p_z + (\alpha_x \beta + \beta \alpha_x) p_x m_0 c$$

$$+ (\alpha_y \beta + \beta \alpha_y) p_y m_0 c + (\alpha_z \beta + \beta \alpha_z) p_z m_0 c.$$

The two sides of this equation agree if

$$\alpha_x^2 = \alpha_y^2 = \alpha_z^2 = \beta^2 = 1$$

$$\alpha_x \alpha_y + \alpha_y \alpha_x = \alpha_y \alpha_z + \alpha_z \alpha_y = \alpha_x \alpha_z + \alpha_z \alpha_x = 0$$

$$\alpha_x \beta + \beta \alpha_x = \alpha_y \beta + \beta \alpha_y = \alpha_z \beta + \beta \alpha_z = 0.$$

The last two lines establish that the α's and β do not commute. They are mutually "*anti*commuting":

$$\alpha_x \alpha_y = -\alpha_y \alpha_x, \quad \alpha_y \alpha_z = -\alpha_z \alpha_y, \qquad \text{etc.}$$

What possible mathematical identity can the α and β coefficients have if they do not commute? They cannot be simple numbers, as one would expect offhand, because numbers of all kinds commute. Evidently we have entered that realm of algebra, which should be

† Remember that p_x, p_y, and p_z are commuting quantities. This was proved on page 202. m_0 and c are constants and therefore commute with everything. No commuting properties are assumed for the α and β coefficients.

familiar by now, where commutation is not a strict rule and algebraic symbols do not always represent simple numbers.

If the α's and β are not simple numbers, what are they? A logical step beyond numbers is to write matrices. Matrices that are non-commuting can easily be found. For example, if

$$x = \begin{pmatrix} 0 & 1 \\ 1 & 0 \end{pmatrix} \quad \text{and} \quad z = \begin{pmatrix} 1 & 0 \\ 0 & -1 \end{pmatrix},$$

the product xz is noncommuting, $xz \neq zx$. Furthermore, if

$$x = \begin{pmatrix} 0 & 1 \\ 1 & 0 \end{pmatrix} \quad \text{and} \quad y = \begin{pmatrix} 0 & -i \\ i & 0 \end{pmatrix},$$

the product xy is anticommuting, $xy = -yx$. Unfortunately, it proves impossible to find a third and fourth 2×2 matrix which anticommute with the x,y pair or any other pair. The four anticommuting coefficients α_x, α_y, α_z, and β cannot therefore be expressed as 2×2 matrices. It is also impossible to find four 3×3 matrices that are mutually anticommuting. A suitable collection of four 4×4 matrices can, however, be defined; in fact, *many* such sets of 4×4 matrices can be found. The particular ones used in the Dirac theory,

$$\alpha_x = \begin{pmatrix} 0 & 0 & 0 & 1 \\ 0 & 0 & 1 & 0 \\ 0 & 1 & 0 & 0 \\ 1 & 0 & 0 & 0 \end{pmatrix} \quad \alpha_y = \begin{pmatrix} 0 & 0 & 0 & -i \\ 0 & 0 & i & 0 \\ 0 & -i & 0 & 0 \\ i & 0 & 0 & 0 \end{pmatrix}$$

$$\alpha_z = \begin{pmatrix} 0 & 0 & 1 & 0 \\ 0 & 0 & 0 & -1 \\ 1 & 0 & 0 & 0 \\ 0 & -1 & 0 & 0 \end{pmatrix} \quad \beta = \begin{pmatrix} 1 & 0 & 0 & 0 \\ 0 & 1 & 0 & 0 \\ 0 & 0 & -1 & 0 \\ 0 & 0 & 0 & -1 \end{pmatrix},$$

are chosen largely for expedience; others are also mathematically satisfactory.

With the linearity coefficients expressed in this way, with the momentum written in the usual operator form, and with the negative sign chosen † in (21), the Dirac linear Hamiltonian becomes

$$\hat{H} = V + ic\hbar\alpha_x \partial/\partial x + ic\hbar\alpha_y \partial/\partial y + ic\hbar\alpha_z \partial/\partial z - \beta m_0 c^2.$$

† An arbitrary choice. It is not intended to imply that only the negative energy states are valid. Both kinds of energy states must ultimately be included in the theory.

And this is used, for example, in the energy eigenvalue equation,

$$\hat{H}\psi = E\psi,$$

a relativistic counterpart of the Schrödinger time-independent equation which is known as the Dirac equation. This statement, although it looks simple, is actually four separate equations. The four elements in the rows of the α and β matrices must multiply four column elements in something else, this something else being supplied by taking ψ and derivatives such as $\partial\psi/\partial x$ to be four-element, one-column matrices:

$$\psi = \begin{pmatrix} \psi_1 \\ \psi_2 \\ \psi_3 \\ \psi_4 \end{pmatrix} \quad \text{and} \quad \partial\psi/\partial x = \begin{pmatrix} \partial\psi_1/\partial x \\ \partial\psi_2/\partial x \\ \partial\psi_3/\partial x \\ \partial\psi_4/\partial x \end{pmatrix}.$$

Spinning Electrons and Antielectrons

The Dirac theory brought out two extremely important theoretical facts. First, and most important for our particular purposes, is that the theory shows the existence of a kind of electron rotational motion that has come to be known as "spin." When the Schrödinger procedures, especially the operator commutation rules, are applied to the description of rotational motion, it develops that an operator which represents electronic "orbital" motion, rotational motion around an external center such as a nucleus, commutes with an atomic Hamiltonian operator written in the Schrödinger form. This orbital operator, which is known as the "orbital angular momentum" operator, is therefore appropriate for the characterization of electron rotational motion. The mathematical problem is to solve for the operator's eigenvalues and eigenfunctions.†

The problem changes significantly when the Schrödinger atomic Hamiltonian operator is replaced by the corresponding Dirac Hamiltonian. The simple orbital angular momentum operator is no longer sufficient; there is added to it, when the commutation rules are obeyed, a second operator which tells of a distinctly different kind of rotation. This is not a rotation around a center external to the electron; it seems to be rotation around an *internal* center or axis, an

† The details of this calculation are the subject of a chapter in a sequel volume.

"intrinsic" kind of rotation most nearly comparable to classical spin motion. The mathematical problem now involves eigenvalues and eigenfunctions for *both* kinds of rotational motion, orbital and spin.

The explanation of spin motion was, perhaps, the greatest triumph of the Dirac theory. Electron spin was known before Dirac's work, and a nonrelativistic spin theory had been grafted on to the Schrödinger method, but this approach required that the existence of spin motion be postulated. The Dirac theory produced the spin concept as a simple and direct consequence of the workings of the equations.

The second major achievement of the Dirac theory seemed at first to be of rather dubious value. This is the strange matter of negative energy states. To display this concept, consider a free electron, for which $V = 0$ and (21) reads

$$E = \pm c \sqrt{p^2 + m_0^2 c^2}. \tag{21a}$$

Diagram this equation as follows:

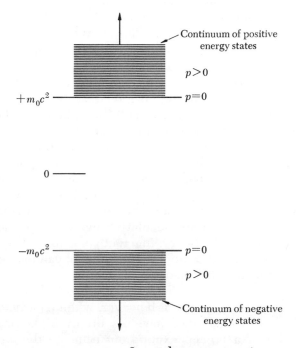

For electrons at rest, $p = 0$, and two energies are possible, $E = +m_0 c^2$, an ordinary positive energy, and $E = -m_0 c^2$, a negative energy. Electrons in motion have appreciable momenta, leading to a continuum of positive energy states above $E = +m_0c^2$ and also to a continuum of negative states below $E = -m_0c^2$.

Do electrons in negative energy states have any physical reality? In a sense they do not, because in the Dirac theory they are not observable. The continuum of negative energy states is assumed to be filled with electrons according to the dictates of the Pauli exclusion principle (one electron, and only one, occupying each state). With the negative energy continuum completely filled and no electrons in the positive energy continuum, no physical effects can be observed. This is an infinite, continuous "sea" of negative-energy electrons, exactly the same at all points in space. Properties such as negative charge can have no observable manifestation. The sea of negative-energy electrons by itself is, in other words, a complete vacuum.

But if sufficient energy (a minimum of $2m_0c^2$) is supplied to an electron in a negative energy state there is no reason why it cannot be made to move up to a positive energy state where it becomes a recognizable positive-energy electron. And there is left in the sea of negative-energy electrons an imperfection, a "hole," which must give rise to observable physical effects. What kind of physical effects? Since a one-electron hole is an absence of negative charge, it must itself have an effective positive charge $+e$. The fact that $+e$ is also the observed charge on the proton prompted Dirac to assume at first that protons are holes in the negative-energy electron sea.

The proton-hole idea was criticized by Oppenheimer, who showed that an ordinary piece of matter would annihilate itself in about 10^{-10} sec with electrons falling into proton holes, the downward transitions being accompanied by emission of gamma-ray photons. Apropos of these disastrous falling electrons, Pauli was inspired to produce his "second principle," to the effect that any theory should first be tested by applying it to the theoretician who invents it. This test would apparently be spectacularly negative when applied to Dirac and his proton-hole theory: in a tenth of a billionth of a second theoretician-Dirac would disappear in a burst of gamma rays and no one would ever hear of his theory.

Later the humor was reversed, however, when a particle was discovered which obviously *did* have its origin in Dirac's famous holes. Once again a crucial experiment came to the rescue of a worthy but faltering theory. And again the experiments followed a logic of their own, mostly unrelated to the theory. The experimental work in this case was done by Carl Anderson, a former student of Robert Millikan and a research fellow at the California Institute of

Technology. Anderson was concerned with studying the energy spectrum of secondary electrons produced by cosmic radiation. His apparatus was a Wilson cloud chamber operated vertically in a magnetic field strong enough to produce measurable curvatures in the paths of highly energetic electrons.

Anderson expected that his cloud chamber photographs would show secondary electrons produced by interactions of the sort described by Compton. He soon found that he was wrong, however; most of the secondary particles turned out to be *positively* charged. At first Anderson naturally assumed that the positive particles were protons, but this assumption was not supported by the cloud chamber tracks in air and through small thicknesses of lead, which showed ranges and specific ionizations belonging to particles much less massive than protons. In 1933 Anderson reported in the *Physical Review* the discovery of a positive electron, a particle with the mass of an electron and one positive electronic unit of charge. Anderson's term for the new particle was "positron," a contraction of the words positive and electron.

Dirac's theory certainly held the key to a fine explanation of Anderson's results. A negative-energy electron can absorb energy from one of the ingredients of the cosmic radiation, usually a gamma-ray photon, and undergo an upward transition to one of the positive-energy states:

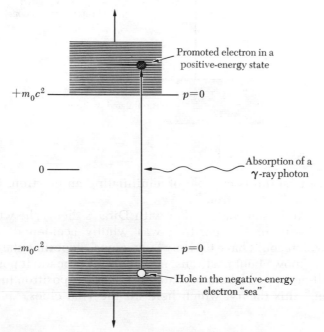

Promoted electron in a positive-energy state

$+m_0c^2$ —— $p=0$

0 ——

Absorption of a γ-ray photon

$-m_0c^2$ —— $p=0$

Hole in the negative-energy electron "sea"

Such a transition, as Dirac had assumed, creates a hole in the sea of negative-energy electrons. This hole has a positive charge and it also evidently has the mass of an electron. The hole is, in other words, one of Anderson's positrons. Since the positron-creating events are very rare, the density of holes is always very sparse and loss of electrons by falling into the holes is no longer the total disaster it was with the holes identified as protons. But each *individual* electron-hole encounter, or electron-positron encounter in Anderson's terminology, is a disaster for the electron and positron involved, since both particles lose their identity and two gamma-ray photons appear in their place. This is the reverse of the process diagrammed above:

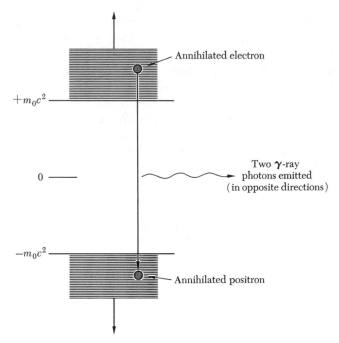

Because a positron is capable of annihilating an electron, it is also in a sense an "antielectron."

Though Anderson was familiar with Dirac's theory, he writes that "the discovery of the positron was wholly accidental." Dirac's theory, which could have told any "sagacious" experimentalist all he needed to know about positrons, and could have made it possible in "any well-equipped laboratory" to "discover the positron in a single afternoon," this theory, which held all the vital clues, "played no part whatsoever in the discovery of the positron." Like Planck's quantized black-body resonators, Einstein's light quanta, Bohr's stationary states, and de Broglie's matter waves, Dirac's holes were too "unphysical" for most physicists to accept with confidence. They were not willing to guide their experiments with concepts as "esoteric" as negative kinetic energy.

Anderson's positron, or antielectron, was the first of a long series of antiparticle discoveries, including (in 1955) the antiproton and antineutron. Physicists are convinced today that all of the elementary particles have their antiparticle counterparts. And it is conceivable that the universe contains entire antiworlds built of antimatter. Somewhere, on some antiworld, inventing theories to confound ordinary antimortals, there may well live an anti-Dirac.

Afterword

A Better View

Our story ends happily enough. It has told of obstinate groping along labyrinthine paths, guided mainly by profitable accidents and rare flashes of insight; of problems so foreign to ordinary ways of thinking that sometimes the questions can hardly be stated, to say nothing of the solutions; and of conceptual controversies so tangled that no complete resolution appears possible. There have been monumental mistakes and frustrations, but the last chapter has finally brought us to a working theory of quantum physics.

The way was cleared by simply converting to a mathematical language. A system of postulates was formulated and with this as a foundation a series of theorems was deduced comprising a mathematical quantum theory. The marvel is that this theory, unlike the speculative conceptual theories mentioned earlier, is accepted with no controversy. To be sure, several of the postulates, with implications of the statistical interpretation, are possible sources of argument. But once these assumptions are accepted—and few physicists feel they can afford not to accept them, if only for the sake of expediency—the theory builds in clear, unmistakable directions. Other versions of the mathematical theory of quantum physics are known (for example, the Heisenberg-Born-Jordan matrix method), but everyone agrees that they and the more commonly used Schrödinger method presented here are mathematically equivalent; preference for one or another is largely a matter of convenience. Here is the miracle of the mathematical method which prompted Dirac's remark, ". . . God is a mathematician of very high order . . . ."

Well, then, where do we stand? Is it true that the riddle is finally solved? Can we say that the achievement of this admirable mathematical theory closes the matter? With a mixture of regret and fascination it must be said that the answer is clearly, No. The theory as I have developed it is broadly applicable to the determination of electronic structures in atoms and molecules. But attempts to carry it further than that, to deal with electron-photon and other particle interactions, have exposed some unfortunate loopholes. The theory of electrons and photons works well from the physical viewpoint, but it is beset by mathematical inconsistencies. Other particles, especially those involving "weak" and "strong" interactions, seem to exist in a realm that the present quantum physics is not quite able to grasp physically; it is often difficult, for example, to arrive at a suitable Hamiltonian operator for a system involving such particles.

Beyond these shortcomings lies the ancient, unmanageable problem of "meaning." Where does the real truth lie? Is quantum physics irreducibly statistical and indeterminate? Or is there a "micro-micro" physics which sees beneath all this, restoring determinism and the continuum? Or is it possible that the ultimate truth is simply the intrinsic mathematical beauty of the theorems, and the pure, efficient line of the argument leading precisely toward the equations of greatest simplicity and utility? After all, do we attempt to find elaborate conceptual meanings in a Beethoven symphony? The truth of the symphony lies in the eloquence of its technique and language. Ought we to judge physics in the same way, listening only for the beauty and power of the mathematical language?

These are open questions, and it is not particularly remarkable that they should be. Quantum physics is faced with a profoundly difficult task: an attempt to penetrate the smallest, most intricate details of the pattern of the physical world. That human observers can *ever* find a quantum physics that is unified, complete, and non-controversial may be pure conceit. To the nineteenth-century physicist, a complete and permanent atomic physics seemed within reach. But a few "unexpected vistas" have appeared since then (and continue to appear). It seems more likely now that science develops by an endless evolutionary process. Dirac has written in this vein:

> I should like to suggest that one not worry too much about . . . controversy. I feel very strongly that the stage physics has reached at the present day is not the final stage. It is just one stage in the evolution of our picture of nature, and we should

expect this process to continue into the future, as biological evolution continues into the future. The present stage of physical theory is merely a steppingstone toward the better stages we shall have in the future. One can be quite sure that there will be better stages simply because of the difficulties in the physics today.

For the present there is an imperfect theory which is, nevertheless, beautifully constructed, fascinatingly provocative, and marvelously useful. For the future there is the promise of continual improvement and refinement toward new theories so revolutionary, powerful, and lovely that the older theories will seem dim and clumsy in comparison.

Notes and Comment

Feeling that the pages of this book are already too cluttered with footnotes, I have omitted from the text a number of incidental remarks and all references to additional reading material. Also, in the interest of keeping the reader to his main task, I have left out the sets of exercises customarily attached to textbook chapters. All of these things—notes, reading references, practice exercises, and assorted other comments—are collected here for the reader to use as he sees fit.

Chapter 1

References
It is regrettable that quantum physics first appeared in connection with the theory of thermal radiation, a subject far from the main purpose of this book. There is no choice but to present radiation theory in a somewhat narrow and sketchy form, and to refer the reader who lacks background to other books. A good elementary introduction to many important aspects of the subject, keeping the historical viewpoint in sight, is given by Holton and Roller:

1. Gerald Holton and Duane H. D. Roller, *Foundation of Modern Physical Science* (Addison-Wesley, 1958), Chap. 31.

More detailed and more advanced accounts can be found in Born's book,

2. Max Born, *Atomic Physics* (Blackie, 1935; Hafner, 7th Ed., 1962), pp. 250–59,

and in the recent book by Tomonaga,

3. Sin-Itiro Tomonaga, *Quantum Mechanics*, Vol. I, *Old Quantum Theory* (North-Holland, 1962), Chap. 1.

Klein has written very well of Planck's work. I have enjoyed and made use of Klein's papers, particularly

4. Martin J. Klein, "Max Planck and the Beginnings of the Quantum Theory," *Archive for History of Exact Sciences* 1, 459–79 (1962),

5. "Planck, Entropy and Quanta, 1901–1906," *The Natural Philosopher,* (Ginn-Blaisdell, 1963), Vol. 1, pp. 83–108, and

6. "Thermodynamics and Quanta in Planck's Work," *Physics Today,* November 1966.

Planck himself wrote extensively and had a remarkable facility for making physical science intelligible to the general reader. As further reading on the material in Chapter 1, sample

7. Max Planck, *Scientific Autobiography and Other Papers* (Philosophical Library, 1949), and

8. *A Survey of Physical Theory* (Dover, 1960).

Two of Planck's papers translated into English are given in

9. D. ter Haar, *The Old Quantum Theory* (Pergamon, 1967).

The Planck papers translated by ter Haar are

10. Max Planck, "On an Improvement of Wien's Radiation Law," *Verhandlungen der Deutschen Physikalischen Gesellschaft* 2, 202–4 (1900), and

11. "On the Theory of the Energy Distribution Law of the Normal Spectrum," ibid. 237–45 (1900).

The first of these papers introduces Planck's radiation formula and the second contains Planck's epoch-making derivation of the radiation formula.

Planck's theory and its antecedents are discussed by Jammer, with particular attention to the sources:

12. Max Jammer, *The Conceptual Development of Quantum Mechanics* (McGraw-Hill, 1966), pp. 1–28.

Jammer's book is by far the most comprehensive one available on the development of quantum physics. His coverage is so general I will not attempt to make reference to all the pertinent material. B. L. van der Waerden's book,

13. B. L. van der Waerden, *Sources of Quantum Mechanics* (North-Holland, 1967; Dover, 1968),

is also valuable as an examination of the origins and evolution of quantum mechanics.

Three more general and less detailed accounts of the history of modern physics are:

14. Victor Guillemin, *The Story of Quantum Mechanics* (Scribner's, 1968),

15. A. d'Abro, *The Rise of the New Physics,* Vol. II (Van Nostrand, 1939; Dover, 1951), and

16. Henry A. Boorse and Lloyd Motz (eds.), *The World of the Atom* (Basic Books, 1966).

Although not written from the historical viewpoint, the text by Ruark and Urey,

17. Arthur E. Ruark and Harold C. Urey, *Atoms, Molecules and Quanta*
     (McGraw-Hill, 1930),
frequently shows quantum theory as it developed.

The statistical method in thermodynamics may not be familiar to all readers,
particularly the Boltzmann evaluation of entropy with $S = k \ln W$ and the
Planck expression $W = (N + n - 1)!/n!(N - 1)!$. For an elementary and entertaining discussion of these matters see
18. Henry A. Bent, *The Second Law* (Oxford University Press, 1965), Chap.
     20–25.

The glimpse of Einstein in his early years is taken largely from a paper by
Klein:
19. Martin J. Klein, "Einstein and Some Civilized Discontents," *Physics
     Today,* January 1965.
Einstein's remarks on his education are taken from the "Autobiographical
Notes" written for
20. Paul A. Schilpp (ed.), *Albert Einstein: Philosopher-Scientist* (Library
     of Living Philosophers, 1944; Harper and Row, 1959), pp. 3–95.

The 1905 Einstein photon paper,
21. Albert Einstein, "On a Heuristic Viewpoint Concerning the Production
     and Transformation of Light," *Annalen der Physik* **17**, 132–48 (1905).
is translated into English in
22. A. B. Arons and M. B. Peppard, *American Journal of Physics* **33**, 367–74
     (1965).
Klein has presented an interesting analysis of this paper:
23. Martin J. Klein, "Einstein's First Paper on Quanta," *The Natural
     Philosopher* (Ginn-Blaisdell, 1963), Vol. 2, pp. 59–86.
Einstein's role in the development of the wave-particle duality concept is
examined in another paper by Klein:
24. Martin J. Klein, "Einstein and the Wave-Particle Duality," *The Natural
     Philosopher* (Ginn-Blaisdell, 1964), Vol. 3, pp. 3–49.
Tomonaga (in Chap. 2, Ref. 3, above) gives a treatment of the energy-
fluctuation calculations with which Einstein was concerned in his duality
discussions.

On the subject of the photoelectric effect, Chap. 32 of Holton and Roller
(Ref. 1, above) can be consulted. Millikan tells his own story well, including his outspoken 1916 criticism of the Einstein photon concept:
25. Robert A. Millikan, *The Electron* (University of Chicago Press, 2nd
     Ed., 1924), Chap. X.

Compton tells of his controversy with Duane and of other matters in
26. Arthur H. Compton, "The Scattering of X-Rays as Particles," *American
     Journal of Physics* **29**, 817–20 (1961).

For a portrait of Compton see

27. Samuel K. Allison, "Arthur Holly Compton, Research Physicist," *Science* **138**, 794–97 (1962).

Compton's theory is clearly presented in his original paper:

28. Arthur H. Compton, "A Quantum Theory of the Scattering of X-Rays of Light Elements," *Physical Review* **21**, 483–522 (1923).

If a study or review of the principles of special relativity seems advisable see

29. Robert M. Eisberg, *Fundamentals of Modern Physics* (Wiley, 1961), Chap. 1, and

30. Herbert Goldstein, *Classical Mechanics* (Addison-Wesley, 1950), Chap. 6.

Chapters 2 and 3 of the Eisberg book also contain good general accounts of Planck's theory, the photoelectric effect, and the Compton effect.

There is no substitute, it seems to me, for reading widely. If time is limited browse in several papers and books on each topic of interest. This is far more profitable and entertaining than laboring over every detail in a single book. Diverse opinions and approaches make the best teachers.

Practice Exercises

1. The energy distribution function $\rho(\nu,T)$ has several peculiarities that are worthy of special note. What units does ρ have? What are the units of $\rho d\nu$? In Planck's theory what does the frequency variable ν refer to? What meaning does the temperature variable T have? This is the temperature of what?

2. The "classical" form of the energy distribution function, in which ρ is a quadratic function of the frequency, $\rho(\nu) = (A/B)(\nu^2 T)$, (see p. 13) leads to a critical difficulty which Ehrenfest called the "ultra-violet catastrophe." This difficulty arises when the total energy density from all frequencies is calculated. What problem does this calculation raise? What is the meaning of Ehrenfest's term? How is the "catastrophe" avoided?

3. Use the Planck radiation law to prove the Stefan-Boltzmann law (equation (1) in Chapter 1).

4. An energy distribution function must be defined so that it can be placed in an integral and integrated to give the full radiation density. The distribution function introduced in Chapter 1 is suited to integration over all frequencies; it forms the integral $\int_0^\infty \rho d\nu$. When the integration is done with respect to wavelengths instead of frequencies a distribution function ρ' with a different appearance becomes necessary. The integral formed in this case is $\int_0^\infty \rho' d\lambda$. Show that

$$\rho' = 8\pi hc/[\lambda^5(e^{hc/\lambda kT} - 1)].$$

5. Prove that Wien's law can be restated to say that the wavelength-dependent distribution function ρ' introduced in the last exercise has the general form $\rho' = g(\lambda T)/\lambda^5$, where $g(\lambda T)$ is a function of λT alone.

6. From the form of Wien's law just proved show that the wavelength of maximum radiation density λ_m (for which $\rho'(\lambda,T)$ is maximum) is inversely proportional to the temperature, that $\lambda_m T =$ constant. Use the Planck radiation law to calculate a theoretical expression for the constant $\lambda_m T$. (This calculation, and aspects of the calculations mentioned in the previous problems, are outlined in p. 60 of Ref. 17, above.)

7. Derive the necessary equations for the method of evaluating the Boltzmann and Planck constants h and k, mentioned in the footnote on p. 28.

8. Einstein used the title, "On a Heuristic Viewpoint Concerning the Production and Transformation of Light," for his 1905 paper on the photon concept. Comment on Einstein's use of the word "heuristic." (Holton tells us that when Newton communicated *his* theory of light particles to the Royal Society in 1672 he was careful to remark that the theory was heuristic.)

9. It is sometimes said that Planck introduced the concept of "quanta of energy" whereas Einstein introduced "quanta of radiation." What is the distinction between these two terms?

10. The equation derived on p. 31 expresses the angle of photon scattering θ in the Compton effect. The angle of electron scattering ϕ can be expressed by the equation.

$$\cot \phi = \left(1 + \frac{h\nu_1}{m_0 c^2}\right) \tan (\theta/2).$$

Derive this equation.

Chapter 2

References
In spite of the almost universal practice in chemistry and physics textbooks of introducing atomic physics with an account of Bohr's theory, very few books actually build the story around Bohr and his papers. I have found good material on Bohr's work in only a few places, particularly in Chap. 2 of Jammer's book (Ref. 12, above) and also in Behrens's papers,

31. Carl E. Behrens, "The Early Development of the Bohr Atom," *American Journal of Physics* 11, 135–47 (1943), and

32. "Further Developments of Bohr's Early Atomic Theory," *American Journal of Physics* 11, 272–81 (1943).

Most readers will not have the perseverance to read all of Bohr's 1913–1915 papers. I recommend the first and last of this series:

33. Niels Bohr, "On the Constitution of Atoms and Molecules," *Philosophical Magazine* 26, 1–25 (1913), and

34. "On the Quantum Theory of Radiation and the Structure of the Atom," *Philosophical Magazine* 30, 394–415 (1915).

The 1915 paper gives the best summary of the postulates which are used as a basis for the discussion in Chapter 2.

Much has been written about the life of Bohr and his Institute. Perhaps the best of this material is contained in the memorial volume,
35. S. Rozental (ed.), *Niels Bohr* (North-Holland and Wiley-Interscience, 1967).
There is a recent biography,
36. Ruth Moore, *Niels Bohr* (Knopf, 1966).
Another recent book,
37. Barbara Lovett Cline, *The Questioners: Physicists and the Quantum Theory* (Crowell, 1965),
also tells of personalities and events during the Bohr era. A collection of reminiscences,
38. J. B. Birks (ed.), *Rutherford at Manchester* (Heywood, 1962; Benjamin, 1963),
gives a valuable picture of the Rutherford Manchester establishment. One of the articles is written by Bohr.

The Balmer paper on the hydrogen spectral series,
39. Johann Jakob Balmer, "A Note on the Spectral Lines of Hydrogen," *Verhandlungen der Naturforschenden Gesellschaft in Basel* **7**, 548–60 (1885),
is given in English translation in
40. W. R. Hindmarsh, *Atomic Spectra* (Pergamon, 1967).
This book also contains a translated excerpt from the Rydberg monograph dealing with the combination principle,
41. Janne R. Rydberg, "On the Emission Spectra of the Chemical Elements," *Den Kongliga Svenska Vetenskaps Akademiens Handlingar* **23**, 11 (1889).

For sketches of Moseley and his world see
42. Charles G. Darwin, "Moseley and the Atomic Numbers of the Elements," in Ref. 38, above, and
43. L. A. Redman, "H. G. J. Moseley," *Physics Teacher* **3**, 151–57 (1965).
The Moseley papers on X-ray spectra are
44. H. G. J. Moseley, "The High Frequency Spectra of the Elements," *Philosophical Magazine* **26**, 1024–1034 (1913), and
45. "The High Frequency Spectra of the Elements, Part II," ibid. **27**, 703–13 (1914).
A thorough and readable analysis of Moseley's research is given by Heilbron,
46. John L. Heilbron, "The Work of H. G. J. Moseley," *Isis* **57**, 336–64 (1966).

The Franck-Hertz paper,

47. James Franck and Gustav Hertz, "Collisions between Electrons and Mercury Vapor Molecules and the Ionization Potential of Such Molecules," *Verhandlungen der Deutschen Physikalischen Gesellschaft* **16**, 457–67 (1914),

is translated in Chap. 46 of Ref. 16, above. The discussion of the paper is misleading, however, since it seems to accept the Franck-Hertz misinterpretation of the critical potentials as measurements of the ionization potential. Another important Franck-Hertz paper,

48. James Franck and Gustav Hertz, "On the Excitation of the 2536Å Mercury Resonance Line by Electron Collisions," ibid. 512 (1914),

is translated in Ref. 9, above. James Franck's remarkable comments on his ignorance of the Bohr theory are quoted by Holton in

49. Gerald Holton, "On the Recent Past of Physics," *American Journal of Physics* **29**, 805–10 (1961).

De Broglie's theory of matter waves is not easy to comprehend. Because of its vagueness, it leaves unsaid as much as it says. This was, in fact, de Broglie's intention. He could only glimpse the outlines of a theory. He knew that there was more beyond the outlines which he could not grasp well enough to clarify. His statements are deliberately incomplete. He speaks of the electron's "internal process" or "internal phenomenon" without saying much about what this is. He introduces particle waves or "phase waves" without giving us any concrete picture of them. The limitations of his theory are therefore as important as its positive assertions (though perhaps the same should be said of any theory). These subtleties are best approached by reading de Broglie's original papers. Useful excerpts from de Broglie's thesis,

50. Louis Victor de Broglie, "Investigations on Quantum Theory," *Annales de Physique* **3**, 22–128 (1925),

are translated in

51. Gunther Ludwig, *Wave Mechanics* (Pergamon, 1968).

Jammer's comments (pp. 236–47 of Ref. 12, above) are, as usual, accurate and helpful. The de Broglie Nobel Prize Address is also illuminating; it is given in Chap. 63 of Ref. 16, above. De Broglie has written and lectured extensively. Try his most recent volume of essays,

52. *New Perspectives in Physics* (Basic Books, 1962).

For a satisfactory understanding of the de Broglie wave theory and the Schrödinger theory which follows, it may be desirable to review the rudiments of the physics of wave motion. It is necessary to see that periodic functions such as $\sin 2\pi(\bar{\nu}x - \nu t)$ and $e^{2\pi i(\bar{\nu}x - \nu t)}$ express traveling waves ($\bar{\nu}$ and ν represent wave number and frequency). The general equations for the phase velocity $u = \lambda\nu$ (λ is the wavelength) and for the group velocity

$w = dv/d\bar{v} = dv/d(v/u)$ are also essential. The sense of these equations is well-expressed by Eisberg in pp. 141–44 of Ref. 29, above, and by Born in pp. 92–93 and 348–49 of Ref. 2, above.

The intricacies of the Davisson-Germer experiments are clearly presented by Davisson,

53. Clinton J. Davisson, "Are Electrons Waves?" *Franklin Institute Journal* **205**, 597–623 (1928).

The original Davisson-Germer paper is

54. C. J. Davisson and L. H. Germer, "Diffraction of Electrons by a Crystal of Nickel," *Physical Review* **30**, 705–40 (1927).

Germer tells the law-suit story in

55. L. H. Germer, "Low-Energy Electron Diffraction," *Physics Today*, July 1964.

Thomson's work on electron diffraction was first reported in

56. G. P. Thomson and A. Reid, "Diffraction of Cathode Rays by a Thin Film," *Nature* **119**, 890 (1927).

The early history of electron-diffraction experiments is told in an absorbing article by Thomson,

57. G. P. Thomson, "Early Work in Electron Diffraction," *American Journal of Physics* **29**, 821–25 (1961).

Electron diffraction had been lurking in the wings for many years before its formal entrance in 1927. It appears that cathode-ray experiments such as those done by Lenard in the late nineteenth century might have shown diffraction effects had the focusing techniques produced electrons which were more nearly monoenergetic. Jammer finds it attractive to speculate on the course physics might have followed if electrons had first been revealed as waves rather than particles.

Practice Exercises
11. From the equation $T = Ze^2/2a$ for the kinetic energy of a classical system comprised of an electron of charge $-e$ separated by a distance a from a nucleus of charge $+Ze$, it follows that, as the electron and the nucleus become very widely separated, the kinetic energy decreases toward zero. On the other hand, the kinetic energy of an electron rotating around a nucleus at a distance a and with a rotation frequency ω is $T = 2\pi^2 ma^2\omega^2$. This implies that the kinetic energy becomes *large* for wide electron-nucleus separations. Which of these two conflicting statements is correct?
12. Calculate the Rydberg constant R using modern values for the constants e, m, c, and h. Compare this with Bohr's result, given on p. 48.
13. Show that the Bohr theory not only predicts that combinations involving sums of observed frequencies can occur in an emission spectrum (as established on p. 49) but also that combinations involving frequency differences can occur.
14. Use the Bohr postulates and the classical equations of motion to show

that, besides the kinetic energy quantization according to $T = nh\omega/2$, there is also an angular momentum quantization: $l = nh/2\pi$. In the subsequent versions of the quantum theory (old and new) angular momentum quantization became much more important than kinetic energy quantization.

15. Franck and Hertz observed the 2536Å "resonance line" that appears when the first critical potential is reached. What is the origin of this "resonance line"? Show that the energy of the photons in this emitted radiation is the same (within experimental error) as that measured by the critical potential.

16. Davisson and Germer found that, at a given angle of incidence, the intensity of electrons simply reflected from the face of a nickel crystal (as shown on p. 65) was particularly strong at certain accelerating potentials. Using the simple Bragg theory of X-ray diffraction, and ignoring any refraction effects, prove that at these maximum reflections the accelerating potentials V_m satisfy the equation

$$V_m{}^{1/2} = 12.25n/2d \cos \theta, \tag{1}$$

where n is an integer, θ is the angle of beam incidence, and d is the spacing between crystal lattice planes. Also prove that when refraction is taken into account the potentials of maximum reflection satisfy the equation

$$V_m{}^{1/2} = (12.25n)/(2d)(\sqrt{\mu^2 - \sin^2 \theta}), \tag{2}$$

where μ is the index of refraction of the crystal medium. The last equation is somewhat more complicated than it looks since μ is not constant but decreases toward unity with increasing accelerating potentials. Use the approximate equation (1) and the exact equation (2) to refine the explanation given on p. 65 for the plot of $V^{1/2}$ versus reflected electron intensity. Account for the fact that the spacings between the intensity peaks are not exactly constant.

Chapter 3

This chapter tells what is probably the most critical part of the story of quantum physics—the events of 1925 and 1926 which brought forth the Schrödinger and Heisenberg-Born-Jordan methods of quantum mechanics. Like some of the other developments in this story, this one is difficult to follow in all its refinements. To a large extent Heisenberg and Schrödinger were guided by classical methods; the classical theories resembled the new quantum theories just enough to supply some vital clues. Unfortunately, these classical methods are not as familiar to the modern reader as they were to Schrödinger and Heisenberg. Readers of this book are not likely to be fluent in the language of Fourier analysis and Hamiltonian mechanics. Nevertheless, I think it is valuable to see the Heisenberg and Schrödinger lines of reasoning at least in outline. Their work brought the dawn of modern quantum physics. The peculiar ways of change in science are only perceptible if the story is followed from the beginning.

If that argument is not persuasive I must admit, reluctantly, that the sections in Chapter 3 on Heisenberg's matrix mechanics, Hamilton's analogy, and Schrödinger's wave mechanics (pp. 79–97) *can* be omitted. The matrix method is not used again in this book and the vital Schrödinger equation is rederived in Chapter 5 in a way which is more suited to its modern usage.

References

For further details on Heisenberg's marvelous manipulation of Fourier techniques into the first quantum mechanics see van der Waerden's penetrating account (pp. 19–36 of Ref. 13, above) and Chap. 5 of the Tomonaga book (Ref. 3, above). Heisenberg's paper itself,

58. Werner Heisenberg, "On a Quantum-Theoretical Re-Interpretation of Kinematic and Mechanical Relations," *Zeitschrift für Physik* **33**, 879–93 (1925),

makes good reading, especially in the clear way it shows the classical-quantum parallel. This paper is translated by van der Waerden (in Ref. 13, above) along with the Born-Jordan paper,

59. Max Born and Pascual Jordan, "On Quantum Mechanics," *Zeitschrift für Physik* **34**, 858–88 (1925),

and the "three men's" paper,

60. Max Born, Werner Heisenberg, and Pascual Jordan, "On Quantum Mechanics. II," ibid. **35**, 557–615 (1926).

These last two papers gave the first general formulation of matrix mechanics.

Hamilton's analogy and Schrödinger's use of it are given a clear presentation in Goldstein's book (pp. 307–14, Ref. 30, above). Goldstein (Chap. 2) also gives an excellent introduction to the use of variation principles in classical mechanics. The rest of Goldstein's book is recommended as a fine portrayal of classical mechanics in a modern context.

As far as I am aware the only biography available on Schrödinger is

61. William T. Scott, *Erwin Schrödinger* (University of Massachusetts Press, 1967).

This is a fine book. It sketches Schrödinger's life and also evaluates the scope of his thought and writing. For a vivid picture of Schrödinger in Vienna shortly before his death see

62. Jeremy Bernstein, "I Am This Whole World," in *A Comprehensible World* (Random House, 1967).

The four communications responsible for the introduction of the Schrödinger wave mechanics are:

63. Erwin Schrödinger, "Quantization as an Eigenvalue Problem," *Annalen der Physik* **79**, 361–76 (1926),
64. ibid. **79**, 489–527 (1926),
65. ibid. **80**, 437–90 (1926),
66. ibid. **81**, 109–39 (1926).

The first two and the fourth of these are translated by Ludwig (see Ref. 51), who also translates Schrödinger's comparison of his method with the matrix method:

67. Erwin Schrödinger, "On the Relationship of the Heisenberg-Born-Jordan Quantum Mechanics to Mine," *Annalen der Physik* **79**, 734–56 (1926),

Schrödinger's analysis of Hamilton's analogy, and the line of reasoning which led him to a wave equation, is best summarized in

68. Erwin Schrödinger, *Four Lectures on Wave Mechanics* (Blackie and Sons, 1928).

An excerpt from this book is included in Chap. 64 of Ref. 16, above.

Schrödinger was prolific as an essayist. For a sample of his writings pertaining to Chapters 3 and 4 of this book see

69. Erwin Schrödinger, *Science and Humanism* (Cambridge University Press, 1951).

The short volume of philosophical essays,

70. *My View of the World* (Cambridge University Press, 1964),

gives a clue to Schrödinger's complex personality. Many of Schrödinger's remarks quoted in Chapter 3 are taken from

71. "Are There Quantum Jumps?" *The British Journal for the Philosophy of Science* **3**, 109–23, 233–42 (1952).

In this paper Schrödinger summarizes his anti-quantum-jump argument, the subject of the debate with Bohr.

Schrödinger's article,

72. "What is Matter?" *Scientific American*, September 1953,

is recommended as a summary of his position on the interpretation of quantum physics.

Heisenberg's account of the Bohr-Schrödinger meeting in Copenhagen is given in pp. 103–4 of Ref. 35, above. In this same article Heisenberg recalls his collaboration with Bohr which marked the beginnings of the Copenhagen interpretation of quantum physics.

The comment is made on p. 99 that a single atomic transition produces a wave train at least a foot long. This remarkable conclusion is justified by A. A. Michelson's experimental work on "coherence lengths." The Michelson apparatus splits a light beam into two components, sends these components along two different paths, recombines them and finally focuses the recombined beam onto a detector. If the two beam components are coherent the detector shows distinct concentric interference patterns. The condition for coherence seems to be that the apparatus splits and recombines a single wave train, that is, the light emitted in a single transition. To show the length of the wave train Michelson made the two beam paths of different lengths. He found that when the path difference was one or two feet (depending on the wavelength of the light) the interference pattern was lost. Presumably the component of the wave train traveling the longer path is just prevented from recombining with the component sent along the shorter path.

The famous double-split experiment was first done in 1909 by G. I. Taylor, who used a weak light source. He reported the results in

73. G. I. Taylor, *Proceedings of the Cambridge Philosophical Society* **15**, 114 (1909).

The mysterious ramifications of this experiment have been fascinating physicists ever since. Nothing puts the difficulties of the quantum riddle more insistently than the spectacle of a single photon or electron diffracted by a double slit. A multitude of textbook chapters have dealt with the paradox of the double-slit experiment. The most readable and comprehensive account I have seen is

74. Richard P. Feynman, Robert B. Leighton, and Matthew Sands, *The Feynman Lectures on Physics*, Vol. III (Addison-Wesley, 1965), Chap. 1.

This chapter from the Feynman book and the two which follow it form an excellent supplement for the material of Chapters 3 and 4 of the present book.

A good introduction to the uncertainty principle is given by Born in pp. 96–104 of Ref. 2, above. Heisenberg's book,

75. Werner Heisenberg, *The Physical Principles of the Quantum Theory* (Dover, 1930), Chap. II,

discusses a variety of measurements and the uncertainty products which describe their limitations.

Practice Exercises

17. De Broglie arrived at the expression $u = c^2/v$ (equation (14), Chapter 2) for the phase velocity of his particle waves. Schrödinger, using a different approach, also derived a phase velocity $u = E/\sqrt{2m(E - V)}$ (equation (6), Chapter 3) for the waves comprising a "particle ray." Are these two phase velocities identical? If so, prove their identity.

18. Compare de Broglie's derivation of the relation $p = h/\lambda$ with Schrödinger's derivation for the same equation. Does either derivation have important advantages over the other?

19. Schrödinger based an important part of his argument on the assumption that when the total energy E is constant the wave amplitude Ψ is periodic in time according to

$$\Psi = \psi(x)e^{\pm 2\pi i E t/h} \tag{1}$$

(for the one-dimensional case), where $\psi(x)$ depends only on the position variable x. Making use of the Einstein energy-frequency relation $E = h\nu$, develop a line of reasoning which justifies this equation.

20. Use the expression (1) from the last exercise to derive $\partial\Psi/\partial t =$

$\pm(2\pi iE/h)\Psi$ and then combine this with equation (7) of Chapter 3 to derive the two equations

$$-(\hbar^2/2m)(\partial^2\Psi/\partial x^2) + V\Psi = \pm(h/2\pi i)(\partial\Psi/\partial t). \tag{2}$$

One of these equations (the one with the minus sign on the right is usually chosen) can be taken to be the general time dependent equation which determines $\Psi(x,t)$. It will be derived again in Chapter 5.

21. Comment on Heisenberg's use of the term "kinematic" in the title of his first paper on quantum mechanics: "On a Quantum-Theoretical Re-Interpretation of Kinematic and Mechanical Relations."

22. De Broglie's wave mechanics postulates a certain periodic "internal process" and periodic particle waves or "phase waves" which move with the particle and stay in phase with the internal process. His theory was incomplete, however, in that it failed to identify or explain in more fundamental terms the internal process or the phase waves. Schrödinger's wave mechanics also had its incomplete aspects. What were they?

23. Make a general comparison of the advantages and disadvantages of the de Broglie and Schrödinger systems of wave mechanics.

24. When an electron whose associated waves have the wavelength λ is passed through a small hole with a diameter d the beam is diffracted so that its angle of divergence is θ, related to λ and d by $\sin\theta = \lambda/d$. What is the uncertainty in the component of the electron's momentum parallel to the hole's diameter? What is the electron's uncertainty of position in the same direction? Show that the product of the two uncertainties is approximately equal to Planck's constant. Whereas the gamma-ray microscope disturbs the particle aspect of an electron while it measures position, the small hole device disturbs the wave aspect of the electron while making a position measurement. The physical processes are entirely different in the two cases, but the limiting uncertainty product is approximately the same.

Chapter 4

References

Margenau's firefly analogy is mentioned in the article,

76. Henry Margenau, "Advantages and Disadvantages of Various Interpretations of the Quantum Theory," *Physics Today*, October 1954.

Margenau states the basic difficulties facing the quantum physicist with clarity and style. If the student of modern physics reads nothing else on the controversy concerning the interpretation of quantum physics, he should at least read this paper. Margenau's viewpoint is perhaps not the final one, but he makes it abundantly clear that the conventional Copenhagen doctrine is no better than several others.

I recommend again Feynman's Chapters 1, 2, and 3 of Ref. 74, above, for an elementary yet thorough presentation of the argument which justifies the

peculiar statistical methods of quantum physics. Chapters IV and V in Born's
book (Ref. 2, above) and Born's Nobel Prize Address,

77. Max Born, "Statistical Interpretation of Quantum Mechanics," *Science*
    122, 675–79 (1955),

also provide valuable material on the statistical interpretation. A non-
technical and entertaining book,

78. Banesh Hoffmann, *The Strange Story of the Quantum* (Dover, 2nd
    Ed., 1959),

simplifies the complexities of the statistical description with wit, ingenuity
and a vast fund of analogies.

Besides the invaluable *Atomic Physics* (Ref. 2, above) the following of
Born's books make absorbing general reading:

79. Max Born, *Physics in My Generation* (Pergamon Press, 1956),
80. *Experiment and Theory in Physics* (Dover, 1956),
81. *My Life and Views* (Scribner's, 1968), and
82. *The Restless Universe* (Dover, 1951).

Complementarity and the Copenhagen interpretation have been so widely
advertised there is no difficulty in finding discussions of the basic viewpoint.
For instance, look into Heisenberg's excellent book,

83. Werner Heisenberg, *Physics and Philosophy* (Harper and Row, 1962).

Two other authoritative articles are

84. Norwood Russell Hanson, "Copenhagen Interpretation of Quantum
    Theory," *American Journal of Physics* **27**, 1–15 (1959), and
85. Leon Rosenfeld, "Foundations of Quantum Theory and Complemen-
    tarity," *Nature* **190**, 384–88 (1961).

Two of Bohr's collections of essays,

86. Niels Bohr, *Atomic Theory and the Description of Nature* (Cambridge
    University Press, 1961), and
87. *Atomic Physics and Human Knowledge* (Wiley, 1958),

contain various comments on complementarity. As usual with Bohr and the
written word, these books cannot be recommended as introductory treat-
ments.

Bohr's account of his long debate with Einstein was originally published in
Ref. 20, above; it is also included in Ref. 87. The movable-mirror paradox invented by Epstein in the image of the Einstein-Podolsky-Rosen argument
can be found in

88. Paul S. Epstein, "The Reality Problem in Quantum Mechanics,"
    American Journal of Physics **13**, 127–36 (1945).

Rosenfeld tells the story of Bohr's reaction to the Einstein-Podolsky-Rosen
"onslaught" in pp. 128–29 of Ref. 35, above.

A volume of letters,

89. K. Przibram (ed.) and Martin J. Klein (trans.), *Letters on Wave Me-
    chanics* (Philosophical Library, 1967),

speaks the feelings of the Copenhagen opponents, Planck, Einstein, and Schrödinger. The informal, candid style of these letters is a delight to read. In a letter to Schrödinger, Einstein comments on "the Heisenberg-Bohr tranquilizing philosophy — or religion? — so delicately contrived that, for the time being, it provides a gentle pillow for the true believer from which he cannot very easily be aroused." No matter, decides Einstein: ". . . let him lie there."

Landé's book,
90. Alfred Landé, *New Foundations of Quantum Mechanics* (Cambridge University Press, 1965),
is a good antidote for too much dogma in your physics. The Bohm work referred to in Chapter 4 is presented with simplicity and clarity in his book,
91. David Bohm, *Causality and Chance in Modern Physics* (Van Nostrand, 1957).
The paper in which Margenau writes of fireflies and our somewhat unsatisfactory alternatives for understanding quantum physics has already been mentioned (Ref. 76, above).

Practice Exercises
25. Frame an answer to the question originally put on p. 75: "If not the photon itself, what *does* pass through the double slit spreading out on the other side in two fields which overlap and produce regions of cancellation and reinforcement?"
26. Write the wave function used on p. 119 (to represent an electron equally likely to be in two separate beams) so that it satisfies the normalization requirement.

Chapter 5

Quantum mechanics may not be easy to learn, but a student of the subject has the consolation that he can choose from a considerable variety of introductory, intermediate, and advanced books for his reading. If one book proves impenetrable don't give up, try another, or another. It seems rather useless to try to offer a complete guide to these books. I shall, however, list a few of them here and in the References to Chapter 6; these seem to me to supplement the viewpoint presented in Chapters 5 and 6.

References
The plausibility of the Schrödinger equation is best argued, I think, by showing it to be a simple energy equation in differential operator disguise. Many authors take this approach and I have followed suit. The most comprehensible presentation of this argument I have seen is in Eisberg's book (Chap. 7, Ref. 29, above). Two other well-organized versions of this introductory discussion are found in

92. Robert H. Dicke and James P. Wittke, *Introduction to Quantum Mechanics* (Addison-Wesley, 1960), Chap. Three, and
93. Leonard I. Schiff, *Quantum Mechanics* (McGraw-Hill, 2nd Ed., 1955), Chap. II.
These references can also be consulted on the matters of operator associations, average-value calculations, and energy eigenvalues. Eisberg's treatment of the potential-well calculation with an asymmetrical potential function shows that the symmetrical well is not essential to the main features of the eigenvalue argument. Besides the potential-well problem, Dicke and Wittke also briefly treat the interesting case of a potential *hill*. On the subject of operator manipulations, Rojansky's discussion,
94. Vladimir Rojansky, *Introductory Quantum Mechanics* (Prentice-Hall, 1938), Chapter III,
is also recommended.

The normalization condition $\int \Psi^* \Psi dx = 1$ is not always easy to apply when the wave function depends on the time variable. The probability function $\Psi^* \Psi$ is dependent on time in these cases, and this raises the possibility that the normalization integral itself may be time-dependent. A time-dependent normalization integral cannot be allowed, however, since it implies creation or loss of particles. It is a fundamental requirement of the theory, then, that $\int \Psi^* \Psi dx$ be constant at all times: $(d/dt)\int \Psi^* \Psi dx = 0$. Using the Hermitian property of the Hamiltonian operator $\hat{H}$ this can, in fact, be proved as a general theorem. See Exercise 34.

The electron-in-the-box problem is justifiably popular with textbook authors. Schiff's discussion (Ref. 93, above) is good; he includes the case of a box which allows the electron to penetrate its walls. A variety of one-dimensional barrier, step, and well potentials is discussed by Eisberg (Chap. 8, Ref. 29, above). The problem of a three-dimensional box is considered by Pauling and Wilson, in
95. Linus Pauling and E. Bright Wilson, *Introduction to Quantum Mechanics* (McGraw-Hill, 1935), Chap. IV.
Electrons in rings and spherical boxes can be found in Linnett's book,
96. J. W. Linnett, *Wave Mechanics and Valency* (Wiley, 1960), Chaps. II and III.
The case of the spherical box serves as a good introduction to the use of spherical coordinates in more complex problems.

In a manner of speaking, most physical problems of interest are just one step beyond the problem of the electron in the box. In the box the potential energy function vanishes: $V = 0$. In other cases one simply substitutes another potential function and proceeds with the solution of the resulting form of the Schrödinger equation. But this is vastly more easily said than done, due to the considerable mathematical complexity of even the most elementary case. Unfortunately for us Schrödinger's equation is by no means a simple differential equation. It is certainly valuable to note, however, that a large part of the difficulty is *mathematical*, not physical. To sample some of these mathematical complexities look at the problem of the harmonic oscillator. The potential function $V(x) = kx^2/2$ (k is a constant) is used here to simulate the two nuclei of a diatomic molecule held together by a simple spring force. See Eisberg (Chap. 8, Ref. 29, above) and Pauling and Wilson (Chap. III, Ref. 95, above).

Practice Exercises

27. Show that the second choice of signs in the derivation of the Schrödinger equation, $\alpha = +i$, adds nothing to the equation which is physically important.

28. Schrödinger's 1926 paper was brought to Einstein's attention by Planck. In his first hurried look at the paper Einstein misread the proposed equation and wrote to Schrödinger with two objections: "If I have two systems that are not coupled to each other at all, and if E_1 is an allowed energy value of the first system and E_2 an allowed energy value of the second, then $E_1 + E_2 = E$ must be an allowed energy value of the total system consisting of both of them. I do not, however, understand how your equation is to express this property." His other objection had to do with the "integration constant" of the energy. This is determined, for example, by the point on the energy scale where the energy is assumed to be zero. In non-relativistic mechanics the choice of the energy zero-point is arbitrary. Therefore Einstein remarked that Schrödinger's equation, which is non-relativistic, must not be affected by constant additions and subtractions to the total energy E or to the potential energy V. Show that Schrödinger's time-independent equation (13a) is not subject to either of these objections. (In his letter Einstein suggested an equation which fulfilled his two requirements. Much to Schrödinger's delight this equation sketched "free-hand" by Einstein was identical to the equation as it was originally proposed, and he wrote to Einstein in reply: ". . . one's confidence in a formulation always increases if one — and especially *you* — construct the same thing afresh from a few fundamental requirements.")

29. Referring to the remark on p. 152, that $\hat{A}\hat{B}$ is not always the operator associated with the physical quantity AB, consider $\hat{x}\hat{p} = -i\hbar x\partial/\partial x$ as the operator for xp. Show that neither this nor $\hat{p}\hat{x} = -i\hbar(\partial/\partial x)x$ lead to real values for the average value $\overline{xp}$. On the other hand, prove that if the average value is calculated using $(\frac{1}{2})(\hat{x}\hat{p} + \hat{p}\hat{x})$ for the operator the result is real. This kind of difficulty sometimes complicates the problem of deciding how to formulate operator associations. Also see Exercise 48.

30. Write operators for:

(a) the square of the total linear momentum

$$p^2 = p_x{}^2 + p_y{}^2 + p_z{}^2;$$

(b) the x and y components of the angular momentum

$$l_x = yp_z - zp_y \text{ and } l_y = zp_x - xp_z;$$

(c) the square of the total angular momentum

$$l^2 = l_x{}^2 + l_y{}^2 + l_z{}^2;$$

(d) the Hamiltonian of an atom containing N electrons and a nucleus with charge $+Ze$ (remember that the electrostatic potential energy of two particles with charges q_1 and q_2 separated by the distance r is q_1q_2/r).

31. Prove that the Hamiltonian operator $\hat{H}$ and the momentum-squared operator $\hat{p}_x{}^2$ have the Hermitian property.

32. Prove that solutions of the Schrödinger time-dependent equation (6) must be complex. Also prove that the time-independent equation (13a) does not require imaginary solutions, although they are possible.

33. The electron-in-the-box problem leads to a Schrödinger equation of the general form $d^2\psi/dx^2 = k^2\psi$. The problem was solved in Chapter 5 by assuming that the constant factor k^2 is inherently negative; this leads to periodic solutions of the type $\psi = \psi_0 \sin kx$. What difficulties arise if the constant factor k^2 is assumed to be positive, leading to solutions of the type $\psi = \psi_0 e^{-kx}$? Assuming that k^2 is negative implies what concerning the energy E?

34. The probability function $P = \Psi^*\Psi$ can change with time but it is necessary that the *total* probability $\int \Psi^*\Psi dx$ be time-independent. It is therefore an important requirement that $(d/dt)\int \Psi^*\Psi dx = 0$ be true in general, and a theorem to this effect should be proved. As a first step in the proof write

$$(d/dt)\int \Psi^*\Psi dx = \int [(\partial\Psi^*/\partial t)\Psi + \Psi^*(\partial\Psi/\partial t)]dx.$$

Continue the proof from here making use of Schrödinger's equation and the Hermitian property of the Hamiltonian operator $\hat{H}$.

35. Another, more specialized, version of the time derivative of the probability integral can also be proved. When the Hamiltonian operator has the particular form

$$\hat{H} = -(\hbar^2/2m)(\partial^2/\partial x^2) + V,$$

the derivative of the probability integral is

$$(d/dt)\int \Psi^*\Psi dx = (i\hbar/2m)[\Psi^*(\partial\Psi/\partial x) - \Psi(\partial\Psi^*/\partial x)].$$

The expression on the right is evaluated for the limits of the integral. Derive this equation.

36. Comment on the significance and intention of the general title, "Quantization as an Eigenvalue Problem," chosen by Schrödinger for his four 1926 communications.

Chapter 6

The formal structure of quantum physics, like that of any other science, begins with a collection of postulates. The choosing and refining of these postulates is an absorbing mental pastime which has apparently given pleasure to many authors of quantum mechanics texts. The various elegant and sophisticated systems of postulates found in these books have much in common. Those that build on the Schrödinger operator method begin with an explicit or implied statement of the existence of the wave function, or "probability amplitude" as some call it, and the probability function which the wave function forms. Beyond this, it is at least necessary to postulate the time rate of change of the wave function according to the Schrödinger equation; the basic prescription for formulating operator associations, the procedure for calculating average values; and the method for eigenvalue and eigenfunction calculations. These matters are dealt with in Postulates I, III, IV, V, VI and VIII, given in Chapter 6. To these postulates I have added three more, asserting the existence of probability waves (II), the Hermitian property of physical operators (VII) and the possibility of arbitrary eigenfunction expansions (IX). These additional postulates are not logically and mathematically necessary. The Schrödinger equation in its usual forms, together with the interference property of wave functions, assure that the probabilities come in waves, and if the mathematical apparatus is developed sufficiently the Hermitian and expansion postulates can be avoided. The theorems needed to prove the latter are complex, however, and beyond what is justified in this introductory treatment. I think there is something to be said for bypassing the more formidable aspects of the mathematical structure by adding a few more postulates. The probability-wave postulate I have included as a basic *physical* postulate. I realize that the probability fields are not always wavelike and that the separate assertion of the existence of waves is redundant. Nevertheless, there is nothing more fundamental in the workings of most atomic and molecular systems than the various kinds of standing and traveling probability waves.

Although it is not part of the story told in this book, one further postulate is needed to make quantum physics completely operable. When a system containing more than one particle is considered—an atom or molecule, for instance—it proves necessary to assume that no two of these particles can exist in the same state. This assumption is known as the "Pauli exclusion principle." It is indispensable for an understanding of such things as atomic spectra and the chemical properties of the elements. Since these matters are beyond the scope of this book, the Pauli principle, and Pauli himself for the most part, have been left out of the story. Most of the general textbooks cited below can be consulted for good accounts of the statement and uses of the Pauli principle.

References
The system of postulates of quantum physics can be found in a number of excellent books. Some of these are

97. Henry Margenau and George Moseley Murphy, *The Mathematics of Physics and Chemistry* (Van Nostrand, 1943), Chap. 11,

98. Henry Eyring, John Walter, and George E. Kimball, *Quantum Chemistry* (Wiley, 1944), Chap. III, and

99. Walter Kauzmann, *Quantum Chemistry* (Academic, 1957), Chap. 5.
Dicke and Wittke (in Chap. 6, Ref. 92, above) also present the postulates

very well. The Margenau and Murphy book is particularly good for its close attention to the mathematical requirements. The text by Eyring, Walter, and Kimball, besides giving an excellent statement of the fundamentals, is famous for its handling of problems relating to atomic and molecular structure. The Kauzmann text is also written along these lines.

To complete this prejudiced list of favorite books on quantum mechanics two more should be added.
100. David Bohm, *Quantum Theory* (Prentice-Hall, 1951),
is very useful for its careful building of the physical viewpoint. Finally, and to my way of thinking better than all the rest, there is the fine book by Landau and Lifshitz,
101. L. D. Landau and E. M. Lifshitz, *Quantum Mechanics* (Addison-Wesley, 1958),
a model of concise and thorough textbook writing. Its level is somewhat above that of the other texts mentioned, but it is worth any additional reading effort.

In the interests of mathematical simplicity all eigenvalues appearing in the theorems of Chapter 6 and elsewhere are assumed to be discrete. The case of continuous eigenvalues, with its additional mathematical requirements, is omitted. The method of handling continuous eigenvalues and applications to the description of collision processes are shown in most of the texts listed above. For example, see Ref. 92, Chap. V.

The requirements that all observable quantities have associated operators and that the operators form eigenvalue equations sometimes lead to rather strange mathematical difficulties. Consider the position operator $\hat{x} = x$. Its eigenvalue equation might be $\hat{x}u = au$ or $xu = au$, where u is an eigenfunction of x and $x = a$ is one of its eigenvalues. The eigenvalue a is the observed value of the position variable x. But what is the eigenfunction u? It must be an eccentric kind of function which vanishes for any value of x other than a: if $u \neq 0$ for $x \neq a$ then the eigenvalue equation necessarily leads to the contradictory statement $x = a$. "Functions" which vanish except at a certain point can, in fact, be constructed. Consider, for example, the function $\exp[-(x-a)^2/\epsilon^2]$, where ϵ is a constant. When $x = a$ this function has a value of unity; for $x \neq a$ it rapidly decreases toward zero. The parameter ϵ determines how narrow the region of non-zero x values is around $x = a$: as ϵ becomes smaller the width of this region decreases. To make the non-zero region infinitesimally small define the limit in which ϵ approaches zero:

$$\lim_{\epsilon \to 0} \exp[-(x-a)^2/\epsilon^2].$$

This is a "function" of the desired kind with values of zero everywhere but at $x = a$. It is not, however, useful as an eigenfunction unless it is normalized: it must be such that

$$\int_{-\infty}^{+\infty} u^* u \, dx = \int_{-\infty}^{+\infty} u^2 dx = 1.$$

To accomplish the normalization multiply the exponential function by the factor $(2/\pi)^{1/4}(1/\sqrt{\epsilon})$; the normalized eigenfunction is therefore

$$u = (2/\pi)^{1/4} \lim_{\epsilon \to 0} \exp \left[-(x-a)^2/\epsilon^2 \right] / \sqrt{\epsilon}.$$

This is a function which is zero everywhere but at $x = a$, where it forms a peak infinitesimally narrow and infinitely high, the width and height being balanced so that the integral $\int_{-\infty}^{+\infty} u^2 dx$ is finite and equal to unity. The peculiar art of handling functions of this kind was extensively developed by Dirac.

The method I have used to prove the uncertainty principle is given in Born's book (pp. 399–401, Ref. 2, above). Proofs of the other theorems of Chapter 6 can be found in most of the books cited above. I recommend reading the proof of each major theorem in at least one other book.

A good presentation of Dirac's theory of the electron is given by Rojansky (Chap. XIV, Ref. 94, above). Dirac's book,
102. P. A. M. Dirac, *The Principles of Quantum Mechanics* (Oxford University Press, 4th Ed., 1958),
is said to be *the* quantum mechanics classic, and no doubt it is. I am not sure, however, that it should be recommended as reading to supplement the chapters of this book. Dirac speaks in a highly individual idiom which is more abstract than anything appearing here. Dirac has indeed found the essence of "beauty in one's equations" but listening to him, like listening to a Beethoven quartet, takes an experienced and refined ear.

Anderson gives his interesting account of the positron discovery in
103. C. D. Anderson, "Early Work on the Positron and Muon," *American Journal of Physics* **29**, 825–30 (1961).

Practice Exercises
37. Prove that two eigenfunctions u_1 and u_2 belonging to different eigenvalues a_1 and a_2 ($a_1 \neq a_2$) are linearly independent. This involves proving that no relation such as $c_1 u_1 + c_2 u_2 = 0$ can be found in which the constants c_1 and c_2 are not zero. In other words, prove that $c_1 = c_2 = 0$.
38. Prove that if $u_1, u_2, \ldots, u_m$ are degenerate eigenfunctions of the eigenvalue a then any linear combination of these eigenfunctions is also an eigenfunction of a.
39. Show the extension of the Schmidt orthogonalization procedure to a third and fourth degenerate eigenfunction.
40. Illustrate the theorems of Chapter 6, pp. 184–95, by applying them to the calculation of energy eigenvalues and eigenfunctions.

41. Show that the three components of the angular momentum satisfy the following commutation rules:

$$[\hat{l}_x, \hat{l}_y] = i\hbar\hat{l}_z$$
$$[\hat{l}_z, \hat{l}_x] = i\hbar\hat{l}_y \tag{1}$$
$$[\hat{l}_y, \hat{l}_z] = i\hbar\hat{l}_x$$

Consult Exercise 30 for the individual component operators, $\hat{l}x$, $\hat{l}y$, and $\hat{l}z$.

42. With rather extensive mathematical manipulations the operator $\hat{l}^2$ for the square of the magnitude of the angular momentum of a rotating electron can be shown to commute with each of the three angular momentum component operators:

$$[\hat{l}^2, \hat{l}_x] = [\hat{l}^2, \hat{l}_y] = [\hat{l}^2, \hat{l}_z] = 0 \tag{2}$$

From this set of commutation relations and the set (1) derived in the last exercise what can be said about the quantum description of the angular momentum vector whose magnitude is l and whose components are l_x, l_y, and l_z? Much of the highly important theory of electron orbital motion can be derived in a simple algebraic manner beginning with the six commutation relations (1) and (2).

43. The quantum equation of motion $d\bar{A}/dt = (i/\hbar)[\overline{H,A}]$ was derived with the assumption that the operator $\hat{A}$ for A is independent of time. Carry out the proof without this restricting assumption and derive a more general equation.

44. Why is it necessary that *two* gamma-ray photons be formed in the positron-electron encounter which annihilates both particles?

45. It has been proved (p. 202) that the energy operator $\hat{E}$ and the time operator $\hat{t} = t$ do not commute ($[\hat{E},\hat{t}] = i\hbar$), and therefore that E and t cannot be measured simultaneously. On the other hand, the Hamiltonian operator $\hat{H} = -(\hbar^2/2m)(\partial^2/\partial x^2) + V(x)$, which is also an energy operator, *does* commute with the time operator: $[\hat{H},\hat{t}] = 0$. This seems to indicate that the energy *can* be measured at a definite time. How can these two apparently contradictory statements be reconciled?

46. Prove that the adjoint of an operator product is the product of the adjoints in reverse order, that $(\hat{A}\hat{B})^+ = \hat{B}^+\hat{A}^+$.

47. Prove that Hermitian operators are self-adjoint and vice versa.

48. Prove that, even though $\hat{A}$ and $\hat{B}$ are Hermitian, $\hat{A}\hat{B}$ is not Hermitian unless $\hat{A}$ and $\hat{B}$ commute. Make use of the theorems proved in Exercises 46 and 47. If $\hat{A}$ and $\hat{B}$ do not commute and $\hat{A}\hat{B}$ is therefore not Hermitian show that $(\hat{A}\hat{B} + \hat{B}\hat{A})$ is Hermitian.

49. Most of the major steps in the story told in this book were made by men who were very young, in their twenties or early thirties. The exceptions are Planck and Schrödinger, who were about forty when their greatest work was done, but they, too, were not able to sustain for long the full brilliance and force of their scientific inspiration. There is something about scientific creativity that does not last. As Jeremy Bernstein remarks: "It is impossible

to think of a figure in science comparable to a Stravinsky, a Picasso, or a Thomas Mann—someone whose creative genius flowered undimmed to a tremendous age." Why this difference between the work of the scientist and the work of the artist? Are scientists subject to more ruthless criticism than artists? Is a scientist's genius so specialized that it cannot adapt to changes? Are great scientific achievements made only during a relatively short "revolutionary" period? How important are "accidental" circumstances?

50. If this book has accomplished nothing else I hope it has shown that scientists have their idiosyncrasies, and that some of an individual's personality may be reflected in his research. Bohr and Schrödinger were particularly inclined to present their work (at least part of the time) with personal opinions attached. How successful were they? What factors determined their success or failure?

51. Notice once more the patterns of Heisenberg's and Schrödinger's thoughts as they developed the methods of quantum mechanics. They were inclined to begin with classical concepts and reshape them in a way that suited the peculiar needs of quantum physics. When the next revolutionary change is made in physics, to form the new mechanics—mechanics?—of the future, is it likely to begin in this same way, with classical analogies? How else might the change be guided?

Symbol Index

F = a separation constant, 162

g = acceleration of gravity, 129

h = Planck's constant, 16
$\hbar = h/2\pi$, 96
H = Hamiltonian function, 153

$i = \sqrt{-1}$, 80

k = Boltzmann's constant, 14

l = angular momentum, 41
l_x, l_y, l_z = components of angular momentum, 159
L = size of a one-dimensional box, 164

m = mass, 25
m_0 = rest mass, 29

n = the number of energy units in the Boltzmann-Planck statistical method, 14
   = a quantum number, 43
   = the nth stationary state, 49
   = an integer in Bragg's formula, 64
   = subscript designation on eigenfunctions and eigenvalues, Chaps. 5 and 6
N_0 = Avogadro's number, 14

p = linear momentum, 30
p_x, p_y, p_z = components of the linear momentum, 180
P = work parameter in Einstein's photoelectric equation, 26
   = probability function, 115; Chaps. 5 and 6

$q_1, \ldots, q_f$ = coordinates in f-dimensional phase space, 181

R = gas constant, 14
   = Rydberg constant, 46
R' = Rydberg constant ($= Rc$), 46

s = path length, 91
$S(E,\nu)$ = average entropy of black-body resonators, 11
$S(\nu)$ = entropy of monochromatic radiation, 22
S_T = total entropy of black-body resonators, 14

t = time, 60
T = absolute temperature, 8
   = kinetic energy, 41

u = phase velocity, 60; Chaps. 3 and 4
$u_n(q)$ = the nth A-eigenfunction, 184

v = volume, 22
   = speed, 25
v_l = degenerate eigenfunctions, 197
$v(t)$ = a perturbation, 194
V = applied potential, 25
V_0 = minimum applied potential, 26
V = potential energy, 42; Chaps. 5 and 6
V_0 = a constant potential energy, 141
   = minimum potential energy in a potential well, 169
V_m = potential of maximum reflection, 229

w = group velocity, 61
W = disorder, 14

x = position variable, 60

Z = nuclear charge, 41

Greek Letters

α = a constant in Wien's radiation formula, 9
   = a constant in Bohr's theory, 43
   = separation constant, 95
   = constant in electron-in-a-box problem, 164
$\alpha_n(t)$ = time-dependent expansion coefficients, 194
$\alpha_x, \alpha_y, \alpha_z$ = Dirac matrices, 210

β = a constant in Wien's formula, 9
   = the ratio v/c, 29
   = a Dirac matrix, 210
β_{ij} = constant coefficients in the calculation of simultaneous eigenvalues, 197

δ = the variation operation, 91
δ_{mn} = Kronecker delta, 188
Δ = uncertainty in the quantity whose symbol follows (as in Δx), 107
$\overline{(\Delta A)^2}$ = mean-square uncertainty in A, 160

ϵ = the indivisible energy units in Boltzmann's statistical method, 14

θ = photon scattering angle, 30
   = angle of incidence (with respect to a line drawn *normal* to a surface), 64

θ = angular aperture of a microscope, 104
  = angle in the double-slit experiment, 126

λ = wavelength, 31
  = small constant, 80
λ_1 = incident-photon wavelength, 31
λ_2 = scattered-photon wavelength, 31
λ_0 = wavelength of photons before scattering, 106
λ_1, λ_2 = wavelengths for forward- and backward-scattered photons, 106

μ = index of refraction, 67

ν = frequency, 8
ν_0 = frequency of a particle's "internal process" according to the particle's "own clock," 59
ν_1 = incident photon frequency, 30
  = frequency of a particle's "internal process" according to a fixed observer, 59
ν_2 = scattered photon frequency, 30
$\nu(n,m)$ = frequency emitted or absorbed in the transition $n \rightarrow m$, 49
$\tilde{\nu}$ = wave number, 46

ρ = wave amplitude in the classical wave equation, 94
$\rho(\nu,T)$ = energy distribution function, 8
$\rho'(\nu,T)$ = energy distribution function, 224

σ = Stefan-Boltzmann constant, 9

τ_0 = period for a periodic process occurring in a particle at rest, 59
τ_1 = the same period seen by an observer who is moving with respect to the particle, 59
τ,τ' = summation indices, 85

ϕ = phase angle, 60
  = electron scattering angle, 225
$\phi(\rho,\nu)$ = entropy distribution function, 21
$\phi(t)$ = time-dependent part of the wave function, 95, 161

$\Psi(x,t)$ = one-dimensional, time-dependent wave function, 95
$\Psi(q,t)$ = generalized, time-dependent wave function, 181
Ψ_n = nth energy eigenfunction, 176
$\Psi_n^{(0)}$ = nth unperturbed wave function, 195
$\psi(x)$ = one-dimensional, time-independent wave function, 95
$\psi(q)$ = generalized, time-independent wave function, 181, 191
ψ_n = nth energy eigenfunction, 176

ω = frequency of rotation, 41
ω_0 = a constant in the equations of motion for oscillators, 79

Miscellaneous Symbols

$\dot{\ }$ = differentiation once with respect to time (as in $\dot{\theta}$), 41
$\ddot{\ }$ = differentiation twice with respect to time (as in x), 80
$*$ = complex conjugate (as in Ψ^*), 115
$\bar{\ }$ = average value (as in $\bar{x}$), 117
$|\ |$ = absolute magnitude (as in $|\Psi|^2$), 115
$|$ = the expression to the left is evaluated between two limits, 146
$\hat{\ }$ = an operator (as in $\hat{p}$), 149
$\nabla^2 = \partial^2/\partial x^2 + \partial^2/\partial y^2 + \partial^2/\partial z^2$ = del operator, 180
$[A,B] = AB - BA$, commutator, 202
$+$ = adjoint operator (as in G^+), 203

Author and Subject Index

Page citations such as 224r refer to references listed in the "Notes and Comment" section. Citations such as 28n refer to footnotes.